THE MENTALLY RETARDED

Second Edition

THOMAS E. JORDAN
Southern Illinois University

Charles E. Merrill Books, Inc., Columbus, Ohio

PREFACE

In the study of mental retardation the inquirer faces a number of serious problems. He must develop a set of concepts which adequately contain the essentials of a broad problem; he must make sense out of a body of knowledge going well beyond the scope of his own immediate interests, and he must learn the literary sources through which future variations in knowledge will emerge. Since these items may well affect the welfare of human beings who depend on others for assistance with the complexities of life, it is important that the concepts determining action be accurate, realistic and comprehensive.

The primary purpose of this book is to provide a guide to the basic concepts and issues in the field of mental retardation. The secondary purpose is to equip the reader to explore the primary literary sources of a large and continually expanding body of knowledge. Attention is called to what we concretely know about mental retardation and to the areas from which new information may be expected to emerge. The materials are integrated in the sense that, first, a consistent idiom runs through the chapters, second, cross-referencing from one chapter to another is provided, and, third, one point of view and corresponding set of values determine the content and organization of the entire work.

The book consists of eleven chapters which may be thought of in groups. Chapter One deals with the uses and abuses of definitions and delineates the nature of mental retardation. Chapters Two and Three consider the two social contexts most prominent in the welfare of the retarded: the family and the institution. Chapters Four, Five, and Six contain analytic presentations of the attributes and functional traits of mentally retarded persons, together with a consideration of ways to

v

study these characteristics. Chapters Seven and Eight constitute a treatment of developmental issues. The mechanisms and patterns of growth peculiar to the various conditions are treated separately rather than combined under the conventional arrangement which starts with the syndromes. Chapters Nine, Ten, and Eleven consider the possibilities of amelioration and progress towards a higher level of functioning.

Let me express my thanks to Miss Carol Ann DuBiel for her editorial support. Professor Oliver P. Kolstoe has precipitated a good deal of reflection on my part during the last several years, and I thank him for it. Ralph Darr has helped with some of the last minute detail.

Thomas E. Jordan

Carbondale, Illinois
March, 1966

CONTENTS

Chapter 1 **DELINEATING MENTAL RETARDATION** 1

Mental Retardation and Mental Illness, 2
Problems of Definition, 3
An Inductive Approach to Mental
Retardation, 11
Summary, 30
Bibliography, 31

Chapter 2 **THE FAMILY** 35

The Discovery of Mental Retardation, 36
Family Adjustment to Mental
Retardation, 40
Strategies, 49
The Family and Child-Rearing, 51
The Family and the Counseling Process, 59
The Family Which is Mentally Retarded, 68
Summary, 72
Bibliography, 73

vii

Chapter 3   **RESIDENTIAL LIVING**   **81**

Types of Institutions, 83
The Choice of Residential Living, 90
Admission to Residential Living, 92
Leaving Residential Living, 95
The Social System, 97
Child Care Through Residential Living, 101
Summary, 102
Bibliography, 103

Chapter 4   **CHARACTERISTICS OF THE
MENTALLY RETARDED**   **109**

Theories of Behavior, 110
The Severity of Mental Retardation, 112
Age and Retardation, 115
Social Competence and Mental
   Retardation, 117
Adaptive Behavior, 122
Ambiguities in Behavior, 123
The Retarded as a Threat to Others, 127
Characteristics by Syndrome, 128
Investigations of Cognitive Processes, 131
Functional Achievements of the
   Mentally Retarded, 134
Summary, 136
Bibliography, 137

Chapter 5   **LANGUAGE**   **143**

The Nature of Language, 144
Acquisition of Language—Description, 148
Acquisition of Language—Explanations, 151

Negative Influences on Language, 153
Incidence, 156
Articulation, 159
Vocabulary, 160
Syndromes, 163
Speech Therapy, 168
Research, 169
Summary, 177
Bibliography, 178

Chapter 6   **PSYCHODIAGNOSTICS**   **187**

Levels of Analysis, 188
The Purposes of Evaluation, 189
A Case Study, 195
Diagnostic Instruments, 202
Measures of Intelligence, 202
Measures of Social Development, 207
Measures of Personality, 207
Special Tests of Intelligence, 213
Educational Tests, 216
Decisions in Differential Diagnosis, 218
Diagnostic Possibilities, 231
Summary, 231
Bibliography, 232

Chapter 7   **THE SOURCES OF MENTAL RETARDATION**   **239**

A Reformulation, 241
Descriptive Approaches, 241
Inferential Studies, 243
Research and the Disciplines, 243

Tools of Research, 244

Sources of Mental Retardation, 247

Heredity and Mental Retardation, 248

Development, 251

Mental Retardation and the Problems of Birth, 259

Mental Retardation and Other Factors, 261

Mental Retardation and the Growing Child, 265

Summary, 267

Bibliography, 267

Chapter 8   PATTERNS OF DEVELOPMENT   277

Mind, Mental Retardation, and Development, 278

The Mechanisms of Mental Retardation, 280

Disorders of Body Structure, 281

Disorders of Body Chemistry, 302

Summary, 306

Bibliography, 306

Chapter 9   THERAPEUTIC CONSIDERATIONS   317

Terms, 319

The Nature of Therapeutic Agents, 322

Schools of Therapy, 323

Functional Therapies, 324

Psychotherapies, 335

Surgical Therapies, 341

Chemotherapies, 347

Summary, 354

Bibliography, 355

Chapter 10   **EDUCATION**   **365**

Enrollments, 366
Theoretical Problems I, 368
Theoretical Problems Il, 371
Applied Considerations, 374
Conceptual Issues, 393
Summary, 398
Bibliography, 398

Chapter 11   **INDEPENDENT LIVING**   **405**

Intelligence and Work, 408
Training, 414
Summary, 423
Bibliography, 423

Chapter 1

DELINEATING MENTAL RETARDATION

One of the striking aspects of human nature is its endless variability. It is only rarely that one sees two human beings who look alike, and yet all have the same number of limbs or fingers, and all are of approximately the same height and weight. In those instances where people are singularly tall or thin, the differences may be noted as extreme forms of normality and as another illustration of the uniqueness of human characteristics.

Mental retardation is the condition which accounts for the lower end of the curve of intellectual abilities, and the study of mental retardation illustrates the extent to which one human being can differ in *intellectual* characteristics from his fellows.

There is, however, a slight note of caution to be observed at this point. To speak of weight and height as we have done is to speak of attributes that are relatively apparent to the everyday observer. One either

1

is or is not very tall or very thin. We can tell by looking because the condition is obvious.

This is the point at which mental retardation, the *intellectual* caliber of the individual, differs from height and weight. Height and weight are observable phenomena, even when the individual is doing nothing; they are attributes which do not leave him when he sleeps. Unfortunately, we cannot make a similarly accurate judgment of intellectual height, or tell by inspection who is a mental heavyweight.

In this chapter we will attempt to consider the theme of the entire book—*the nature of mental retardation*. This must be done cautiously and systematically; for mental retardation is at once a symptom and a central issue, a scientific concern and a source of much folk-lore, a personal-family problem and a social issue. It can be held to no disciplinary line; mental retardation crosses the vista of workers in virtually every discipline from literature (66)[1] to genetics (71).

MENTAL RETARDATION AND MENTAL ILLNESS

One perennial source of confusion is the doubtful terminology in this area. Let us begin our analysis of mental retardation by distinguishing between two common terms.

Mental Illness is the term used to cover a broad range of personal problems and disorders. It is applied, broadly, to those problems which arise when an individual is in a state of dissonance, or maladjustment, with his life-situation. As a result, he may have distorted perceptions of people and the world around him. He may have radical disturbances of mood which leave him at the mercy of his feelings. Such disturbances—neuroses (the mild ones) and psychoses (the severe ones)—are usually considered acquired conditions amenable to treatment.

Mental Retardation, while it is *mental* too, does not automatically connote maladjustment, nor does it clearly involve disturbed perceptions. Typically, mental retardation is not acquired in adult life, nor is it amenable to treatment once its presence has been established positively. In general terms, it describes inherent limitations of the individual's growth in ability to perform tasks of abstraction and organization, and it sets limits to the ceiling his abilities will eventually reach. Interests, skills, and the like, are usually those of a younger person, and the level of performance in tasks of an intellectual nature is below expectations.

One result of this preliminary analysis of the term *mental retarda-*

---

[1] This and similar numbers throughout each chapter are references to numbered entries in the bibliography appended to each chapter.

tion should be a general awareness that *mental* is a very vague word and that we need to be more careful in our application of the word to human problems.

PROBLEMS OF DEFINITION

In the course of studying the substantive forms of mental retardation, the typical reader encounters many definitions, each reflecting the views of a particular theoretician and each generally incompatible with those of any other. So far the author has found thirteen types of definition. Following is a list of the types with an example of each drawn from current thought on mental retardation.

1. *Synoptic.* In this approach to definition, authorities try to give a summary of the condition. An example is the definition given by Doll (*17*): ". . . we observe that six criteria by statement or implication have been generally considered essential to an adequate definition or concept. These are (1) social incompetence, (2) due to mental subnormality, (3) which has been developmentally arrested, (4) which obtains at maturity, (5) is of constitutional origin and (6) is essentially incurable" (*17*).

2. *Discriminative.* In this form an attempt has been made to indicate that the condition may be several entities which while related are genotypically distinct. Kanner (*41*) provides an example when he discusses:

1. *Absolute Feeblemindedness.* One variety consists of individuals so markedly deficient in their cognitive, affective, and constructively conative potentialities that they would stand out as defectives in any existing civilization . . . they would be equally helpless and ill-adapted in a society of savants and in a society of savages.

2. *Relative Feeblemindedness.* . . . individuals whose limitations are definitely related to the standards of the particular society which surrounds them. In less complex, less intellectually centered societies, they would have no trouble in attaining and retaining equality of realizable ambitions . . . their deficiency is an *ethnologically determined phenomenon.* . . .

3. *Apparent Feeblemindedness* or *pseudo-feeblemindedness.* . . . individuals who appear to be limited at the time of the psychometric rating but who at other times, under different circumstances, . . . attain much higher IQ's (*41*, p. 9-10).

3. *Residual.* This approach to definition is essentially negative. It connotes a condition whose existence is indicated by the progressive

elimination of other conditions by a differential analysis. Thus, we may sequentially consider the following etiological entities when attempting to account for deviant behavior, (1) hearing loss (2) aphasia (3) delayed speech (4) schizophrenia (5) pseudofeeblemindedness, and so forth. The failure to find these and other entities may leave only one condition unconsidered—mental retardation. A more rigorous example of residual definition can be found in the *demotic* pattern of mental retardation identified by Stein and Susser (65).

> When careful examination reveals no positive neurological sign or history suggestive of brain damage, and no obvious physical incongruity or metabolic disturbance; when investigation shows no chemical abnormality in the urine, a normal electro-encephalograph, the expected sex-chromatin on oral smear and no abnormality of chromosomes; and when there is no other psychiatric disorder, then the diagnosis can be inferred from the social background.

It should be observed that the *demotic* pattern refers to mental retardation in school children from working-class homes in Great Britain. Such homes do not have precise equivalents in the United States, and the ideas of Stein & Susser are presented here in order to discuss modes of defining, rather than ways of diagnosing, retardation.

4. *Tautological.* This is a generic sort of definition arising not so much from an examination or a case study as from a prior construct. The construct is the IQ the relevance of which to normality and retardation may be approximate rather than accurate. Instead of going to the literature for this sort of definition, we may consider a practice. Were this practice recognized in a formal definition it would appear roughly as follows: "All school children who have an IQ below 70 shall be considered retarded and placed in a special class." This approach ties the condition to a distortion of the IQ concept. Mental adequacy and inadequacy are the literal equivalent of IQ's without regard for the many intrinsic and ecological factors that influence IQ's.

5. *Ontological.* In an ontological approach to definition the position is taken the condition can be directly connected to the innate constitution of the person. Benoit, for example, considers brain cells at least the proximate site of mental retardation. He says, "Mental retardation may be viewed as a deficit of intellectual function resulting from varied intrapersonal and/or extrapersonal determinants, but having as a common proximate cause a diminished efficiency of the nervous system, thus entailing a limited general capacity for growth in perceptual

and conceptual integration and consequently in environmental adjustment" (7).

6. *Phylogenetic.* Interestingly, at least one research worker has put mental retardation in a context drawn from the study of evolution. Yakovlev considers mental retardation a phenomenon which exists only in man. He says that mental retardation ". . . is peculiar to man. Except for the operationally expedient analogies with this phenomenon as studied in the experimental rats and monkeys, there is nothing homologous to it in other biological systems" (70). He adds, of course, that it has other aspects, but he places the biological aspect first in his discussion.

7. *Functional.* To continue with Yakovlev's work it is interesting to see the condition of mental retardation equated with definite limitations of typical human functions. "Thus the behavior of the moronic scullery maid who breaks dishes, of a mechanic's helper who breaks tools, and of an adextrous recruit who does not know right from left . . . is pragmatically rated mainly on the basis of their shortcomings in their effective productive performance, i.e., in their manufactorial dexterity; and this shortcoming represents the pragmatic part of their own predicament as individuals and of the public problem they represent" (70).

8. *Phenomenal.* Jordan has suggested that mental retardation be approached on the basis of manifest failure at some developmental task or in an important life situation, with a descriptive statement resulting that is restricted to the current status of the individual. "It makes no assumptions about etiology and no conclusions, even tentative ones, about the future. It is applicable to all types, degrees, and combinations of disorders which we accept as germane to intellectual inadequacy" (36).

9. *Codified.* The last few years have seen practically every state legislature pass laws designed to help the handicapped. Legal procedure has required that concepts be codified and thus rendered applicable to problems in the common weal. The need to define mental retardation to the satisfaction of the law is found as early as 1534 in Fitzherbert's *De Natura Brevium,* according to Hilliard and Kirman (34). The author has found work contemporary to Fitzherbert's in the State papers of Henry VIII, where it is recorded that William Paulet conducted the affairs of the "King's Widows and Idiots," meaning those dependent persons who were wards of the crown. All man-

ner of proceedings passed through Paulet's hands, and, as today, it was necessary to codify mental retardation in order to conduct business of a legal nature. Unfortunately, contemporary codification of mental retardation and legal responsibility have been confounded by the McNaughton decision in Scottish law, and legal codification does not always provide mechanisms to handle retarded persons' problems equitably in many circumstances (44). A suggestion for remedying ambiguities in the care has come from Porteus and Corbett (60). They have suggested that a good statute on mental retardation should cover the following topics: (1) definition of the condition (2) commitment procedures (3) establishment of an examining bond (4) prior notice of adjudication to all parties (5) certification and (6) discharge.

More recently, in 1964, the state of California sponsored a survey of all its laws, which was conducted by Mrs. Kay Werdegar (67). The investigation explored the implications of California state statutes for the welfare of persons who are mentally retarded. The result is a collation of statutory provisions in twenty-three categories covering topics as far apart as medical quackery and the explicit bases for dental care in state institutions. Parallel activity resulted in submission of a set of recommendations for programming to the governor in 1965.

10. *Nuclear.* The President's Commission on Mental Retardation, Task Force on Education and Habilitation, adopted a definition of mental retardation in 1962. They defined mental retardation as referring to, ". . . sub-average general intellectual functioning which originates during the developmental period and is associated with impairment in adaptive behavior." This approach has several precursors, and it shows traces of an attempt to be all-inclusive while not being invidious. It is considered nuclear since it could easily be expanded into a very comprehensive definition. It flirts with etiology in the phrase ". . . which originates . . . ," it touches on "adaptive behavior," that is it appears to be non-ontological, and it recognizes the broad cognitive nature of the disability rather than showing a concern for a narrow intellective formulation. In many ways this definition seems uncontroversial, but it is probably capable of provoking wide disagreement because of its eclecticism.

11. *Factorial.* Another interesting conception of mental retardation has been provided by Jastak, who feels that the judgment of mental disability should be broadly based in the behavior of the individual (35). He would see up to fifty attributes measured and evaluated, with final judgments derived from masses of data. Jastak considers the "alti-

tude," the ability which yields the highest score, an approximate index of latent intellectual power. Clearly, Jastak considers mental retardation, indeed any level of intellectual performance, a function of the total psychological make-up. This interesting approach has been analyzed, on the whole favorably, by Cassel (15).

12. *Social.* Dexter has suggested the social significance of the retardate's behavior as a focal issue (16). Kratter, and Benton have reiterated the "relative" nature of behavior in excellent summaries of what they call *pseudo-mental deficiency* and *pseudo-feeblemindedness* (43) (8). Gibson's paper on the changes in our conceptual analysis of mental retardation indicates the shifts over the years in our starting point for studying mental retardation (24).

13. *Neural.* Perhaps the most different formulation of mentally retarded behavior is that implicit in the Soviet studies of "higher nervous activity." Pevzner's work is a representative example, and in it we see a set of postulates—implicit rather than explicit—which are at variance with most of those held in the Western world (59). As in Luria's writing, Pevzner formulates the issue as disorganization of activity within the nervous system due to organic damage. Formulations of *oligophrenia* consist of statements of degree and description based on neurological data such as EEG patterns developed in laboratory and studies. The idiom is a development of nineteenth- and twentieth-century terms introduced by I. W. Pavlov. The findings of Soviet workers are quite provocative, despite the apparent dearth of studies of social aspects of the problem.

We may end this account of attempts to conceptualize the problem by referring to a most promising development of the Technical Planning Project of the *American Association on Mental Deficiency* (31). In the 1959 monograph supplement to the *American Journal of Mental Deficiency,* the following judgment is offered formally, "Mental retardation refers to subaverage general intellectual functioning which originates during the developmental period and is associated with impairment in one or more of the following: (1) Maturation, (2) Learning, and (3) Social adjustment" (31). In a concluding paragraph the authors reiterate a position taken earlier by Jordan (36) when they state, "Within the framework of the present definition mental retardation is a term descriptive of the current status of the individual with respect to intellectual functioning and adaptive behavior. . . ." They continue, ". . . level of efficiency always being determined in relation to the behavioral standards and norms for the individual's chronological age group" (31). They further suggest that there must be "demonstrated deficiencies" in *adaptive behavior and measured intelligence* in order to qualify as mental retardation. *Measured intelligence* to demonstrate current intellectual functioning, and *adaptive behavior* refers "to the effectiveness with which the individual copes with the natural and social demands of his environment."

This pronouncement offers a resolution to many problems and provides an adequate basis for making decisions. By avoiding rigid formulae the A.A.M.D. has placed the locus of decision-making *in situ,* proportionately increasing the care to be taken when human lives are involved. We shall have more to say about this work later. For the moment we can observe that "adaptive behavior" is currently a much more dynamic field of thought and inquiry than "measured intelligence" (*47*).

We may now attempt to gain a little perspective on the preceding definitions. To start with, it is obvious that we need verbal symbols in order to think about things. Naming is the first step, and this is followed by definition as we begin to deal in a sophisticated way with a problem. The definitions just given have emerged after long and careful thought and are representative of the best we have. The range of definitions of mental retardation makes direct comparisons of worth fruitless. Usually analyses of definition are negative in tone and arise over disagreement about the meaning and value of specific words. What usually does not occur is prior discussion of what a definition, and therefore its components, is intended to do. This means that disparity between the several definitions may reflect not so much differences in terms as differences in direction, differences about what any definition is supposed to do. The nature of a definition in turn decides whether it is appropriate to use a particular noun, for example, *childhood* or *developmental period,* and whether entire concepts such as *incurability,* and *etiology* should be included.

Let us now consider the role of definition, definition as a tool in the manipulation of knowledge. It follows from the previous statement that definition has some formal properties as well as some informal ones. Among the formal properties of definition in knowledge are the following:

1. *Giving a full description of phenomena by ordering the data.* An example of this is seen in the steady accretion of knowledge about changes in the biological order. In the nineteenth century this was formalized in the work of Darwin and Wallace who gave order to a series of piercing if disconnected observations that had been made in previous generations. The pronouncement we know as the *Origin of the Spe-*

cies is essentially a definition in the earliest sense of giving order to knowledge. The definition of the word *evolution* not merely gives the connotations of the word, but imposes order on a previously informal set of observations.

2. *Conceptualizing the hypothesized.* Men think in words. That which has no name or label has no existence except in the privacy of one person's mind. The act of bestowing a name gives people a handle to grasp a concept by. The verbalization of that handle is the act of creating a tool for thinking. In science we see the use of definition to conceptualize the hypothetical in the introduction of terms to describe atomic and sub-atomic particles. Recall that "atom" comes from the negative, residual definition as that which could be no further reduced.

3. *Explication of a causal-genetic set.* One of the most interesting physical aspects of the western United States is the San Andreas fault. This is the site of vast slippage between geological strata, and its reverberations are evident in earthquakes. To merely identify earthquakes is to describe an alarming experience. To identify two adjacent but dissimilar strata of rock is to be observant. However, to identify the dimensions of an immense and still unstable stratal defect is to do more. To show a relationship between thousands of miles of defects in strata and earthquakes is to offer a concept which not only names but also explains the origins of past and present phenomena and enables one to explain future occurrences. The definition of this geological *fault* is naming plus the vital step of explaining.

4. *Prediction of a lawful course of events.* Until very recently we could all take comfort in the natural order of things. Objects observed the classic law of moving bodies. One could be reasonably sure that what went up would come down. Obviously the ground rules of natural observation have changed. The comprehension of phenomena and their interdependence is probably the hallmark of science. Crucial to this step has been the formulation of lawful statements whose function has been the prediction of future relationships of objects in space. Planetary motion, tidal effects, and so on give us a good example of prediction as a vital form of definition. Thus, the sun can be defined as a minor star which is the source of heat. It can also be defined in terms of lawful relationships between it and its satellites whose movements can be accurately predicted.

5. *Relating one construct to another.* One of the more useful aspects of definition is that it enables us to relate one object to others that are identical, or entirely dissimilar. Chemistry provides an example of

this function of definition. Matter is classified in many terms but the familiar ones of *acid, base, metal,* and so forth illustrate the point, while the less elementary ones suggest that there are relationships that go unguessed until classes of things are fully elucidated and defined. As new concepts were defined in chemistry, new relationships could be explored. Thus, mental retardation is currently profiting from definition of the amino-acids, which have many applications in relating clinical symptoms to pathology.

6. *Description of a phenomenal state.*   It is interesting to see that men of science often place communicability above many considerations. Astronomers undoubtedly feel it best to delay the start of their work "until the sun goes down." And yet the sun does not go down, nor does it set, least of all in the minds of astronomers. In fact the phenomenon consists of the curvature of the earth progressively occluding the light of the sun from specific regions of its third satellite. What a dismal way to describe a sunset, and yet how meaningful in the fullest sense is that definition: yet, how meaningless it is in the sense of helping plan the everyday procedures of the world, how awkward. This is not to fall into the error of oversimplification but rather to indicate that issues may be selectively pursued at several different levels when different goals are held. The difficulty with awkward if correct definitions lies in the concept of *surplus meaning;* that is information may be correct but inappropriate at a given moment. The controversy definitions arouse is partially due to surplus meaning, that is connotations which are correct but are often unnecessary. Not every disposition in cases of mental retardation requires a statement on etiology, certainly not the applied matters of instruction and rehabilitation. This matter is paralleled by the partial relevance of disease as a scientific construct. Taxonomic endeavors in educating retarded children suggest that the concept of disease, for example, mongolism, color-blindness and left-handedness, is only partially relevant because of surplus meaning (37).

7. *Codification.*   A definition is a convention; it is all the things George Herbert Mead (53) meant when he spoke of a symbol, particularly at the point of agreement over meaning to all parties. Thus, to define may well be the most important step in a discussion; but it may properly come at the end rather than the beginning. It may enable all parties to recall by decoding, to use Osgood's expression, that which was found agreeable and acceptable. A definition may be a vital step in any serious discussion acting *as capstone rather than foundation* to the development of ideas.

It appears that we have many types of definition for mental retardation. In many cases they are doing quite different things, suggesting different objectives in the minds of the people who constructed them. More importantly, the definitions emerge from no common framework in the philosophy of science or the equally applicable subject of epistemology. Defining mental retardation has been and continues to be a rather loose and informal process in which people summarize what their personal experiences inductively suggest. An alternative strategy might be to discard the act of defining in favor of the process of delineating.

AN INDUCTIVE APPROACH TO MENTAL RETARDATION

Let us attempt to sharpen the meaning of the term *mental retardation* by a particular procedure which may be called *inductive*. Rather than proceeding deductively from a formal definition to illustrative instances, we will consider a number of settings in which mentally retarded persons function. The settings show a slightly different aspect of living; they are (1) education, (2) social-vocational efficiency, (3) poverty, (4) mental testing, (5) cognitive processes, and (6) epidemiology.

Education

There are few life situations which impose such rigorous demands on a child as school. His earliest years are a period of learning, but it is learning in the familiar context of the family circle. He learns from mother and from his brothers and sisters. Nevertheless, a young child may not feel that he is learning since he usually construes his own activities as play, which is, of course, hard, busy work.

As he reaches his fifth or sixth birthday, he leaves home for an alien setting, encountering new children and the mass machinery of education which society provides. If he is one of the many middle-class youngsters who enter kindergarten and first grade, he will probably find that the values of his teacher and the actions of his playmates are predictable and can be handled within the framework of his previous experiences.

There are two exceptions to this: there is the child whose home and background are not congruent with the middle-class orientation of the teacher and the school, and there is the child whose problems illustrate the nature of mental retardation. This is the child whose intellectual growth has not kept pace with the passage of time.

Now what is the nature of the school and how does it help us understand mental retardation? Consider a child entering school, a child who is of less than normal intellectual height.

The elementary school is intended to educate all children. It usually assumes a number of qualities in children and bases the curriculum on these qualities, though it also tries to account for individual differences. Early in the school experience the assumption is made that most—if not all—first graders are ready to read. Reading is the connection of meaning—an abstract proposition—with arbitrary signs called words. This ability to relate meanings and signs is conditional upon developing or previous experiences. Thus, an assumption is made regarding both antecedent experience and the ability to apprehend its essential meaning.

Yet the facts occasionally belie the assumptions, and most teachers have to cope with the child who is not ready for academic learning, despite the correct age and the happy congruence of his birthday, school regulations, and the conjunctions of the planets.

Such a youngster was rarely considered until Binet's studies, begun in the 1890's. Binet was asked to study the many poor students and devise some way of evaluating them fairly. His work was successful and found a basis for examining individual differences (9). A further elaboration of the extent of this problem came from Burt several years later (12).

Many children starting school simply do not connect meanings and printed words efficiently, regardless of how hard they try. This issue can be defined sharply by noting the extreme opposite, the child who reads easily or even comes to school already reading. Both types of children may look alike, but one simply does not learn. His attention span may be shorter and he seems to approach the task like one much younger. For example, he may derive more satisfaction from manipulating the book than from deciphering the magic signs it contains or enjoying the pictures.

Here then is a clue to the entity we call mental retardation. The clue is that the child may play with the physical book rather than enjoy pictures in a meaningful way. As a child progresses through the grades, a similar picture emerges. The fifth grader may be more at home with second grade material; the seventh grader may find the course of study quite beyond him in interest and difficulty. Thus, we may say that the school places intellectual demands on children and that these may be consonant with or, in the case of mental retardation, considerably ahead of the child's level of growth. Using this last statement, we may construe the school and its challenges as a way of demonstrating the degree to which a child's maturity is on a level with, or behind, children of about the same age. The child who lags behind his fellows to a significant extent may be giving us evidence of a delay or retardation in his intellectual aptitude for school work.

At this point the issue is deceptively clear. Some children do poor school work; poor school work follows slow growth of ability; therefore poor school work means delayed or retarded growth of intellectual ability. Apart from the inadequacy of the syllogism, there are other reasons for doubting that school failure and retarded intellectual growth mean the same thing.

A way of indicating the uncertainty in this connection is to look at the post-school, or vocational, performance of poor students. While many of them fail at all tasks, others perform in a rather striking way.

John S. lives near the seat of a rich, Midwestern county. He and his wife, who is a teacher, have known each other all their lives. She was a good student who graduated from college, and has performed successfully as a teacher. He was a failure in school and never became a fluent reader. He was considered slow in his school days but survived those trying years and currently farms the most profitable and efficient farm in the county. His wife conducts the clerical side of the business, keeping the records and balancing the books. He makes the managerial and technical decisions that have made him one of the best farmers in a prosperous rural community.

It would be very foolish to label such a man as mentally retarded. Further, if one chooses to consider economic efficiency—earning money—man and wife can only be compared with absurd results. In all probability what is involved is the dissonance of school-related abilities and personal aptitudes. One must either accept this resolution of the problem or accept the notion that the man in question was able to lift himself by his own intellectual bootstraps—at about age sixteen.

It may be that the school's demands on children are insensitive to special abilities and exert most force in those areas where a child may be least competent. In commenting on the scholastic implications of this diversity of abilities, Burt said: "By the age of eleven, there are clear signs of a distinction between two broad types: some children seem to belong to what has been termed (in a rather narrow sense) the intellectual or academic type; these, if they are of high intelligence, are obvious candidates for the grammar school; others belong rather to a more practical or mechanical type; and these, provided they possess the requisite intelligence, are better suited to an education with a technical bias" (13).

Burt is discussing British education with its radical attempts to meet both qualitative and quantitative differences in intelligence. He clearly does not equate non-verbal ability with a lack of ability. As a common-sense observation, few of the nineteenth-century mechanical geniuses —Edison, for example—appeared at their best in the almost totally verbal culture of the schools of that time.

In our own generation people have called attention to the number of men rejected by the military on grounds of unsuitability. It has been pointed out that many rejectees have a similar background. They have a low level of educational attainment, due partially to a lack of opportunity, partially to an insensitivity to the value of education, to give the issue an explicit middle-class bias.

In their basic reference book, Masland, Sarason, and Gladwin consider this issue (51). Working from the differential rates of military rejection on grounds of mental retardation, they react to the almost 6:1 ratio for comparative rate of rejection in the Southeast and far West; resisting the impulse to attribute the cause to educational standards, they wonder if the problem might not be approached by asking how important education is in the various sub-cultures and how value-centered and instrumental it appears to people in different regions of the United States.

This relatively cautious approach is broad in outlook. There is a price to be paid, however. As one widens the scope of inquiry the issues tend to become vague. Research becomes concerned with entire cultural matrices, and the ideas lose clarity. If one can maintain a reasonable grasp of the issues, this cultural approach is promising. Its promise is derived from its fundamental validity; mental retardation is intertwined with schooling, but the relationship is not clear. What is needed is more research. The alternative is to accept the hazy notion that intellectual subnormality and educational subnormality are palpably the same thing.

Up to this point in our discussion of the school as a setting which can throw light on our attempts to understand mental retardation, we have cast the school in the role of a villain. That it is not necessarily so has been pointed out by Kirk, who has accepted the inadequacy of some pre-school children and vindicated the school as a force for good.

Kirk devised a project several years ago to "determine the effects of pre-school education on the social and mental development of young educable mentally handicapped children" (42). He selected eighty-one children between three and six years of age, and studied them for periods ranging from three to five years. Four groupings were assembled and labelled *Community Experimental Group, Institution Experimental Group, Community Contrast Group, and Institution Contrast Group*. He summarized his findings, which we shall consider further in a later chapter, by saying: "The over-all effects of pre-school education on the development of young mentally retarded children were positive. In general, pre-school education has some favorable effects in modifying the development picture of mentally retarded children, for on the whole, the pre-school experimental groups showed increased rates of growth following educational opportunities at a young age" (42, p. 205).

It should be noted that the pre-school experience was carefully planned, and the results would probably have been otherwise had the children been exposed to anything but the best experiences.

The role of the school as a means of illuminating the nature of mental retardation can now be summarized. First, school is a place where children may be exposed to tasks beyond their level of intellectual maturity. Second, in many cases a spurious picture of inadequacy may emerge because of the curriculum's emphasis on verbal skills. And third, while apparently cast as the villain of the piece, the educational process may potentially help the child, rather than merely focus attention on his inadequacies.

Social-Vocational Efficiency

Schools have not always existed; yet people have recognized that some of their fellows are incompetent, that they are unequal to the day-by-day stresses of living. Kirman has noted the legal provisions of the middle ages which, without the benefit of IQ's or psychologists, nevertheless made some distinctions which escape us even today. He reported fourteenth-century legislation designed to deal equitably with the property of "idiots (i.e., natural fools) . . . and . . . lunatics (i.e., persons of unsound mind). . ." (34). These are distinctions which present-day provisions for the handicapped do not fully reflect in many states.

Most communities have some people who do not hold jobs or who support their families only marginally and become public responsibilities. As a way of delineating social-vocational efficiency, let us consider some of the problems that the normal individual faces in any given day.

For the homemaker there are decisions about child care and buying food. The children must be looked after, and the food must be chosen for the meals by multiple criteria of cost, nutrition, and availability. There is the selection of household chores and the planning of time in which to do them. For the working man there is the need to get to work in time, to use judgment and discretion in his assigned tasks, and in his relations with co-workers. At times independence of judgment may be necessary to fulfil the demands of one's position. The school-age child is expected to find his way to school, avoiding the more enticing invitations to play that he meets on the way. He must get there on time and in much the same state of cleanliness that marked his departure from home. Once in school, he must be alert to the subtle ways in which the teacher indicates her demands, as Henry has pointed out (33). He must subdue impulses and work in the presence of many distracting stimuli on material that is usually of an abstract order.

To a considerable extent social-vocational skills are independent of ability, and yet they may be direct illustrations of ability. This is less paradoxical if we attempt to specify the level of social-vocational competence. In some instances people may be wholly lacking in fundamental ability and yet be successfully adapted to a working situation.

Roger is the last born of a family of six children. He is considerably younger than the other children and was born some fifteen years after the previous child. The family owns a moderately large department store in a middle-class area of the community.

Psychometrically and academically Roger is well below average. In his late teens now, he reads at about a third-grade level and has a Stanford-Binet IQ of about 65. In physical appearance he is clearly not well formed, but the disparity in structure is not gross. In contrast to Roger's native endowment there is his training and experience in a very pleasant home. He can pick out a tune on the piano—only one tune, however—and he has acquired the polish, the veneer of adequacy that comes with simple exposure to the home and its culture.

Roger is at a disadvantage in school; he is at a disadvantage in abstract tasks; and yet Roger shines in his own circumscribed lifespace. Life is a simplified thing for Roger; he has a prescribed routine to his days which takes him to the family business, by bus, and then home. On the bus Roger is a master of small talk. He yields his seat to ladies with an almost extinct graciousness. He pays for his fare with aplomb and is entirely adequate for the demands of his daily peregrination.

At work Roger makes a contribution. His is the job of escorting the carriage trade. He meets the upper-middle-class ladies, many of whom he has known from early childhood, and escorts them to the right department. His stock of stereotyped conversational material gets him through the few minutes of talk his job requires. He is a well-mannered young man, and he opens the door, as the shoppers leave, with a smile for all.

Now what accounts for Roger's social-vocational competence? And he *is* competent. First, there is the stereotyped, routined program of his day. Second, there is the rare circumstance of the job being created for the worker. Finally, there is the total lack of responsibility for decision-making. Asked to make change, a rarity in the age of credit, Roger would be incompetent. Asked to find his way to another job, he would get lost; asked a question beyond stereotyped words of greeting, he would founder.

How does this example of social-vocational competence illustrate the nature of mental retardation? The typical human being in the course of the day must meet all the demands that Roger's happy niche protects him from. The retarded individual usually has to compete with those who *can* make decisions, who *can* count their money at the end of the week, who *can* strike out on their own in the face of the economic facts of life.

Typically, as Jordan and deCharms have noted, the retarded child does not move towards independence (38). The retarded child is often led, as are many other handicapped individuals, away from, rather than toward, the development of traits necessary for social-vocational competence. It has been the exceptional retarded person who has achieved vocational adjustment or economic independence in the past. Only rarely did people think of useful retardates. Even today many people think of educables as totally ineffective people. The significance of contemporary programs for the retarded lies in their insistence that proper education and training from the beginning can lead to eventual social-vocational competence. The level of competence aspired to is not great, but even partial economic sufficiency is a strong contrast to the plight of the retardate who is a totally dependent person.

In summary, we have suggested that the area of human affairs which involves the day-by-day tasks of living provides a useful setting in which to study the problems of mental retardation. Some of the tasks which normal adults and children perform indicate the complexity of the working day. People sometimes have a veneer of adequacy which will be sufficient for limited, stereotyped roles but which is inadequate for important decisions and responsibilities. Such inadequate people have been known for generations and the law today attempts to cope with the problems they present, as it tried to do in the middle ages.

Poverty

John is a poor boy, the oldest of several children. He has an IQ in the upper sixties, and he is enrolled in a regular class because no special class is available. His life at school has been a series of problems as he encountered verbal materials which both frustrated him and bored him. His frustration is due to the increasing gap between the reading level he needs and the reading skill he possesses. Reading also bores him because he is expected to apply his limited ability to stories that have little reference to his life.

At home the picture changes dramatically. There he functions very differently. He takes care of the younger children in an admirable way considering there is no fence separating the door of the house from the railroad tracks fifty yards away. He forages for scrap materials which his father sells in order to supplement the family income. Both John and his brothers and sisters have a warm family life, although the material things are often in short supply. In freezing, wet weather his torn sneakers let in the cold, and he reaches school in tears.

Here we have a picture which emerges when our perspective on a child's life style is based on IQ's and school matters. Including observations based on other aspects of society—its institutions and their implicit evaluations of people—makes the picture darker. Poor choice of foods, alienation from middle-class values, doubtful hygiene, all of these can make a child's life seem bleak. Reality, in subjective terms, is a little less bleak once the the school doors close. John becomes not only marginally competent but remarkably so as he copes successfully with the gambits of nature in a lower-class milieu. Further, John loves and is loved by his parents and he enjoys the only way of life he has known.

Such children are common and constitute a sizeable proportion of what used to be called the poor and are now labelled culturally deprived. What needs to be added is a sensitivity to the changing demands made on such children at different stages of maturity. John and his brethren tend to discard their inadequacies at the end of each school day, and they frequently shed them completely when they drop out of school at the first opportunity. Retardation in this particular ambience is not a fixed property or an unchanging reality. Rather, it is a discrepancy between expected and observed performance at one stage of life. To generalize, as we all too often do, is to go beyond the facts and make fallacious statements about the life style and subsequent careers of many children.

If the federal programs of the 1960's, the War on Poverty activities of the Kennedy-Johnson administrations, have any effect it will be by intervening in the economic cycle of poverty and its social consequences. This is not to say that the life style and sub-cultures of families—indeed entire regions—can be changed easily. Nevertheless, an outcome of strategic intervention could well be the deletion of children such as John from the lists of children whose backgrounds produce sharp depression of verbal skills and a degree of alienation from middle-class values. Many children of the poor are in special classes because their linguistic/cultural backgrounds are contrary to those which schools presume. Pre-school intervention through careful social action may free children such as John from eroding experiences and confining milieux. It will not make all children good scholars, but it can help marginal children survive in the non-lower-class context of school and its demands.

Mental Testing

One interesting consequence of early attempts at mental testing was the surprising discovery that the relative abilities of human beings were quite neatly distributed. What seemed to many a further illustration of nature's symmetry was the fact that most people seemed modestly endowed with intellectual ability while the few whose abilities exceeded or fell short of this modest endowment decreased in number with the extent of their difference. Most of the early analyses of this issue took place in the context of education. Binet in Paris (9) and Burt in London (12) both concerned themselves with the study of abilities in school children, concentrating on those not endowed with the normal share of abilities.

Burt came to grips with an issue that still plagues the study of mental retardation. His psychometric findings indicated more than a chance frequency of low test scores in poor districts. As his subjects came from progressively better environments, he found fewer people with low test scores and more with high scores. A parallel example of the complexities of test scores emerged with a series of findings which, when naively interpreted, seemed to show that rural children are duller than urban children (20). A further example of what mental-test scores can mean to the unwary is the finding of an inverse relationship between the size of a family and the level of intelligence (52). Maxwell's comments on the subject based on the extensive 1947 Scottish Survey of Intelligence reported a Pearson correlation coefficient of .32 between IQ and the number of children in a family.

One of the more interesting findings from the demographic IQ studies is that entire groups of people seem to raise themselves to normality in a decade or so. In 1942 Wheeler published an interesting account of changes in tested intelligence in children in the mountains of east Tennessee (68). He reported, "Today the average mountain child is about eight months younger chronologically and nine months older mentally for his grade than the average child of ten years ago." He continues, "The average mountain child has gained ten points in IQ, or nearly one point a year during the past ten years" (68, p. 333). How do we account for such changes in abilities; why do we find IQ and family size inversely related? There are two answers to this sort of question: the first is to note that environmental conditions, even in remote mountain areas, do improve, while the curious finding about family size may be explained, to paraphrase Anastasi, because irrelevant and uncontrolled variables intervene (3).

The point to raising the issue of IQ changes is that it shows the *com-*

plexity rather than the *simplicity* of studying mental retardation as a psychometric issue. Obviously, mental retardation defined as low IQ (a phenomenon often erroneously compared to blood type) is a plastic thing. People do not raise their intellectual stature several cubits by putting their minds to it. What is necessary, then, is a careful analysis of the measuring instrument, the psychometric device.

When we give an intelligence test to a child the purpose is to make comparisons of performance and not to measure the dimensions of the mind.

The goal is to see how a child of given age performs on tasks which have been undertaken by many other children of the same age. There are two corollaries to this assertion: first, we state that the tasks to be performed are indicative of the abilities to be tested, and second, we believe that we can relate one child's performance to that of another in an orderly and significant fashion.

Let us examine the tasks to be performed and see whether this sheds light on the nature of mental retardation. An instrument in use today is the *Wechsler Intelligence Scale for Children*. In the late 1940's Wechsler introduced a scale derived from his work on adult intelligence. It is called a *scale* rather than a test because it actually consists of several sub-tests. The tasks are divided into a verbal section, which contains questions about vocabulary and arithmetic and some of the day-by-day activities of life, and a non-verbal or *performance* section which tests skills of a manipulative or non-language conceptual nature. Roughly speaking, the child plays with some interesting puzzles.

Having briefly considered the tasks, let us consider the assumptions about relating children's performances. In general terms, giving any task to children produces a distribution of skill from very poor, through average, to very good. There are comparatively few performances that are very good or poor, while many more lie midway between these extremes. If the children to whom the tasks are presented are representative of children in general (and that is a very big *if*, as we shall see in a moment) we define those who do very well, about the top 3 per cent, as gifted; we call the bottom 3 per cent or so, mentally retarded.

Thus, when we consider tests as a way of shedding light on the nature of intelligence, we find that we are dealing, not with an absolute phenomenon, but with a relative one. A child is *comparatively* lacking in ability, or vice-versa.

A moment ago we noted that big *if* concerning the sample of children. Several years ago, Carlson and Henderson tested the intelligence of children in Los Angeles of Mexican parentage (*14*). Looking at a total of 8,300 children, they concluded that "the American child of Mexican parentage was found to have consistently lower mean IQ scores than the American children of white non-Mexican parentage" (14, p. 550).

This finding of lower average IQ scores is common when considering minority groups. Its hazards have been discussed by Pasamanick who pointed out the myriad uncontrolled variables in such experiments and the difficulty of finding groups that are validly equated (55). This last point opens up another area of consideration. Many psychometric measures are appropriate for middle-class, white, native-born children. Unfortunately, the children come as they are, without regard for the restrictions in the test manuals. Consequently some children do poorly by virtue of the biases in language and cultural background which underlie the tests, a point commented on by Anastasi (4).

The evidence, up to this point, would suggest that our attempts to comprehend the nature of mental retardation in testing terms is not particularly profitable.

Happily the test-makers have responded to the challenge. There are several scales in use which are available to the examiner who doubts the relevance of the more popular scales. As with all the issues raised in this introduction, we shall have more to say in succeeding chapters about this point.

What then can we conclude about mental retardation on testing terms? What precisely does a low IQ, usually one below about IQ 85, really convey?

The Technical Planning Project of the American Association on Mental Deficiency has come to grips with the issue (31). Attempting to order the dimensions of behavior, they have used the standard deviation concept, a unit which describes how IQ's are distributed above and below the mean. They present a psychometric concept of intelligence as follows:

"The *Measured Intelligence* dimension is scaled into five levels in terms of standard deviations units which describe the distribution of scores in the general population . . ." (31, p. 57). The system they offer is presented in Table 1·1.

It would be misleading to think that the only thing we can learn from the attempts to measure intelligence is a labelling or classification system. Regardless of the numerical findings of testing, there are some important insights to be gained from simply analyzing how a human being approaches a standardized task. Working in New Zealand, Lawrence analyzed failures in performance as children worked on test materials (45). He found that 31 per cent of the errors in performance resulted from inadequate formulation of the task. Fourteen per cent of the time the children simply did not consider all the choices open to them as they worked. In 13 per cent of the cases the children did not express the correct answer in the required terms or idiom. In another 15 per cent of the cases the correct answer came out—but for wholly incorrect reasons.

TABLE 1·1

LEVELS OF MENTAL RETARDATION

Level V	Borderline retardation of measured intelligence
1.01-2.00 standard deviations	
Level IV	Mild retardation of measured intelligence
2.01-3.00 standard deviations	
Level III	Moderate retardation of measured intelligence
3.01-4.00 standard deviations	
Level II	Severe retardation of measured intelligence
4.01-5.00 standard deviations	
Level I	Profound retardation of measured intelligence
-5.00 standard deviations	

Another source of profit when children perform tasks on intelligence scales is the interesting material they volunteer about themselves and their families. Occasionally, unsuspected problems emerge, and a shrewd clinician can often develop some interesting hypotheses about the child's home and interpersonal relationships. Sometimes new hypotheses, issues to be probed at another time, may develop as the child reveals unsuspected difficulties on different sorts of problems.

In summary, it would seem that psychometric data are useful. We can learn something of the way in which a human being operates under controlled circumstances and on tasks which enable us to derive *comparative* estimates of ability. We have seen that one must choose the standard of comparison carefully and that caution is vital in evaluating children in light of the work of other children. While not rejecting test data out of hand, we can see that IQ's are not to be interpreted literally. Care must be taken to ensure sound interpretation; IQ's do not interpret themselves, nor should intelligence test data be considered as relevant only to the particular problem of assessing intellectual performance.

The Cognitive Processes

Presumably whatever diverse methods workers use in mental testing, they agree that they are studying the intellectual processes, or, to use a slightly broader term, the cognitive processes.

It is entirely appropriate to use a broad term since we are dealing with a broad subject. We have seen that mental retardation is a problem for many scientific disciplines. One consideration that we have not yet pursued is the basis in physiology for mental retardation. As pointed out several years ago, "mental deficiency is not a disease as such, but manifestations of an affection—structural or functional—of the nervous system" (58, p. 432).

Unfortunately we open up a Pandora's box when we look at mentality and the nervous system. There is no more uneasy issue than modern—or even medieval and ancient—man's attempt to resolve the dualism of brain and mind. In recent years Hebb has tackled the problem in a way that has been stimulating and productive (30). He phrases a general concern for phylogenetic considerations by asserting that "a hierarchy of 'Intelligence' can be assumed, which corresponds to gross differences (1) in the size of the cerebrum, and (2) in the proportion of afferent to internuncial neural tissues"[1] (29, p. 125).

In another place in his stimulating work, *The Organization of Behavior*, he speaks of "the *intrinsic organization* of cortical activity," a radical statement in view of the prevalent notion of environmental stimulation as a basis for behavior. He documents his assertion by offering EEG data on the intrinsic organization of the cortex, commenting that "It appears at birth in the large slow waves of the infant's electroencephalogram"[2] (29, p. 122).

Generally, Hebb relates the contents of thinking to "cell assemblies." Occasionally they work in "phase sequence," and since there are millions of cells it is not hard to see that an adequate brain has endless possibilities for action. An inadequate brain has proportionately less.

It might well appear that mind and brain are easily interrelated. Such is not the case. In his Wayneflete lectures, Eccles demonstrated the complexities of this relationship (18). Relevant papers on brain function by Magoun and Samuels have shown that there are brain processes which we are only beginning to comprehend (50) (63). Galambos commented on an "excluding" process intrinsic to the cerebral mechanism which "shuts off" some phenomena of a peripheral nature (23). Fretting at American propensities to relate brain processes to machines, the Soviet scientist Frozlov has argued that the origins of behavior are in "participation in society," a not unpredictable position (22). According to Bruner:

> In general, an impoverished environment, one with diminished heterogeneity and a reduced set of opportunities for manipulation and discrimination, produces an adult organism with reduced abilities to

---

[1] Reprinted with permission from D.O. Hebb, *The Organization of Behavior*, John Wiley & Sons, Inc., 1949.

[2] *Ibid.*

discriminate, with stunted strategies for coping with roundabout solutions, with less taste for exploratory behavior, and with a notably reduced tendency to draw inferences that serve to cement the disparate events of its environment such as between the light of a candle flame and the likelihood of its burning when you put your nose into it. . . . Unless certain forms of stimulation-cum-learning take place before a certain point . . . there appear to be certain very intractable changes . . . (10, p. 92).

Here is interesting information indeed for students of mental retardation. What better characterizes the mentally retarded individual who passed his formative years in a slum? The early studies of isolation (e.g., Kasper Hauser) responded to "good" environments, but apparently the basic limitations were "intractable," as Bruner calls them.

One branch of the study of cognition has been the attempt to specify the process of "cognizing." Under this heading there are the conceptual models whose structures are based on speculation and, in some cases, on experimentation. Two examples will illustrate this approach to cognition. Zuk developed a model which he called "optical" and which was based on some little-known writing by Freud (72). Interestingly, he used normal and mentally retarded subjects and established some differences in their cognitive processes. Using the mathematical tool, factor analysis, Guilford developed a partially complete "structure of intellect" which consists of numerous factors and processes (28). He has extrapolated, predicted, and speculated about some elements not yet fully described in his model. Perhaps at this point it would be well to remember the discussion of intelligence testing. Clearly, whenever one develops a scale of intelligence, its numerous sub-tests constitute a model of the intellectual processes. Ostensibly, testing and model building seem far apart; testing seems applied and practical, while the work of the cognitive-model builder seems abstruse. Purely manipulative mental testing (the derivation of IQ's) as a basis for placing children in special programs, seems sterile when compared to work such as that of Bruner and Guilford. On the other hand, we cannot routinely handle large numbers of children on the basis of conceptual models. Our intelligence tests seem to be the only practical tool at hand. While not perfect, they are better than anything else when we wish to make typical, routine judgments about children.

Finally, we may consider briefly the activity now so evident in the study of language. Spradlin (19) has developed an applied model of language behavior and has applied it to retarded children. *The Parsons Language Sample (PLS)* which is discussed in Chapter 5, "Language," measures a number of behaviors in a conventional fashion, but it is distinctive because it flows from Skinner's ideas on verbal behavior. Skinner believes that linguistic-cognitive behavior can be formulated and analyzed like other behavioral phenomena. Spradlin has extended the idiom, and we may expect to see mental retardation better understood as a consequence. In a complementary way Kirk & McCarthy have developed a set of ideas on Psycholinguistic processes developed by Osgood. They have developed the *Illinois Test of Psycholinguistic Abilities* (ITPA). As with the *PLS* the *ITPA* is a behavioral, quantified description of mental-verbal processes. Both scales produce accounts of functioning in children which can be understood through the models developed by Skinner & Osgood.

Does cognitive theory help us understand mental retardation? The answer is that cognitive theory has yielded new insights into mental retardation and may well expect more in the future.

The Epidemiology of Mental Retardation

One way to study mental retardation is to look at the frequency of occurrence and at the peculiarities of the condition as it occurs under different circumstances. There have been very few systematic attempts to measure the absolute number of mentally retarded individuals, and this is understandable in view of the difficulty and scope of such projects. Akesson's summary of investigations best illustrates the problems (1).

There have been rule-of-thumb approaches which are usually phrased as percentages. We can speak of mental retardation as occurring in about 2 or 3 per cent of the population. Yet this kind of estimate has virtues only in the abstract. There are school districts in which the population consists of very bright children and the youngster with an IQ of 110 is at a disadvantage. He is a comparatively slow learner. On the other hand, there are classrooms in which the range of intelligence quotients is in the eighties, with the exceptional pupils being either in the sixties or in the high nineties.

Within the population of retarded persons there are degrees of defect. It comes as a surprise to many people to find after serious study that most retarded persons are mildly affected. Helgason's 1964 analysis of a population in Iceland put the proportions of mild, moderate, and severe retardation at 73.70 per cent, 20.00 per cent, and 6.30 per cent (32). The comparatively low incidence of severe cases is partially explained by the reduction of longevity in persons with profound disorders of the nervous system. A second consideration of severity can be obtained from the slightly more restricted population of retarded children receiving special education. Educators typically use proportions of 80:15:5, to plan for educable, ineducable but trainable, and ineducable and untrainable children. Both this last estimate and Helgason's figures vary slightly, but show a consistent disproportion, i.e., more of the higher grades than middle or lower grades of retardation.

In 1951 Wunsch reported data from the "Rhode Island Mental Deficiency Register" (69). Analyzing data derived from 6,676 individuals, he found slightly more males than females. He reported 'good' adjustment in 3,376 cases, poor adjustment in 1,685. His frequency distributions are interesting. There were 319 cases below IQ 30; 1,051 cases between IQ 30 and 49; 5,036 cases in the IQ range 50-69; with 276 unknown. Clearly, the 50-69 IQ group with five thousand cases is the largest. There are very few cases below IQ 30; it should be noted that IQ 30 is a relatively doubtful concept as a result of the inadequacy with which psychometric devices shed light on serious deficiency.

In 842 cases the individuals were married and over twenty years of age. Three hundred and sixty-four had one child, 219 had two children, and 125 had three children. One hundred and seventy-eight had more than four children.

Rather different strategy in the study of retardation as a population problem is seen in the occasional study of small populations on an intensive basis. Representative examples of this technique are the studies of Rawnsley and Loudon (61), and Brunetti (11). Rawnsley and Loudon examined the two hundred and sixty-four persons living on the remote island of Tristan da Cunha. They had all possible psychiatric categories in mind during their studies. Six adults, or about 3 per cent of the total population, were judged mentally retarded. Brunetti found three of one hundred and two persons mentally retarded, which is consistent with most estimates. The subjects of this study were residents of a small commune in Provence, in the south of France.

Another study of importance in plotting the demography of mental retardation is the study, now some twenty-five years old, by Lemkau, Tietze, and Cooper (48). In reporting data from the 1936 survey of the Eastern Health District of Baltimore, they showed the following breakdown by age when white and Negro, male and female data were amassed. (See Table 1·2)

TABLE 1·2

MENTAL RETARDATION RATE PER THOUSAND PUPILS

Age Group	0-4	5-9	10-14	15-19	20-24	35-44	45-54	55-64	65+
Frequency	.7	11.8	43.6	30.2	7.2	8.1	8.3	2.6	1.9

A brief analysis of these data shows why mental retardation is such a curious entity, why one needs to look at many considerations, as we are doing in this chapter, rather than rely on a sharp IQ cut-off point or on a formal definition alone.

It would appear that mental retardation is a virtually unknown phenomenon in this study's sampling of small children. The elementary school years increase the incidence, and the secondary school years maximize the incidence. From that point on, the incidence decreases to a stabilized level through adult years, dropping off sharply after fifty-five years of age. Figure 1·1 shows a similar situation in a clinic population.

Figure 1·1

Ages of Patients in a Clinic Population

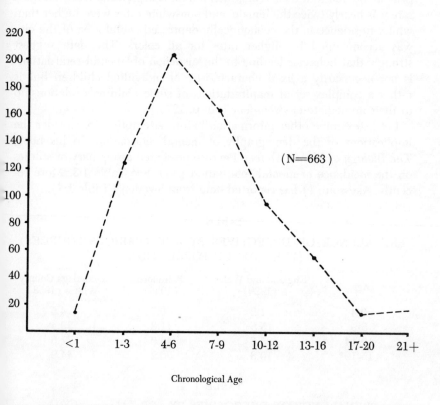

(N=663)

Chronological Age

Relationship to the passage of time is reported in Lee's study of low scoring Negro children in Philadelphia (46). He found that IQ's were higher in the children he studied when they had been in the Philadelphia schools for longer periods of time. Children entering first grade obtained higher IQ scores than those entering school at a higher grade.

Perhaps the most interesting data are from the Onondaga County Study in northern New York State. This useful study gives the following summary data.

A special census of children believed to be possibly retarded was conducted through local child-care agencies in a New York State metropolitan area. One per cent of all children under eighteen years of age were reported as retarded, measured by an intelligence quotient less than 75. Two-tenths (0.2) per cent were severely retarded, with an intelligence quotient greater than 75, a total of 3.5 per cent were referred as "possibly retarded."

Reported suspected prevalence rates were observed to vary markedly with age, sex, color, and place of residence. Rates increased to a peak at age ten to fifteen years, then fell off sharply. The reported male rate was nearly twice the female, and non-white rates were higher than white. Residence in the economically depressed cental area of the city was accompanied by higher rates for all colors. The data suggest strongly that behavior leading to the suspicion of "mental retardation" is not necessarily a fixed characteristic of individual children but is rather a complex set of manifestations of some children's relationship to their immediate environment (73, p. 127).

Let us examine other information before attempting to consider the implications of the demography of mental retardation. In his book, *The Biology of Mental Defect*, Penrose presented a summary of studies on the incidence of mental retardation (58). See Table 1·3. More recently, Akesson (1) has reported data from Sweden (Table 1·4).

TABLE 1·3

PREVALENCE OF DEFECTIVES BY AGE (VARIOUS SOURCES)
(PER 1,000 OF POPULATION)

Age	England and Wales (1929)	Baltimore (1936)	Onondaga County Whites (1953)
0-4	1.2	0.7	4.5
5-9	15.5	11.8	39.4
10-14	25.6	43.6	77.6
15-19*	10.8	30.2	44.9

TABLE 1·4

PREVALENCE OF DEFECTIVES BY AGE (Akesson, 1961)

In Malmohus County

Age group	0-5	5-10	10-15	15-20	20-30
Percentage	1.25	1.84	3.72	1.42	1.97

* 15-17 for Onondaga County, N. Y.

Tables 1·3 and 1·4 show representative data on the incidence of mental retardation. They contain information from Onondaga County in the west to Malmohus County in the east, from the United States to Sweden. The scope of study in mental retardation today is such that we need to maintain wide geographical as well as intellectual horizons. Also, we need to develop a time perspective ranging from the 1929 "England and Wales Study" to the 1961 "Southern Sweden" investigation. It is within the broad dimensions of epidemiology that mental retardation begins to project its diffuse forms. As Gruenberg (27) and the author (39) have pointed out elsewhere, the origins of mental retardation, as well as the forms, can be profitably studied through population studies. However, this method makes professional and personal demands on investigators well beyond those imposed by the use of experimental designs in contemporary behavioral science. Despite some obvious problems probably attributable to differences in methodology, there still remains the interesting reduction of incidence as a result of increasing age. The ten- to fourteen- or fifteen-year-old group is consistently the highest in frequency, and there is a decline after that point. This phenomenon is also substantiated in studies by Essen-Möller (21) in Sweden, and by Scally & Mackay (64) in Northern Ireland.

Another concern is the extent to which individuals of inadequate intellect are a threat to the level of intelligence of the population as a whole. The basis of the argument, generally, is the negative relationship between intelligence and fertility (3) (56). Clearly, mental retardation can be transmitted in a highly penetrative fashion (71), but it does not follow that mere decades separate us from pandemic mental retardation. On the other hand, it is not enough to consider this an academic issue because it has become entwined in the minds of some people with the problems of mental health, fluoridation of water, and the size of public welfare rolls.

Recently the author saw a column on the topic of reproduction by the mentally retarded and its effect on the tax rate. The column, which appears in hundreds of newspapers and is followed assiduously by a large number of people, asserted that the retarded and the mothers of illegitimate children propagate at a high rate and that the result is an increasing strain on the fabric of society. Put in emotional language, the effect was to leave readers with the conclusion that all the ills of mankind are hereditary and that punitive action is called for. Writing in an academic setting, the author cannot help but notice tens of thousands of bright young people, many of whom marry while attending college. If there is an imbalance in reproduction, it is probably a higher incidence of bright marrying bright, and doing so earlier because they are brought together in the flood of enrollments now submerging our colleges.

This issue requires consideration, since it regularly arises to cloud the discussion of mental retardation. Recent papers have taken a fairly broad position on the etiology of mental retardation. They assume that the mechanisms are diverse and that the issues are not susceptible to simple analysis (1).

Perhaps Penrose put the issues precisely when he discussed "Propagation of the Unfit" (57); in another paper he summarized the arguments and treated them with dispatch:

> A decline in the average intelligence level of the population has frequently been predicted as a consequence of the inverse relationship between intelligence and fertility. The evidence for declining intelligence is indirect. There is direct evidence of improvement of physique in the population and physique and intelligence are correlated. The suggestion is made that the population is approximately in equilibrium with respect to genes responsible for intellectual qualities. (56, p. 118).

It is now appropriate to evaluate the evidence presented. The occurrence of mental retardation as a measured, identifiable problem fluctuates a great deal. This means that the standards which measure intellectual adequacy are empirical and differ from one social context to another. The career of a retarded child moves him from the context of the home to school and then into society at large. The primary standards in the home are docility and motor development. The school stresses achievement in language and concept attainment. The society considers making a living and avoidance of law-breaking important. Failure at any stage of a person's career need not mean failure during the other stages. Thus the incidence of cases of mental retardation fluctuates. Empirically, the school years yield the greatest incidence of failure to meet criteria of adequacy.

SUMMARY

The purpose of this first chapter was expressed in the deliberate choice of words in the title, "Delineating Mental Retardation." The goal was not to *define*, but rather to *delineate*, which is a slightly different process.

We have examined several personal and social contexts in which human abilities operate. We have seen that what constitutes inadequate performance in one aspect of living is not necessarily inadequate performance in another.

Two points may stand out in retrospect. First, we began by offering formal definitions, but then we moved to approach the issue inductively, concluding our analysis only after studying mental retardation in several settings. Second, there was no attempt to define the condition by reference to arbitrary IQ standards and levels of attainment. Having given psychometric data a nod of recognition, we considered evaluation *in situ*, ending with reference to the attempt of the American Association on Mental Deficiency to conceptualize the problem— an attempt which deserves ample recognition.

We have seen that mental retardation is a phenomenon diverse in symptom and challenging in its questions. It remains now to examine some of the issues at a somewhat closer range; those issues are the substance of the remaining chapters of this book.

BIBLIOGRAPHY

1. Akesson, H. O., *Epidemiology and Genetics of Mental Deficiency in a Southern Swedish Population*, Institute for Medical Genetics, University of Uppsala, Sweden, 1961.

2. Anderson, G. W., "Current Trends in the Pathology of Human Reproductive Failure," *Am. J. Pub. Hlth.*, 1955, *45*, 1259-1266.

3. Anastasi, A., "Intelligence and Family Size," *Psych. Bull.*, 1956, *53*, 187-209.

4. ———, "Tested Intelligence and Family Size," *Eugen. Quart.*, 1954, *1*, 155-160.

5. ———, "Differentiating Effects of Intelligence and Social Status," *Eugen. Quart.*, 1959, *6*, 84-91.

6. Benoit, E. P., "Relevance of Hebb's Theory of the Organization of Behavior to Educational Research on the Mentally Retarded," *Am. J. Ment. Def.*, 1957, *61*, 497-507.

7. ———, "Towards a New Definition of Mental Retardation," *Am. J. Ment. Def.*, 1959, *63*, 559-565.

8. Benton, A. L., "The Concept of Pseudofeeblemindedness," *A. M. A. Arch. Neurol. Psychiat.*, 1956, *75*, 379-388.

9. Binet, A., and Simon, Th., *Enfants Anormaux*, Paris, Colin, 1907.

10. Bruner, J., "The Cognitive Consequences of Early Sensory Deprivation," *Psychosomat. Med.*, 1959, *21*, 89-95.

11. Brunetti, P. M., "A Prevalence Survey of Mental Disorders in a Rural Commune in Vaucluse: Methodological Considerations," *Acta Psychiat. Scand.*, 1964, *40*, 323-358.

12. Burt, C., *The Distributions and Relations of Educational Abilities*, London, 1917.

13. ———, "General Ability and Special Aptitudes," *Educ. Res.*, 1959, *7*, 3-16.

14. Carlson, H. B., and Henderson, N., "The Intelligence of American Children of Mexican Parentage," *J. Abn. & Soc. Psych.*, 1950, *45*, 544-551.

15. Cassel, R. H., "A Rigorous Criterion of Feeblemindness: A Critique," *J. Abn. & Soc. Psych.*, 1951, *46*, 116-117.

16. Dexter, L. A., "A Social Theory of Mental Deficiency," *Am. J. Ment. Def.*, 1958, *62*, 920-928.

17. Doll, E. A., "The Essentials of an Inclusive Concept of Mental Deficiency," *Amer. J. Ment. Def.*, 1941, *46*, 214-219.

18. Eccles, J. C., *The Neurophysiological Basis of Mind*, Oxford University Press, 1953.

19. Ellis, N., (ed.) *Handbook of Mental Deficiency*, McGraw-Hill, 1963.

20. Emmett, W. G., "The Intelligence of Urban and Rural Children," *Popul. Studies*, 1954, *7*, 207-221.

21. Essen-Möller, E., "Individual Traits and Morbidity in a Swedish Rural Population," *Acta Psychiat. Scand. Suppl.*, No. 100, 1956.

22. Frozlov, Y. P., "Present Day Cybernetics and the Human Brain," *Vopprosy Filosofi*, 1956, *3*, 116-122.

23. Galambos, R., "Suppression of Auditory Nerve Activity by Stimulation of Efferent Fibers to Cochlea," *J. Neurophysiol.*, 1956, *19*, 424-431.

24. Gibson, R., "A Tentative Clinical Classification of the Special Types in Mental Deficiency," *Am. J. Ment. Def.*, 1950, *54*, 382-393.

25. _____, "A Survey of Special Types Encountered in Mental Deficiency Clinics," *Am. J. Ment. Def.*, 1953, *58*, 141-142.

26. _____, "Changing Concepts of Mental Deficiency," *Ment. Hyg.*, 1959, *43*, 80-86.

27. Gruenberg, E. M., "Epidemiology," in Stevens, H., and Heber, R., (eds.) *Mental Retardation: A Review of Research*, University of Chicago Press, 1964.

28. Guilford, J. P., "The Structure of Intellect," *Psych. Bull.*, 1956, *53*, 267-293.

29. Hebb, D. O., *The Organization of Behavior*, Wiley, 1949.

30. _____, "Intelligence, Brain Function, and the Theory of Mind," *Brain*, 1959, *82*, 260-275.

31. Heber, R., "A Manual on Terminology and Classification in Mental Retardation," *Mon. Suppl. Am. J. Ment. Def.*, 1959, *64*.

32. Helgason, T., "Epidemiology of Mental Disorders in Iceland," *Acta Psychiat. Scand. Suppl. No. 173*, 1964.

33. Henry, J., "Docility; Or Giving Teacher What She Wants," *J. Soc. Issues*, 1955, *11*, 35-41.

34. Hilliard, L. T., and Kirman, B. H., *Mental Retardation*, Boston, Little Brown, 1957.

35. Jastak, J., "A Rigorous Criterion of Feeblemindedness," *J. Abn. Soc. Psych.*, 1949, *44*, 367-378.

36. Jordan, T. E., "Towards More Effective Use of the Term Mental Deficiency," *Am. J. Ment. Def.*, 1958, *63*, 15-16.

37. _____, "Conceptual Problems in the Development of a Taxonomy for Special Education," *Excep. Child.* 1961, *28*, 7-12.

38. _____, and deCharms, R., "The Achievement Motive in Normal and Mentally Retarded Children," *Am. J. Ment. Def.*, 1959, *64*, 457-466.

39. _____, "Retrospective versus Prospective Methods of Longitudinal Research," *Bull. Bureau Ed. Res.*, Southern Illinois University, 1964.

40. Kanner, L., "Feeblemindedness, Absolute, Relative and Apparent," *Nerv. Child*, 1948, 7, 365-397.

41. _____, *A Miniature Textbook on Feeblemindedness*, Child Care Publications, New York, 1949.

42. Kirk, S. A., *The Early Education of Mentally Retarded Children*, U. of Illinois Press, 1958.

43. Kratter, F. E., "The Pseudo-Mental-Deficiency Syndrome," *J. Ment. Sc.*, 1959, *105*, 406-420.

44. Lindman, F. T., and McIntyre, D. M., *The Mentally Disabled and the Law*, University of Chicago Press, 1961.

45. Lawrence, P. J., "A Study of Cognitive Error through an Analysis of Intelligence Test Errors," *Brit. J. Ed. Psych.*, 1957, *27*, 176-189.

46. Lee, E. S., "Negro Intelligence and Selective Migration," *Am. Soc. Rev.*, 1951, *16*, 227-233.

47. Leland, H., *Conference on Measurement of Adaptive Behavior*, Parsons State Hospital and Training Center, Parsons, Kansas, 1964.

48. Lemkau, P., Tietze, C., and Cooper, M., "Mental Hygiene Problems in an Urban District," *Ment. Hyg.*, 1942, *26*, 275-288.

49. McCulloch, T. L., "Reformulation of the Problem of Mental Deficiency," *Am. J. Ment. Def.*, 1947, *52*, 130-136.

50. Magoun, H. W., "Non-Specific Brain Mechanisms," in Harlow, H., and Woolsey, C. N., (eds.) *Biological and Biochemical Bases of Behavior*, University of Wisconsin Press, 1958.

51. Masland, R. L., Sarason, S. B., and Gladwin, T., *Mental Subnormality*, Basic Books, New York, 1958.

52. Maxwell, J., "Intelligence, Fertility, and the Future," *Eugen. Quart.*, 1954, *1*, 244-274.

53. Mead, G. H., *Mind, Self, and Society*, University of Chicago, 1934.

54. Oster, J., "Mental Deficiency: Scientific Problems, Progress and Prospects," *Am. J. Ment. Def.*, 1954, *59*, 425-433.

55. Pasamanick, B. A., "The Intelligence of American Children of Mexican Parentage: A Discussion of Uncontrolled Variables," *J. Abn. Soc. Psych.*, 1951, *46*, 598-602.

56. Penrose, L. S., "The Supposed Threat of Declining Intelligence," *Am. J. Ment. Def.*, 1948, *53*, 114-118.

57. ――――, "Propagation of the Unfit," *Lancet*, 1950, *259*, 245-246.

58. ――――, *The Biology of Mental Defect*, Sidgwick and Jackson, London, 1954.

59. Pevzner, M. S., *Oligophrenia: Mental Deficiency in Children*, Consultants Bureau, New York, 1961.

60. Porteus, S. D., and Corbett, G. R., "Statutory Definitions of Feeblemindedness in the U.S.A.," *J. Psychol.*, 1953, *35*, 81-105.

61. Rawnsley, K., and Loudon, J. B., "Epidemiology of Mental Disorder in a Closed Community," *Brit. J. Psychiat.*, 1964, *110*, 830-839.

62. Riggs, M. M., and Rain, M. E., "A Classification System for the Mentally Retarded," *Train. Sch. Bull.*, 1952, *49*, 75-84.

63. Samuels, I., "Reticular Mechanisms and Behavior," *Psych. Bull.*, 1959, *56*, 1-25.

64. Scally, B. G., and Mackay, D. N., "Mental Subnormality and Its Prevalence in Northern Ireland," *Acta Psychiat. Scand.*, 1964, *40*, 203-211.

65. Stein, Z., and Susser, M., "The Social Distribution of Mental Retardation," *Amer. J. Ment. Def.*, 1963, *67*, 811-821.

66. Tilley, W., "The Idiot Boy in Mississippi: Faulkner's *The Sound and the Fury*," *Am. J. Ment. Def.*, 1955, *59*, 374-377.

67. Werdegar, K., *Mental Retardation and the Law*, Study Commission on Mental Retardation, Sacramento, California, 1964.

68. Wheeler, L. R., "A Comparative Study of the Intelligence of East Tennessee Mountain Children," *J. Educ. Psych.*, 1942, *33*, 321-334.

69. Wunsch, W. L., "The First Complete Tabulation of the Rhode Island Mental Deficiency Register," *Am. J. Ment. Def.*, 1951, *55*, 293-312.

70. Yakovlev, P. I., "Anatomy of the Human Brain and the Problem of Mental Retardation," in Bowman, P., and Mautner, H., (eds.) *Mental Retardation: Proceedings of the First International Congress*, Grune and Stratton, 1961.

71. Zellweger, H., "L'Heredité dans La Maladie de Hurler," *J. Genet. Hum.*, 1958, *7*, 308-314.

72. Zuk, G., "The Mind as an Optical System," *J. Genet. Psych.*, 1959, *94*, 113-130.

73. *A Special Census of Suspected Referral Mental Retardation, Onondaga County, New York*, Technical data report: State Department of Mental Hygiene, Syracuse, New York, 1955.

Additional papers of interest may be found in the work, Jordan, T. E., *Perspectives in Mental Retardation*, Southern Illinois University Press, 1966.

1399485

Chapter 2

THE FAMILY

So far we have considered mental retardation in a variety of contexts. The various social aspects of the condition have emerged, and the life of the retarded individual has been discussed in a number of settings. In this chapter we shall see mental retardation in a slightly different perspective. Instead of focussing on the retarded individual, we shall consider the impact of the condition on the basic social unit, the family.

Here we are concerned with the problem of mental retardation as it affects human lives, the careers of retarded individuals, and the careers of those who live with them. Mental retardation as a public issue—as a school problem, a medical problem or a rehabilitation problem—is of secondary significance. Attention to these matters is obviously important, but it is justified only after we have seen the real proportion of the problem, which is the significance of mental retardation as a family issue.

THE DISCOVERY OF MENTAL RETARDATION

Discovery at Birth

The end of pregnancy is a strain in all families. The increasing discomfort of the mother and anticipation of an addition to the family present many problems. The actual process of terminating pregnancy is a serious medical matter and raises anxieties of a special sort. Apart from the intrinsic unpleasantness of delivery, a complex of fears and superstitions exists which can only be allayed by a completed and successful delivery.

The expectations which people hold for newborn children include a faulty conception of normality. Generally speaking, parents assume that a normal child is a perfect one. Such standards do not apply to themselves at the time; for example, most people are aware of some infirmities but do not consider themselves "un-normal." Few of us are wholly sound in mind and limb. Yet we expect perfection in babies. This expectation that babies are usually born without disorders is not supported by the facts. But the expectation persists, and anything less than perfection shocks and frightens the parents.

Clearly, then, the identification of mental retardation at birth comes at a time when parents are vulnerable physically and psychologically. Since mental retardation is usually inferred from severe physical disorders, the combination of symptoms and parent vulnerability creates havoc.

There are several ways in which parents may learn of the tragedy. The most helpful way is through a family physician who knows the couple and can break the news to them gently. Such a method of discovery in no way lessens the ultimate damage to parents, but it is the least overwhelming method under an almost impossible set of circumstances. Occasionally no mention of the subject is made, and the mother discovers for herself the nature of her child's disorders. Since parents expect normality, the result is catastrophic. In one such case the mother simply fled from a hospital, never to return.

A group of Scottish mothers of mongoloid children have provided information on the process of early identification and its consequences. Drillien and Wilkinson asked seventy-one mothers to recall the occasions on which they learned of their children's status and to reflect on their attitudes and subsequent reactions (22). The better reactions were associated with comparatively early disclosure together with support in the ensuing months and years. Resentfulness and current dissatisfaction were more commonly associated with a pattern of evasion or denial by physicians. A number of mothers said they could have been spared ". . . months of uncertainty and unexpressed fears" (22, p. 1307) by earlier disclosure of the problem. Keeping in mind the visible symptoms of mongolism will be helpful in relating these findings to the total problem of early diagnosis and counselling.

The advisability of placing the infant in a residential setting is often introduced at birth. In many places, unfortunately, this option does not occur since facilities do not exist, or are over-crowded. In those cases where the option does exist, several alternatives may be considered. The mother may never see the child, a fact which makes her vulnerable to a host of anxieties based on ignorance. Another alternative is for her to see the child after she has been suitably prepared and then allow the child to be placed in a hospital. Still another way is to let placement come when the mother has seen for herself that the child's growth and development does not match that of her other children. Perhaps the most helpful way to approach this serious problem is to avoid simple prescriptions. Jolly has advised against always insisting on immediate hospital placement (40). It is his suggestion that institutionalizing retarded infants depends on the specific family situation. In some cases it may come immediately, in other cases after a suitable period of time has elapsed.

Perhaps the basic consideration surrounding the placement of children in residential settings in infancy is the guilt and concern this may precipitate in the parents. Institutionalization does not mean abandonment, nor do hospitals and state schools intend that parents avoid all responsibility for a child committed to them for care (57). Walker pointed out that four problems typically present themselves to parents: "(1) the recognition of the child's defect; (2) the recognition that institutionalization is necessary; (3) the recognition that institutionalization be consummated at some definite given date; (4) the recognition that once consummated, emotion should not undo the action" (91, p. 108).

This is a heavy set of responsibilities. It means that the traditional responsibility for rearing children can be put aside and replaced by conviction that the child's welfare must take precedence over parental emotions.

Discovery in the Pre-School Years

Mental retardation is not always gross, nor are mentally retarded children necessarily any different in appearance from other youngsters. As a result, mental retardation may often go undetected for some time, emerging several years after the birth of the child. The discovery by the parents may be less sudden, less overwhelming, than discovery at birth, but its long-range effects may be just as profound.

In recent years most parents have acquired a smattering of knowledge about child development. Apart from this, people usually make comparisons using other people's children as standards. Thus, parents may discover that their child does not reach the developmental stages of growth attained by other children. Sitting may come slowly, language may be slow to emerge, or the youngster may appear dull and unresponsive. Setting aside the tyranny of child-growth norms so often misused by parents, there are cases where children do not grow at the proper rate. This delayed maturation is recognized by parents, and suspicions of retardation slowly develop.

Parents should test these suspicions by taking slow maturing youngsters to competent sources of help. A pediatrician may give insightful advice based on serious evaluation. The probabilities of this have increased in recent years as physicians have become more aware of the scope of the problem. This increased sensitivity is largely the result of parental willingness to discuss mental retardation. Apart from a degree of disinterest in the condition, physicians traditionally have not had the opportunity to consider mentally retarded children, largely because they were not asked to. Today we may say that the best single source of information and guidance is probably the general practitioner.

Other sources of help are the child-study clinics which have diagnostic, counselling, and training functions. The availability of these multidisciplinary units, which are designed to deal with all the problems of the family with a retarded child, is not great. On the other hand, such is the impact of having a young child suspected of mental retardation that parents often do not use clinical facilities when available. Such parents do not wish validation or rejection of their suspicions; they feel suspended judgment is preferable to confirmation of their fears. The same understandable aversion to an unpleasant reality can take a very different form when parents visit many clinics hoping to hear what they want to hear. In the absence of interagency pools for exchanging records and information, it is possible for several agencies in a metropolitan area to see the same set of parents and child in sequence, apart from innumerable visits to pediatricians and even chiropractors.

In an interesting and informative study Caldwell, Manley, and Seelye analyzed the reactions of parents to the series of a diagnostic clinic attached to a medical school (16). The majority of eighty-eight sets of parents clearly found the services of the clinic helpful, while about twenty parents were dissatisfied. The investigators formulated their subsequent analysis in such a way that the administrative and family-centered bases of reaction could be analyzed. The administrative variables generally did not distinguish satisfied from dissatisfied families; the exception was a more positive reaction from parents who made more visits to the clinic. A highly significant family variable, one beyond rectification by a change in procedures, emerged. Dissatisfied parents generally had children with a greater degree of retardation. The investigators could not explain this finding, but its existence was well beyond chance expectations and indicates a need for greater care in assisting parents of seriously retarded children.

Discovery in the Elementary-School Years

Over the years a number of functions originally assumed by other social units, particularly the home, have gravitated to the schools. The family's responsibility for ensuring good meals, for example, is now partially accepted by the schools. Although some of these responsibilities have been accepted reluctantly, others have been voluntarily assumed. In particular, the schools have voluntarily assumed partial responsibility for the health of school children, which has gradually been broadened to include mental as well as physical growth. As a result, the schools play a role in discovering mental retardation in the young.

Because of the particular demands which schools make on children, some young people are identified as exceptionally slow to learn. Typically, the poor performance of a child is called to the attention of the parents, and an investigation of the roots of the difficulty is begun. As we saw in the previous chapter, it is possible for a child to function at different levels during his life. The danger is that the school may place a broad judgment on a child, drawing unnecessary conclusions about all areas of functioning. For example, failure to make satisfactory progress in reading is not an exact diagnostic sign, but it may be construed as a sign of over-all slowness by the school.

Although such dangers exist, early identification by the school of mental disability involves several positive benefits for the child and for the family. As Chapter 11 will show, the family need not abandon all hope that the retarded child may some day make a living. Training is as crucial as ability. Training takes time. The diagnosis of retardation in the early school years provides the needed breathing-space before the child must leave school for industry. In the second place, as a result of early identification, the elementary school years may be adjusted to remove harmful pressures to succeed, such as unrealistic parental demands for school success and the school's equally unrealistic insistence on placing the child in a regular classroom with his age-mates. Further, when the problem is identified in the early school years, there may still be time to reconstruct the roles of the various members of the family. Because of the role they are expected to play as men, boys are valued as potential high-achievers. It is not fair to expect the retarded member of the family to play a role beyond his ability. Sisters may suffer by being forced into mothering roles. Proper identification and counselling may allow the family to shield its girls from this unhappy role. Finally, when retardation is identified in the early school years, the school may help the family develop outside interests and meet people whose experience is similar. Such contacts make a supportive contribution to the welfare of the family and its members.

FAMILY ADJUSTMENT TO MENTAL RETARDATION

Personal Reactions

The impact that mental retardation makes on the individual members of a family is only partially determined by the severity of the condition. Another important factor is the psychological structure of the various people whose lives are disrupted by the presence of a mentally retarded individual (24).

Occasionally people go to elaborate lengths to avoid facing unpleasant realities. Ego-defensive behavior is entirely understandable since it is a first line of defense against the anxieties which parents experience. People take refuge in denying the reality of the disorder. Some find solutions at the phantasy level, a more elaborate process (30) (96). Others, with little defense against their problems, develop psychotic reactions. But people with considerable sophistication sometimes employ more rational defenses. These relatively sophisticated reactions to anxiety are often appealing and may have a scientific connotation which is hard to analyze. Recognizing that the purpose of these more sophisticated defenses is adaptation to an unacceptable situation, let us examine several of the more elaborate.

1. *The Argument in Child Development.* Coleman cites the case of a mother who felt that, in effect, retardation in development indicated remarkable superiority. "One mother, whose nine-year-old son had been diagnosed by several psychologists and psychiatrists as mentally deficient, developed the firm belief that her son was a member of a new species which matured at a slow rate and would in the long run achieve a higher level of mental development" (19, p. 82).

In such instances parents are not reluctant to accept the reality of slow progress, but they reject the interpretation placed upon that evidence. While it is unwise to consider all children who mature slowly as mentally retarded, it is equally unwise to deny all but the name to a condition of extremely slow intellectual growth.

2. *The Argument in Ballistics.* The deviant growth patterns of retarded children are sometimes compared to a rifle bullet aimed at a target. The bullet misses the target as the retarded child misses developmental norms.

A parent may argue as follows: The bullet missing its target by a large error is on an inaccurate trajectory. The size of the error by which it missed its goal was not constant throughout flight. The final error at target distance was much larger than the initial error on leaving the rifle. One may say, therefore, that the error at target distance is not an absolute measure of the bullet's path, in that had the bullet been corrected, or corrected itself, the final error could have been much smaller.

The argument is sound for bullets, but the analogy needs scrutiny in the case of children. To what extent can a child's "trajectory" through life be changed? Studies in Chapter 9 will suggest that change is possible, but these studies claim modest alterations. The clearly demonstrated changes may well be analogous to the alteration of the path of a bullet in flight; but in one case they deal with conditions acquired after birth and functional; in the other they deal with mostly *non-organic children,* or children from deprived or depriving backgrounds. In no case is there the suggestion that *organic children,* or children from "good" homes, will or can make radical changes in their growth patterns when a valid diagnosis has been made.

The argument that the child fails to meet developmental standards as the bullet misses its mark assumes that the point of intellectual origin, birth, must have been correct. There are some children in whom mental retardation is a post-natal, acquired trait; on the other hand, there are those whose disorders are developmental, going back to the first trimester of pre-natal life. In such cases the validity of the ballistic analogy is slim.

3. *The Key to Unlock the Powers of the Mind.* A point of view with considerable appeal to people is the idea that the mentally retarded child is essentially sound. A block, analogous to the "mental block" of mental health literature, is preventing the expressions of a basically sound mind. The key to this block, the device to loosen the dormant powers, is typically a physiological tool. As some endocrine conditions respond to treatment, so the child in question may be helped by some *deus ex machina.* The particular agent may vary; in the past, glutamic acid was a candidate for the role, but it has not produced the

changes so eagerly awaited. Deanol is an agent now receiving similar attention. Currently, the great concern with *phenylpyruvic amentia* reflects the attitude in question. Perusal of the materials on mental retardation shows a degree of concern for this condition, and its dietary implications, that is out of proportion to its occurrence.

What can be said about "magic bullets" for mental retardation? In all probability we will continue to see chemotherapeutic advances. However, these will be agents designed to produce maximum effectiveness *within limits set by an inadequate somatic condition.*

4. *The Uncertainties of Differential Diagnosis.* There are several conditions which produce roughly comparable symptoms. Children who are retarded, children who are deaf, and children who are emotionally disturbed behave in what seems to be, except to the experienced diagnostician, a similar fashion. For example, such children are often similarly unresponsive in interpersonal settings and commonly present grossly disturbed language.

In recent years there has been increasing interest in language problems and in aphasia in particular. This interest, not always coupled with awareness of the comparative rarity of the condition, has brought the concept into the vocabularies of many people. It is therefore entirely possible, in the absence of very good psychodiagnostics, to reserve judgment about a child in the absence of incontrovertible proof that aphasia does not exist.

A parent, offered the idea of aphasia in preference to the term mental retardation, may be led to expect unreasonable improvement. Reasoning that the disorder may be neurologically circumscribed, parents may well expect a more normal course of development than is really warranted.

Obviously part of the trouble is the term. It would seem that a more phenomenal approach to the problem would lead to clearer statements and less confusion. This assumes that a diagnostician is equipped to make judgments precisely, namely, that he can sharpen the issues which constitute a differential diagnosis and can obtain enough evidence to study those issues.

Probably more needs to be written about aphasia. There are people in evaluative positions who encounter more aphasic children, and report more "congenitally aphasic" children, in one year than many see in a lifetime. That the condition of aphasia exists is indisputable; that it exists as commonly as parents are led to believe is less certain.

All four of the personal reactions described above tend to avoid issues. They have a semantic value; namely, they employ ideas which are more acceptable than mental retardation. They also provide an opportunity to shield oneself from the finality which the judgments of mental retardation erroneously seem to imply. It seems safe to say that parents who resort unduly to these reactions may need help in accepting their child's problem. Such acceptance comes hard, but it can be reached through slow, considerate, patient help.

Family Types

Families may be described in many ways, and there are many issues around which descriptions may be built. Benda and associates have offered a description of the family structure of 205 persons without organic complications at the Fernald State School in Massachusetts, whose retardation was slight enough to make residential living unlikely (7). The families turned out to be typical; in virtually all cases (94 per cent) there was one or more retarded individual, apart from the person in residence. In more than half the cases (57 per cent) the family unit was not intact due to divorce, separation, or the absence of a husband for an unwed mother. Of these factors, separation (or desertion) was most frequent. Almost half the families did not provide adequate care and were somehow involved in "social pathology," meaning difficulty with society norms of some type. Limited data indicated that the socio-economic level of the families was low. Wakefield's analysis of families of educable retarded children in special classes considered family income, housing, parental intelligence and parental schooling (90). Analyzing the backgrounds of 619 children from 563 families in metropolitan Los Angeles, Wakefield found they came from lower social status, generally. Family income and expenditure for housing were significally below average as was parental education. Intelligence test results were available for 145 parents who had attended schools in the district. Levels of intelligence were low for both mothers and fathers; nearly twice as many mothers had IQ's below seventy-five. There were no sex differences when the cumulative proportions were considered; about 77 per cent of both sexes were below IQ 90.

Relevant materials from Lancashire developed by Stein and Susser use three concepts to describe support (1) *functioning,* (2) *deviant,* and (3) *dysmorphic,* the latter meaning unable to provide sustaining relationships (84). Dysmorphic families were commonly from the lowest socio-economic levels (55 per cent). Ninety per cent of a small series of illegitimate children come from dysmorphic families. Legal offenses by members of the cohort of former special school students occurred most commonly in dysmorphic families, as did admission to institutional living.

A further contribution to the classification of families has been given by Stein and Susser. Using the characteristics described in the preceding paragraph, these investigators identified families by occupation and education. Some families were classified *aspirant*, because the father's occupation and the educational attainment of the children was above average. In such families, retarded children are more likely to be conspicuous. Their lack of achievement potential is usually perceived clearly and they receive a different pattern of nurture. Because of the pervasive nature of *aspirant* family reaction, the development of the children is affected by socialization as well as by innate limitations. Aspirant families are less likely to be dysmorphic, and they contribute comparatively few cases to the lists of children receiving consideration as "educationably subnormal." When such families have retarded children they are more likely to seek out help from social agencies, and the children are more likely to have neurological forms of retardation. Other families considered by Stein and Susser to be members of a different subculture were designated *demotic*, because of their educational and occupational attainment. The demotic families are distinguished by social and geographic immobility, although the dysmorphic, i.e., non-supportive families, were quite mobile and scattered.

Dysmorphic families are sometimes described by words such as "depriving" or "disadvantaged," or "culturally deprived." The common element of poverty produces a depressing effort on mental maturity when compounded by neglect. Fortunately, there is reason to believe that such families can be helped; in the absence of such therapeutic intervention, residential living is sometimes beneficial. Windle (92), and pre-school care can produce amelioration (50).

A word of caution is in order. The terms used by Stein and Susser were applied to families in Lancashire. While concepts are generalizable, the criteria used to apply them are specific; that is, they might be applied with accuracy to Holt's families in Yorkshire, but not to Farber's families in Chicago. British social classes are not identical with American groupings, and the concepts may be misapplied easily. Cross-cultural studies can be quite valuable, but concepts must be used very carefully in order to avoid errors of application and conclusion.

Another way to describe families of retarded children is to cite the strategies they adopt in attempts to cope with their problems. Farber has pointed out that some families experience a sense of crisis particularly at the time when retardation is diagnosed (25, p. 108). This tragic crisis is similar to the experience of death and the state of bereavement. It may be followed with a chronic state of *role organization* crisis, a condition in which members of the family fail to reach accommodation with the problem by developing suitable roles. Analyzing the reactions of 268 mothers, Farber concluded that his typology of family behavior was generally accurate for families whose retarded child was living at home. He indicated that the tragic crisis is a phenomenon associated with high socio-economic status, while the *role organization* crisis is associated with low socio-economic status; the role organization problem is probably related to problems of marital organization.

Saucier's work with Canadian families whose children have chronic diseases is also relevant (73). Studying families classified as English, French, and Jewish, he has concluded that reactions to disability are predictable to some extent and that the patterns of adjustment are fairly consistent. In general, the English and Jewish families were comparable in their modes of reaction, while French families differed slightly. More important was family size; Saucier considered the meaning of illness and inferred that it might have different significance to large and small families.

Farber has also classified family's strategies as *child-oriented, home-oriented,* and *parent-oriented* (24). Failure to behave in a way which can be subsumed under one of these types generally connected a low degree of marital integration, while adoption of one of the strategies generally favored a higher degree. Use of constructive rather than disruptive patterns of family behavior usually led to good marital integration, regardless of home or residential placement of the retarded child. Farber has observed that the classification of families by strategies is modified by other factors such as socio-economic level, religion, income, and similar ecological considerations. Interestingly, he has not found it satisfactory to classify families as those who place, and do not place, a retarded child in a residential agency. In his own words, it is not a "major solution"; it is meaningful only in specific configurations of ecological factors. Generally, willingness to institutionalize was inversely related to marital integration, with some differences between husbands and wives. Social status was also influential, as was religion, and the sex of the child (28). The finding that highly integrated couples are less willing to institutionalize is comparable to Saenger's observation that the rate of institutionalization in the city of New York is six times higher in broken homes than in intact homes (72). Saenger's analysis of families showed that very few seriously retarded persons living in the community had inadequate parents; they were much more likely to be under residential care. Saenger's study also showed that families cannot be classified as loving or rejecting on the basis of the decision to place a child in a residential agency.

It follows from the observations just reported that there are many ways to describe families and their capabilities for coping with retarded children and the secondary problems they generate. Complexity rather than simplicity distinguishes the reactions of adequate families, and there are probably many more inadequate than adequate family groups. A second comment is in order; the accounts given in the preceding paragraphs all flow from social science concepts and techniques. Formulation of mental retardation and its attendant problems in social science terms seems quite invaluable and can lead to highly productive findings. It is hoped that the modest trend to formulate retardation as a social-familial issue can be encouraged. It seems to merit at least as much support as consideration on medico-biological grounds.

Group Reactions

A family is a miniature society. As a society has a population explosion, so some families have a great number of children. As societies are rent by civil war, so families are divided. As a civil crisis may rock a nation, leading it to analyze its values and goals, so may the presence of a retarded child shift a family from its predictable growth, even to the extent of destroying it.

In this section we are interested in the impact of a natural disaster, the occurrence of a retarded child, on the integrity of family life. The retarded individual is affected by his disorder, but the lives of the immediate family may be equally scarred, though in a different way. Let us begin by considering the effects of a retarded child on the previously planned course of family life.

One consideration is the effect on the atmosphere of family life. A common occurrence is rejection of the child by one parent. The burden may be passed to the other equally rejecting parent whose bitterness then grows. Husband and wife tension is added to parent-child tension. A retarded child is not sheltered from naked feelings by his intellectual limitations. Apart from these admittedly general considerations, there are some empirical findings on family reactions to retarded children.

Schonell and Watts (77) attempted to look at the problems several years ago in Australia. Using essentially a descriptive method, they approached fifty families with subnormal children and asked a number of questions, all designed to survey the effects of the retarded child on the family. From the answers they received, it was apparent that many facets of family life were marred by the defective child's presence in the home. In addition to finding that the child was usually the youngest or the eldest, they noted that: "It is strikingly clear from the evidence collected that the effects on family life may be of an economic, social, or emotional kind and that they may be far-reaching and intensively restrictive and disruptive in nature" (77, p. 218).

In England, Holt (38) has reported the effects of a retarded child upon attempts at family limitation, while Farber has examined the impact of the severely retarded child upon the American family (23) (24).

Holt's study reported data on how the presence of a retarded child affects the family's decision to limit the number of children. Table 2·1 presents data on the desirability of further pregnancies.

TABLE 2·1

THE POSSIBILITY AND DESIRABILITY OF MORE PREGNANCIES
IN 210 FAMILIES WITH RETARDED CHILDREN

Parents indifferent to the question of more pregnancies . 29 families
More pregnancies wanted . . . . 39 families
More pregnancies not wanted . . . . 101 families
More pregnancies not possible (menopause, death or
    separation of parents) . . . . 41 families
Total . . . . 210 families

Of the 210 families only 39 (or 19 per cent) actually wanted more children. The desire for more pregnancies was much greater in mothers under 36 years of age than among those older. When interpreted in terms of the position of the retardate in the family, the young mothers of first-born retardates seemed more in favor of further pregnancies. The severity of a child's retardation did not seem to affect the issue greatly, and no conclusions about religious affiliation, or occupational status were reported. Among the families that did not want more children, and took active steps to avoid pregnancies, the "failure" rate was about 25 per cent. Among those who did not want more children, but took no active steps to avoid conception, the "failure" rate was about 75 per cent.

Farber has worked from a specific, self-conscious point of view, that of the social scientist. As a sociologist, he analyzes people as members of a social unit. Using the conceptual model of the life cycle, he relates the retardate's family to contemporary American families (23). Accepting the idea that the individuals in the family have careers, a changing series of roles, Farber views family integration as derived from consensus on the goals for careers. In essence, this study analyzes family integration by analyzing how the retardate's career affects the life cycle of the family.

While the findings of the study are important, the work also stands because of its excellent conceptual base. In any study, data become valuable insofar as they shed light on the nature of the problem. It is the conceptual aspect of an issue which is its core. If the issues to be analyzed are stimulating, and if the method is more than descriptive, an investigation may create information rather than merely collect it. A common failing in studies is that the collection of evidence is often confused with analyzing it. A fruitful analysis is possible when the conceptual aspect of a problem is thought through. Farber's study is important because of its conceptual significance and sophistication.

The results of the Farber study indicate that the presence of a retarded child has a serious impact on the family. Marital integration suffers when a retarded child lives with the family; the effect is more pronounced when the child is a boy and when the family is lower-class. As the boy grows older, marital integration suffers more. Generally speaking, placing a boy in a residential setting had a positive effect on the parents' marital relationship. The findings on the retardate's impact on the siblings were as follows: The younger retardate affects the siblings' adjustment most. Girls were more affected by the retarded sibling at home than boys. Maladjustment was greater in boys when the retardate was institutionalized.

Farber defined the relationship of the parents to the community as supportive or non-supportive interaction. When other people felt that the parents' procedures were "correct," interaction was considered supportive. In those cases where understanding and encouragement were absent, interaction with other people was considered non-supportive. Religious affiliation was an important factor in support and non-support.

Other considerations of the effects of religion as a supportive factor have been reported by Zuk (96) (97). He has reported that Catholic mothers are less likely to feel that the presence of a mentally retarded child is the fate they deserve for past errors. Zuk feels that Catholicism offers a mother explicit absolution from responsibility (96). He and his co-workers have found that Catholic mothers tend to express attitudes of acceptance more than non-Catholic mothers. According to Zuk, this degree of support in a situation likely to produce catastrophic reactions may also occur in other groups such as the Hutterites. In Switzerland, Répond has noted a difference between French-speaking

Protestant and Catholic traditionalist families (68). The Catholic families seem more likely to accept the problems of children passively, while Protestant families are more likely to seek assistance. He has also pointed out that rural families seem able to absorb handicapped children without disintegration. He wondered, however, whether this would change with industrialization.

STRATEGIES

If we accept the idea that the impact of mental retardation on a family is severe, it becomes appropriate to consider the reality factors to which the parents adjust and to analyze the strategies which they adopt.

Reality Factors

1. A practical problem in the reaction of a family to its retarded member is the consideration of who will assume responsibility for the handicapped person in the future. In some cases the retarded person may not have a great life expectancy, but on the whole it is realistic to ask who will care for the person when the parents are too old or are dead. The eventual disposition of this problem becomes more severe as time passes. There are two reasons for this. First, agencies that would accept a young child may not accept an adolescent or an older person. Second, a child who has grown in a family circle may not consent to enter an institution with its totally different regimen and its necessary concern for more than one person's wishes.

2. Another problem is the obvious matter of severity. A child who is totally dependent does not present the same reality problems as one whose major disadvantage lies in coping with academic school work. It is entirely possible for the educable person to fit into societal living eventually, maintaining a degree of self-care that makes him no intolerable burden. On the other hand, the family may face the reality of a severely retarded child and realize that no real solution is possible except for someone to become responsible for the day-by-day care of the handicapped individual.

3. A related point is the presence of multiple handicaps and the cumulative effects they have on the family. Such persons require a great deal of care and attention. Cerebral palsy cases may present serious care problems because virtually all possibility of self-care may be ruled out.

4. In some places parents have to contend with the problem of limited facilities. In such cases acceptance of the need to place a child in a residential setting may be frustrated by a lack of space in hospitals and

colonies. In cases of moderate and mild retardation the absence of such facilities as special classes and the more pressing problem of post-school training facilities may present reality factors to which parents must adapt. The form of their adaptation is an interesting issue.

Patterns of Adaptation

The way in which families react to the presence of a mentally retarded child has been analyzed by Farber (24). In what is one of the more sophisticated monographs in the voluminous literature on mental retardation, he has shown how a mathematical model can be applied. Taking Von Neumann's "Theory of Games" as his model, and using "Nature" as the opponent, he has described the gambits which families of varying backgrounds employ.

Three general strategies which can be used to meet the disintegrating ploy of "Nature" are described. The family may employ the strategy which Farber calls "child-centered"; in this response the family reacts by concentrating its activities around the functioning of its normal children. In the "home-oriented" strategy the emphasis is on a pleasant home life. Farber feels that male children are appreciated for their intrinsic value, as are girls, de-emphasizing the achievement potential of the boys. The "parent-oriented" strategy requires that family values be built around social skills, achievement, and personal growth. The use of these strategies seems to be generally sound, although Farber has cautioned against overgeneralizing from his findings.

Alternatives to the three courses of action are (1) the "only-child" strategy, which does not necessarily lead to a degree of marital adjustment above the average for parents of retarded children, (2) the "compensated child-oriented" strategy, in which the mother fails to identify with the normal children. Apart from the non-identification, this gambit is generally similar to the "child-centered" strategy mentioned before.

According to Farber, the relevance of this study, based on the problem-situation of 223 families living in the Chicago area, is as follows:

1. The institutionalization of a severely retarded child seems less crucial for marital integration than the orientation of the family.
2. The combination of an acute situation and the particular strategy employed seems to determine the degree of marital integration, more so than either factor alone.

It should be noted that the adequacy of each strategy is partly determined by a number of circumstances. The factors of religion, socioeconomic status, birth-order, and sex all determine the effect of the retarded child on marital integration and the effectiveness of specific attempts to become accommodated to the problems.

An important factor in considering parental reactions is the decision to institutionalize a retarded child. In another of the excellent studies sponsored by the State of New York, Saenger has analyzed the factors and circumstances that attend the process of removing a retarded person from the home to a residential setting (72). The study is concerned with persons in New York City, and the findings are considered in the next chapter.

THE FAMILY AND CHILD-REARING

One of the more gross analyses of human behavior has been the idea that all the characteristics of a retarded person reflect mental retardation alone. In this analysis of human behavior, the way a retarded child acts and his over-all personality are accounted for by considering his mental retardation. This oversimplification ignores the fact that retarded youngsters, like all young people, develop as a result of the way they are raised. Early training determines later effectiveness in retarded youngsters as in normal children. Only the more profoundly retarded child is an exception.

Working from the premise that the retarded behave partly as they have been taught to behave, we may consider the crucial problem of how retarded children are reared. In view of the varied cultural settings into which children are born, it should be stressed that the ensuing comments are relevant to children born in the main stream of society.

In our society child-rearing is largely the mother's responsibility. We may sharpen the focus of the discussion, then, by considering mothers and retarded children.

Becoming a Mother

The process of becoming a mother starts in infancy (56). People raise their children from the beginning with ideas and expectations based on the sex of the child. A boy is evaluated differently from a girl. Once the total dependence of infancy has passed, different sorts of toys are extended to children, and different standards are used to evaluate their behavior.

A girl is expected to learn doll play and to acquire many of her mother's traits and skills. As a girl enters adolescence, caring for other people's children is encouraged, and the girl extends her growth into the eventual adult role of mother. Fulfilling the role of mother is a long-term goal, and it is also a broad goal. The term *total mother person* has been suggested to describe those components of maternal behavior that impinge on the growth of children (6). Certainly several dimensions of maternal behavior, rather than one, are involved in child-rearing. A girl is prepared for child-rearing when she has assimilated her new role to the extent that it is a basic component of personality. As McClelland *et al.* have documented, the particular set of values a girl assimilates as she grows towards motherhood depends on a number of cultural and religious factors (55). The girl entering motherhood has developed her mother-quality as she has grown and in the particular circumstances of her own exposure to child-rearing values. Of course, not all women develop a self concept built around anticipations of starting a family and raising children. Alternatives are self-concepts built around physical beauty and attractiveness. Even bright children can be an irritation to a woman with essentially narcissistic self-perceptions. Pregnancy can be formulated as the loss of one's pleasing appearance; the care of children—meaning diversion of energies from self-nurture to child nurture—may be a reminder of the passage of time. Obviously, retarded children constitute a basis for self-reproach and derogation to a person with a self-centered, non-nurturing attitude.

Schipper has pointed out what can happen when a girl has not reached maturity in her role as a mother (76). Of a series of mothers with mongoloid children, six regressed to a more immature level of behavior and became quite dependent on their own mothers. Schipper pointed out that the reaction of these women was such that they created more family disturbance than the mongoloid child.

A study of perceptions of retarded children by thirty-nine parents, mostly mothers, has been reported by Worchel and Worchel (94). Seventeen normal and twenty-three retarded children were rated on a series of thirty-eight traits, and a rating was made on idealized fictional children. The results took the form of discrepancies between perceptions of the retarded child (I) and normal children (II), and ideal children (III). The investigators found that retarded children were (1) rated less favorably than normal children, (2) rated less favorably than normal children in comparison with ideal children, (3) were considered more different from normal children than ideal children, in a negative rather than a positive way (ideal children). These were, of course, individual differences in perceptions, and some parents saw retarded children more positively than the majority of normal children.

Maternal Behavior and Child Growth

Before discussing the ways maternal behavior can be related to child growth, we may consider those factors whose locus is the mother.

While the "total mother person" may be the unit largely perceived by the child, investigators have usually chosen less gross constructs and have attempted to relate specific maternal characteristics to child development.

Winterbottom has demonstrated that the achievement motivation of boys can be systematically related to maternal attitudes towards independence training (93). Boys who were high in achievement motivation had mothers whose concern for early-independence experiences distinguished them from other mothers.

The highly relevant issue of children's intelligence has been analyzed by Hurley (39). The problem of the level of intelligence in children has been related to the extent to which the mother dominates the child. It is Hurley's conclusion that some middle degree of maternal domination has an "optimal positive impact."

Four areas of child behavior have been related to maternal child-rearing practices. Klatskin, Jackson, and Wilkins have reported data from the Yale Rooming-In Research Project (51). They have found that disorders in the child due to the way the mothers handled the problem of sleep occurred in the first year of life. Feeding, toileting, sleeping, and social problems emerged as significant in the second and third years.

On the other hand, to consider evidence in another direction, Brown was unable to relate children's adjustment to attributes of the mother (15). Working from an initial sample of 500 cases, Brown felt that the extreme groups of children on the continuum of adjustment had mothers who were similar in attitudes toward child behavior.

Klebanoff's study of the values of mothers whose children were brain-injured and retarded, schizophrenic, and normal concluded that only the factor of "overpossessiveness" distinguished normal mothers from the mothers of the two experimental groups of children (52). Higher scores on this factor were identified using Schaefer and Bell's Parent Attitude Research Instrument (74) (75).

Altman was unable to relate mothers' statements of their behavior and attitudes to the personality structures of their children (2). The self-perceived qualities of child-rearing practices do not seem to be the ones that count. On this basis, awareness of one's actions, one's methods, is not the crucial factor.

Furthermore, specific practices may be less crucial than personality. Contrary to the well-formulated interaction of social class and rearing practices (54), Bossard and Boll have asserted that it is people, not methods of child rearing, that are important within a culture (11).

If a conclusion is possible concerning the scarcely explored territory of child behavior and maternal characteristics, it should come from experimentation because the issues defy simple description. Uyeno has studied the hereditary and environmental aspects of dominant behavior in animals (89). The complexity of the sources of behavior in simple creatures is evident in Uyeno's work. About the only adequate conclusion that can be made about humans is that maternal attributes do relate to children's behavior in a significant fashion. The mechanisms involved are not easily comprehended and seem to reflect various degrees of complex interaction.

The Retarded Mother

One of the social realities of retardation is that many persons whose intellectual limitations are clear are entirely capable of procreating, and commonly do so. At one time this reality, which has surely been with us since time immemorial, raised great concerns in the minds of persons who saw retardation in purely biological terms. The involuntary-sterilization movement arose largely because eugenicists wished to limit reproduction. Fortunately, that proto-Nazi movement has been replaced by a more informed view of the sources of retardation, and contemporary eugenicists speak more conservatively of the amount of retardation to be found among the issue of retarded persons (53). In particular, they acknowledge the basis for much retardation in acquired damage to the nervous system.

The retarded girl who conceives is obviously more important than the retarded father since girls are more likely to be burdened with the responsibility of caring for children. Obviously, not all retarded girls are capable of reproduction; those whose retardation is most profound are usually biologically inefficient to the point of infertility, while the brighter are usually biologically efficient. Since the latter group are usually members of the lower social classes, the *demotic* groups, as Stein and Susser term them (84), we cannot easily separate mothering behavior from the social class norms for child care and family maintenance. We have seen earlier in this chapter that retarded children often come from disorganized, non-supportive families. It follows that we generally have a pattern of nurture that is not good, and leads to less than optimal development in the children. It may be that the retarded mother raises children without a husband to help. In such cases the husband either abandoned the family or was never married to the mother. The resultant pattern of nurture is probably attributable to the mother's intellectual limitations as well as to the problem of an unstable home.

An analysis of retarded mothers who left a hospital in London is informative (13). Brandon's group had an average Wechsler IQ around eighty, although Stanford-Binet scores were lower. More of the women under forty, about one-third, were married; about three-fourths of those over forty were unmarried. In general their performances as wives, housewives, and mothers were rated average by a social worker. In all three areas of functioning the effective women were neither brighter nor duller than the ineffective. Brandon concluded that they were capable of bringing up children and running a home when they were compared with normal women in similar circumstances.

It should be pointed out that the women studied by Brandon had maintained some slight degree of contact with the hospital; also, the circumstances in which they functioned were probably not representative, but probably demotic.

Not all retarded girls who became mothers live on the keen edge of social adversity. On occasions there are examples of relatively successful outcomes to pregnancy and child care.

Mary is a quiet, apparently shy girl whose life prior to marriage consisted of meeting the social and cultural obligations which her upper-class family has cultivated for two generations. After completing the course at a private secondary academy, Mary was presented to society, and shortly after married a young man who found her shyness and slight gaucherie quite charming. Currently she lives in a large modern house and spends little of her time at social functions, preferring to look after her baby and to clean her large house without the assistance of a maid.

Here we have a young woman who is happily married and conducting the affairs of her household quite well. With the exception of her still skeptical family, no one knows that Mary has a Stanford-Binet IQ in the borderline range, and that her present life-style is a successful continuation of her great childhood delight—playing house.

Maternal Behavior and the Retarded Child's Growth

Having established that a relationship exists between attributes of the mother and growth in children, we may move on to consider this relationship in the case of retarded children. Evidence on the problem has come from Centerwall and Centerwall (18). Mongoloid children reared in the home were compared with similar children not reared in the home. Two interesting indices of velocity of growth, the intelligence quotient and the social quotient, were compared. In each case the youngsters raised in the home were maturing at a statistically more significant rate. It should be noted that a statistically significant difference in figures is not necessarily indicative of an observable difference in performance. The investigators concluded that growing up in the family circle is the experience which produces optimal growth in retarded children.

Richards and Sands have also examined the growth of retarded children (69). As in the Centerwall's study two settings were considered, the home and the institution. However, a third milieu was introduced, a foster home. The results showed that the intelligence quotients were highest in twenty-two children living at home ($\overline{M}$ IQ = 43.4), and that children of comparable age receiving family care were next in ability ($\overline{M}$ IQ = 24.9), while a comparable third group of eighteen were most retarded ($\overline{M}$ IQ = 19.3). Apart from this comparatively gross finding, Richards and Sands reported rating on twelve personality traits in sixteen mongoloid children living at home, and twenty-five living in a residential agency. In practically all cases the trait (e.g., *affectionateness, aggressiveness, cheerfulness, stability*) was rated higher in children living at home. The exception was a statistically insignificant difference in the rating for patience.

Kenney has examined some of the values and beliefs of mothers of retarded children who are adjusted and maladjusted (49). A "Family Problems Scale" and a sentence-completion test were administered to four groups of mothers of normal and retarded, maladjusted and adjusted school children. From these instruments, data were developed on maternal ego-development and authoritarianism. The findings relevant to this discussion are: (1) mothers of adjusted, retarded children had a higher level of ego-development than mothers of maladjusted, retarded children; (2) mothers of adjusted, retarded children had a higher level of authoritarianism than mothers of maladjusted retarded children. In this last regard mothers of retarded, maladjusted females had the highest scores. Generally speaking, the least authoritarian mothers had better adjusted children, whether retarded or not.

Related work by Aserlind examined characteristics of mothers from lower-class neighborhoods in Milwaukee whose children seemed most and least likely to experience a decline in IQ during the childhood years (5). "High-risk" mothers were not distinguished by age or education, but were distinguished by a greater number of children and by a lesser degree of linguistic maturity. Aserlind concluded that verbally skilled mothers are likely to provide linguistic enrichment vital to normal intellectual maturation.

Pringle and Bossio have reported related information on English children reared in institutions (65). In their sample 188 boys and girls were without parents because of divorce (44 per cent of the cases); illness and poverty, but not specific rejection by parents, accounted for another 20 per cent; confinement of the parents for psychiatric or criminal reasons accounted for another 20 per cent, while 16 per cent were held to be "uncontrollable" at home.

The most relevant findings in this study were that the more severely deprived youngsters were duller, as were those children who had no contact with their parents. All the children were essentially normal, but dullness was more evident in the more deprived.

The mechanisms which produce a change in the development of children are not clear. Goshen (32) suspected failure to evoke linguistic responses; and, as we shall see in the next chapter, there have been some attempts to explain how residential living affects child development. However, home living has not been particularly analyzed, in the sense of mechanisms of behavior through which mothers influence children. It would be valuable to know precisely what achievement- or independence-inducing behavior is, for example. Usually we are forced to consider maternal values and to infer mechanisms where none have been found. For example, the writer has described the values of mothers using the *Parent Attitude Research Instrument, Form IV, (74, 75)* and has related them to intelligence and social quotients in retarded children (42). Using that approach it was possible to establish a rational connection between mothers and children through statistically significant multiple correlation coefficients. That was done, however, for didactic purposes; the results consisted of statements about variables whose locus is in the mother and other variables whose locus is in the child. The value of the statements lay in their demonstration that attributes of the mother affect growth characteristics in retarded children. What this evidence does not do (nor can any study using this model) is to analyze *how* maternal and child variables blend. What is needed are data on interaction between mother and child, and such findings are not possible when using a correlational model. The use of any correlational model, no matter how sophisticated the analysis, cannot yield interactive data. The difficulty is one of construct validity.

The Conceptual Problem. If data are to have construct validity, they should be obtainable only under strict conditions. The alternative is to run the risk of other constructs being applicable. Also, construct validity suggests that the relevant behavior should emerge under experimental manipulation of situational factors. For example, interaction data should be that nexus of behaviors that emerge when actors interact. There should be no other possible circumstances in which the data might emerge. This is an issue which the theoretician Kantor called attention to nearly two decades ago (47). In 1959 Plutchik and Kronovet called attention to some over-all problems (63). They believed that there were three broad problems in studies of parent-child relations: (a) inadequately defined measuring tools, (b) ambiguous or ethically loaded concepts, and (c) the use of non-representative samples.

These suggestions are offered for a second-generation set of studies of a more crucial, more definitive order.

1. The construct of *role* in behavior is a logical starting point.

2. When two people (two roles) are mutually involved, the resultant behavior may be considered interactive.

3. The emergent behavior is interactive data and may be manipulated by altering the circumstances of the two-person group, or *dyad*.

4. The data may be verbal data or may be physical data emerging from the particular purposes of the dyad.

5. As Jones and Thibaut have indicated, the interaction of a two-person group may be schematized as *non-contingent interactions, asymmetrically contingent interactions,* and *reciprocally contingent interactions* (41).

6. A complementary set of ideas is to define one person in the *dyad* and to scale that person's behavior as it initiates the various sets of interactions. This may be done simultaneously for the other person; theoretically, although, as anyone who has tried to record behaviors *in situ* will recall, this poses procedural problems.

Clearly this is an overture to research. It should be reacted to as an attempt to build a limited model of mother/retarded child interaction. Apart from the procedural elements of this proposal, for which several alternatives could be sketched, attention is called to the implicit values of this approach.

To begin with, this model is derived from contemporary theory in the social sciences. It reflects a deliberate preference for small-group theory in social psychology as a matrix within which to analyze group processes (88). Further, it uses recent developments in the study of two-person groups (41). Such formulations are useful in a number of settings. The application of the two-person group to the scarcely explored interaction of retarded child and adult is another illustration of the value of this model. Virtually the only application of small-group theory to retardation can be found in the work on language conducted by Siegel (79), and Siegel and Harkins (80). In those investigations the linguistic behavior of two-person groups was analyzed. The two studies cited might be profitably replicated with mothers used in place of the adults specified in the University of Kansas studies. Until such steps are taken, valuable knowledge of mother-child interaction will remain lost.

We may now consider another contribution which should be applied to studies of interaction in families of retardates. The approach which has validity in the sense of emerging from interaction has been developed by Haley (34). He formulated questions about repetitive patterns among speakers (in this instance members of eighty families) although none had a retarded member. Haley's evidence can be illustrated by pointing to the possible sequence of speakers among a mother (M), a father (F), and a child (C). Any member may or may not speak or be followed by any other member of the triad; such a sequence might be any combination of MF & C, e.g., MCMFC, etc. Haley found it possible to develop a typology based on departure from random occurrence of each person's speech.

THE FAMILY AND THE COUNSELING PROCESS

Up to this point we have focused on the behavior of parents and children. This is entirely reasonable, but it would be misleading to leave the problem in that form. After countless informal evaluations in the form of comparisons with other children, the parents of retarded children may seek help of some sort. They may seek advice from someone who they feel can offer expert advice. Let us examine the manner in which parents may be helped in counseling interviews. The discussion will place more emphasis on content than on technique and process, an approach self-consciously selected and apparently shared by others (9).

Counseling Defined

Basically, the counseling process starts with two people. One, the client, has a problem; the other, the counselor, has relevant information and some skill in helping people. Typically, the process of counseling consists of a conversation between the two which, ostensibly, treats the issue by negotiation and discussion.

A more penetrating analysis reveals other things, however. Different counselors use different techniques and work from different premises. The goal is typically the same—the counselor hopes to help the parent of a retarded child see issues more clearly and reach necessary decisions. This is quite the opposite of telling the client what to do, and what to think, as many people wish the counselor to do.

Let us examine, now, some of the frames of reference within which counselors work and attempt to derive some idea of their means and ends in the counseling interview.

Non-directive Counseling

Carl Rogers has suggested, over a period of years, a series of procedural steps which enable the counselor to facilitate change with a minimum of intervention in the client's attempts to come to grips with his dilemmas (70). The counseling technique emphasizes the client's ability to help himself, the value of communication, and the special role of insight into one's problems.

Properly construed, the non-directive counselor has plenty of time at his disposal, the urgency of the problem sets no immediate deadlines to be met, and the client is capable of solving his own problems, given the appropriate therapeutic milieu. On the surface, the counselor seems to do very little; he sits, waiting for the client to verbalize. When the client does verbalize the counselor comments minimally, not so much replying to the client as choosing his language to increase the client's perception of the issues. Again, naively construed, the counselor mumbles a judicious comment, clears his throat strategically, or merely repeats the client's statement in a slightly different way.

There are few things in counseling more intrinsically appealing than the wholly false notion that all problems are amenable to non-directive counseling or that this technique is easily mastered and should be used by all counselors in virtually all settings. In those cases where one can set aside months to deal with issues, non-directive counseling can be most helpful to families; however, one should not forget that other therapies also respect the client, allow for judicious silence, and try to generate a permissive, therapeutic milieu.

The Psychoanalytic Orientation

Historically, the process of helping people solve their problems by manipulating conversation began with Sigmund Freud, who found that people with severe problems sometimes experienced relief of symptoms when problems were discussed in an accepting fashion. Working from the frame of reference of "man the irrational," a major reformulation of Western ideas on the nature of man, Freud found that he could help people if they would talk and if he could attempt to interpret some of their perceptions and dreams. Unlike Rogers, Freud erected a huge theoretical edifice which can be examined in such works as those by Fenichel (29).

The therapeutic interview, conducted under contemporary neo-Freudian considerations, views parents of retarded children as a neurotic issue, stemming from realistic problems. The issues are to be manipulated by the therapist in a fashion which prescribes a fair degree of direct involvement in the conversation. Forrer has given an interesting formulation of such a problem (30). Unfortunately, counseling within the psychoanalytic orientation is contingent on a rare degree of training and is both time consuming and far reaching in its ambitions for the client.

The Eclectic Approach

There are as many theoretical orientations to counseling as there are counselors. Most people engaged in clinic or agency work do not have the time at their disposal, the minimal case load, and the precious gift of faith that the orthodox Rogerian and the psychoanalyst, with his non-empirical frame of reference, possess.

In a typical agency, with more families seeking attention than can be immediately served, certain economies must be observed.

Time is a prime consideration. Instead of "analysis terminable and interminable" of the analytic school, and the less than expeditious "waiting" of conventional non-directive technique, most clinical workers pursue short-term, realistic goals. They may subscribe to what Fromm-Reichman has called "intensive psychotherapy" (31).

In this orientation one sets up realistic goals and, by generating a permissive atmosphere, encourages the client to talk freely. One manipulates the "conversation" to encourage discussion of relevant issues and pays careful attention to their emotional components.

In recent years S-R learning theory has been used to demonstrate that clients' behavior is subject to, and therefore responsive to, what we generally consider laws of learning. With additional knowledge, the therapist shapes verbal behavior, reinforcing desirable behavior and extinguishing undesirable by non-reinforcement. In this fashion the therapist accepts the client's problems and handles them expeditiously. There is generally room and atmosphere for the client to express his concerns, and these are responded to with great care; but the therapist is also able to move the conversation from profitless or threatening issues to more pertinent problems.

Practical Issues

Kanner, with commendable forethought, has set down issues that most commonly arise when parents seek help:

> "What is the cause of our child's retardation?
> Have we personally contributed to his condition?
> Why did this have to happen to us?
> What about heredity?
> Is it safe to have another child?" (46).

It should be noted that the questions which Kanner has listed are partially factual but that all of them have a strong affective, or emotional, component. The interviewer typically responds to the implicit emotional issues rather than to the explicit, factual, neutral way in which the issues may be raised. This is because the family of a retarded child is faced with a problem that is, to a large extent, an affective issue. It is not the objective reality of the child's retardation which counts but rather the subjective reality of personal responsibility and the resulting accommodation to the problem (30) (96).

The Parent with Counseling Needs

At the time when parents present themselves to physicians and clinical personnel, they are usually unable to face their problems realistically and to resolve them constructively. Usually, they are aware that they face a problem, but it is a clouded awareness. The typical process of helping parents involves moving them from their present level of understanding and awareness to some more realistic, positive level. The counselor must know where the parent is before he can assess the degree of change needed and determine the direction which this change should take. Stone has indicated some ways of judging parental awareness:

Considerable Awareness

1. The parent states that the child is retarded.
2. The parent recognizes the limitations of any treatment.
3. The parent requests information about suitable care and training, usually placement in an institution.

Partial Awareness

1. The parent describes the symptoms of retardation with questions about the causes.

2. The parent hopes for improvement, but fears that treatment will not be successful.

3. The parent questions his own ability to cope with the problems.

4. The worker evaluates him as having partial awareness of the child's real problem.

Minimal Awareness

1. The parent refuses to recognize that certain characteristic behavior is abnormal.

2. The parent blames causes other than retardation for the symptoms.

3. The parent believes that treatment will produce a normal child.

4. The worker evaluates the parent as having minimal awareness.
   (87, p. 363)

Usually this sort of judgment is made in a clinical setting by a social worker in the initial interview. Most social workers have developed a sensitivity to parental problems that enables them to evaluate parent and child quite accurately. Altman has noted the facility of social workers in making clinical judgments and has pointed out that when social workers judge maternal self-perceptions, some interesting connections can be inferred between the mother's personality and the child's (2).

Problems in Counseling

A practical problem which is faced in helping the family with a retarded child is deciding, in the light of counseling facilities and family needs, how much time should be spent on the counseling process. A modifying issue is the extent to which parental growth proceeds at an optimal pace. Generally speaking, these issues arise in individual family counseling and in the group process too. This is a complex issue; it has already been the topic of one book and will assuredly attract more attention as time goes by (82).

Yet it seems possible to specify some objectives for the counseling sequence which is short-term, rather than intended to rebuild entire personalities. Clearly, when parents are at sea, overwhelmed by their family problems, the counselor has a supportive role. He is not moving towards the remission of all disabling symptoms, since that would be impossible. Usually there are the specific problems mentioned by Kanner (46), and these provide a reasonable basis for predicting the manifest content of the interview. As a function of the socio-economic level of the parents, one may expect some issues to be more important to some families. Generally, the matter of school achievement and placement is found in most series of interviews at one time or another.

How does one decide what constitutes a sensible direction for growth and change in parents? Obviously, solution by prescription will not do; each family setting is different, and its constellation of issues is unique. Doll has suggested that one view the situation as a whole and make the tentative hypotheses on that basis. In what he has commented on as a "cluster" approach he has said that, "one takes account of the total family situation in advising as to the best management or ultimate disposition of the patient" (20, p. 115). When one recognizes that there are many lives involved, lives which have been, and will be, intertwined with that of the retarded child, one moves slowly and carefully.

A trend in the literature on counseling parents with retarded children is interesting. Over the years experts have discussed the goal of parental acceptance. They have put perception of limitations in children and a willingness to come to terms with them fairly high on the list of desirable outcomes of casework. To this there seems to have been added another consideration which progresses from parent to child. It is the goal of facilitating child growth through parent counseling. We have seen earlier in the chapter that parental values shape child growth. It is only reasonable that we should want to influence parents in order to advance the welfare of their children. Such vital processes as language stimulation for young children, and constructive attitudes towards residential living (1) can be facilitated through parent counseling.

In an article previously touched on, Jolly has discussed the institutional placement of seriously retarded children (40). He rejects the idea that early infancy is automatically the best time, suggesting, rather, that a delay might help the parents better understand the problems. His over-all judgment is that one should set the precise time for placement when the family situation suggests it. A corollary to this is that one should be sure that it is absolutely necessary.

It was about 1950 that the drive to convert state hospitals and schools into something better than low-grade custodial facilities was started. As institutions began to look at their populations, they found some normal individuals—a rare occurrence—and a number of children who were suitable for community school facilities rather than institutions.

Meyer has discussed the problems precipitated by discharging children and returning them to their communities and families (57). He has pointed out: "Parents who had in their own minds 'shelved' their child within our institution, were asked to reaccept him within their own family. The traumatic impact of this demand proved to be as punishing as the demand for the original separation" (57, p. 272).

A further counseling issue arises when Meyer points out: "We must consider the welfare of the patient in returning him to his community. Precipitation of schizophrenia may result from pushing an introverted child back into a hostile environment. . . . It is important that . . . one look closely for signs which indicate child-parent . . . incompatibilities" (57, p. 275).

Truly, the attempt to help a family and its retarded child is demanding. Conflict has been commented on by Sheimo as the crux of parental behavior. As Sheimo has also pointed out, while parents have blind spots and conflicts, they may have rather striking, valid insights into the status of their retarded child. One may well wonder how it can be that people have perceptual blinders on when considering their child and may yet be able to estimate mental age with striking accuracy (78). It would certainly make the counselor's job easier if he could find some unifying principle or issue which he could use to thread his way through the labyrinth of personal problems.

There are some constancies, to be sure; but they tend to be of a superficial order. Obviously, as Kanner has pointed out, there are some initial issues which need attention. There are the problems of feeding, clothing, and schooling. There are, as Morris has indicated when trying to point out training needs for caseworkers, "the concrete, daily issues that arise in the home" (59, p. 515).

But these give us no real basis for understanding why the problems arise, the confusions, the compounding of realistic problems and defensive attitudes and complexes. Perhaps the common denominator of all the unique problems that parents present is, as Grebler has suggested, *frustration* (33). Perhaps it is the frustration of what might have been, what was anticipated in the expectation of the child's birth. Perhaps it is the frustration of not knowing what is for the best or the frustration of being unable to change things.

If we take frustration or any similar construct as the keystone when trying to build a rationale for parental behavior in the counseling interview, perhaps we bypass a common sense source of information. The parent himself, if not able to verbalize how he reacts, may be able to suggest how the counselor should act. Patterson, a parent who has experienced the problems, has the following suggestions:

1. Tell us the nature of our problem as soon as possible.
2. Always see both parents.

3. Watch your language.
4. Help us to see this is OUR problem.
5. Help us to understand our problem.
6. Know your resources.
7. Never put us on the defensive.
8. Remember that parents of retarded children are just people.
9. Remember that we are parents and that you are professionals.
10. Remember the importance of your attitude towards us (62, p. 15).

In examining these recommendations one may discern many of the problem areas in counseling. One might parallel Patterson's comments with ten commandments for counselors:

1. Be honest in your appraisal of the situation and explain it without unnecessary delay.
2. Deal with both parents, since they are a natural unit.
3. Be precise, but do not be unnecessarily technical in your explanation.
4. Point out who must be responsible ultimately.
5. Help the parents grasp the issues.
6. Keep in mind the referral agencies that can be of assistance.
7. Avoid precipitating ego defensive reactions in the parents.
8. Do not expect too much too soon from the parents.
9. Allow parents their quota of concern and uncertainty.
10. Try to crystallize positive attitudes at the outset by using good counseling techniques.

Boyd has pointed out the stages through which a parent goes in developing an understanding of the problems presented by his retarded child (12). Perhaps his short address illustrates an observation. The observation is that there are very few human beings who are truly mature, who possess inner resources that make them spiritually superior to their fellows, but those few include parents of retarded children who have transcended the problems that beset them.

Up to this point we have considered the counseling process as a series of steps by the counselor and a series of hoped-for changes in the client. Several authors have commented on the process of change in parents during counseling. Stowe has documented the increase in "acceptance" under counseling (87). Rosen applied Dewey's five steps in thinking to the development of understanding in thirty-six mothers. He found that mothers followed a general pattern in the development of understanding. (71).

Zuk analyzed the nature of distortions in parents' thinking about retarded children. In those cases where there were no motor handicaps, he found one mode of perceiving children; in those who had motor handicaps, he found another (95). He expressed the mechanism of these autistic distortions as follows: "In the case of the parents whose children were not handicapped, unconscious (i.e., non-verbalized) desires for normalcy could be reinforced by their perception of relatively normal motor functioning, despite the lag in learning ability" (95, p. 176).

Group Process

Perhaps one of the most important advances in attempts to help families with retarded children has been the formation of parent groups. Organizations such as local associations for retarded children have a series of goals which are laudable. In the course of pursuing such goals parents usually derive much mutual and reciprocal aid.

A parallel concern has arisen from the work of local crippled children societies and other organizations for handicapped youngsters. Problems arise, however, when several organizations pursue allied goals. Occasionally, cross purposes develop, and a certain amount of regression rather than progress occurs.

A further possibility inherent in group processes is that a number of people may profit by jointly learning more about their problems. Popp, Ingram, and Jordan devised a curriculum for parent education with the following specific subjects:

1. The causes and effects of mental retardation
2. How the child feels
3. Family and neighborhood relations
4. A trip to a state school
5. Meeting the child's needs—the parent's contribution
6. Meeting the child's needs—the community contribution (64)

A series of classes such as this communicates facts. It also does something more; it brings people with common problems together in such a fashion that a sense of mutual sympathy and support is engendered, while people are ostensibly pursuing the problems at an emotionally neutral level. Equally valuable is a practice reported by Standifer at the Abilene State School (83). Faced with serious problems attendant to admission, the social service department asked twenty-one sets of parents to help other parents with the problems which arise when a child enters residential living. Asking parents of residents to help by providing information, helping with admission procedures, and giving personal assistance to parents was considered successful on the basis of two years' experience.

Indirect Help

There is a tendency in any field to think that the problems are unique and that all attempts to solve them can only start from scratch. This is not the case when we attempt to find models for studying the impact of disabled children on the family with a view to therapeutic intervention (44, 45). Nor need it be the case in our attempt to help parents through group processes of one kind or another. There is, for example, the possibility that techniques for stimulating child development could be disseminated to parents long before children are of school age. The education of young deaf children has been advanced in many instances by use of the correspondence course developed by the John Tracy Clinic in Los Angeles. The system is not simply uncontrolled material which parents are free to ignore; the process consists of sequential, developmental acts which parents use after some initial instruction. Probably a parallel activity could be initiated for parents of retarded children so that the growth potentials of the vital early years would not be lost. Obvious starting points would be language stimulation, motor development, and sensory and experiential stimulation. Development of such materials would have a beneficial effect on retarded children and would also help parents burdened with a feeling of helplessness.

THE FAMILY WHICH IS MENTALLY RETARDED

In our consideration of the family of the retarded child we have considered the family to whom mental retardation is an unknown thing; we have considered the normal family, of normal intelligence. In any consideration of the total issue of mental retardation and the family, we must consider, also, the family to whom mental retardation is no stranger. This is the family for whom mental retardation is an everyday matter, since it occurs on a predictable basis in many members of the family.

This issue, clouded by socio-economic considerations, is encountered in public welfare and school situations. There are, for example, the families whose nominal leaders are not capable of supporting themselves or their children. These are the families, well-known to private agencies, who consume social welfare services at a rate out of proportion to their number and who may be under the scrutiny of several social agencies at the same time. Their children are health problems; they are, as total family units, community problems.

Such families may have one or more children in school. It is a fairly familiar issue in those elementary schools that derive their students from distressed or disorganized neighborhoods to have brothers and sisters in schools, all of comparable mental level, typically "garden-variety" defectives. Such children present their teachers with many problems, and, in such cases, there is no obvious recourse to worried, cooperative parents. The parents usually have enough problems without going to school to see how their children are doing.

Studying ninety families in Minnesota, Mickelson had this to say: "The mentally deficient parent emerges from this study not as a different kind of parent but as a more vulnerable one. . . . His mental deficiency was not the primary factor determining his adequacy as a parent . . . (rather) . . . the number of pregnancies, the number of children in the home, the adequacy of income, the satisfactoriness of the marital relationship and the mental health of the parents, especially the mother" (58, p. 532).

Looking at the children of mentally defective mothers, children identified as illegitimate, Brill and Joynson found them to be lower in intellectual performance and social adjustment than deprived children of non-defective mothers (14). Clearly, not all family units give children the right sort of start, nor do all present schools and welfare agencies with serious problems.

One might speculate on the effects of removing the child from the environment generated by mentally defective parents and placing them in an adoptive home. Such actual manipulation is most unlikely, and we have no real evidence of anything but an intuitive sort. On the other hand, we do know something about the effects of adoption on children moved from the depriving atmosphere of the orphanage to an adoptive home. Skodak and Skeels looked at this issue about twenty years ago and, discussing their sample of one hundred children, commented: "The intellectual level of the children has remained consistently higher than would have been predicted from the intellectual, educational, or socio-economic level of the true parents, and is equal to, or surpasses the mental level of own children in environments similar to those which have been provided by the foster parents" (81).

The size of families and the implications of this for mental retardation are interesting. Traditionally, intelligence has been associated negatively with the size of the sibship (4). It would seem, on a gross basis, that the more siblings there are, the less the intelligence of each child. And yet this picture is uncertain. Altus looked at families with two to thirteen children and made an interesting discovery; he reported that when he compared 268 last-born children with 988 children born in another ordinal position, the higher intelligence level was found in the last-borns, with the difference significant at $P = .05$. He further commented that good adjustment was positively related to being the last born in very big families, families with ten or more children (3). Herndon has spoken crisply on the unnecessary judgment of mental incompetence on the basis of superficial differences. He has further substantiated his position with evidence. Studying families in the Blue Ridge Mountains, an area which has been the locus of several investigators of intelligence, he said:

> We have recently been interested in studying the distributions and intra-family correlations of certain characteristics in a normal population in Western North Caroline (sic), the major purpose being to study factors involved in selective mating. The area under study was Watauga County, located in the Blue Ridge Mountains, . . . The county is predominantly rural, with no heavy industry, and with a population in 1950 of 18,342. Although the area is mountainous and the more remote sections might be considered rather isolated, the county is traversed by a system of good roads providing access to the surrounding areas.

> The area was chosen for the study as being typical of this mountain district. During the nineteenth century there was a steady stream of emigration from this region to the lands then being developed in the western states. Migration into Watauga was considerably less, with no major trends of origin being apparent. . . .

> The distribution of IQ scores for the entire sample of 223 individuals was found to approximate the expected normal distribution, with an average of 94.52   0.87.

> A further point that may have some interest . . . is the unusually high cousin marriage rate and with presumably small size of mating isolates (36, p. 55-57).

Having considered the facts in families to whom mental retardation is ascribed, let us consider those families in which it is a demonstrable, familial disorder. Book analyzed some Swedish data and reported in Table 2·2(10). Speaking of the size of the families in which mental retardation is known, he said: "Data collected by Dahlberg (1951) from four counties in Sweden indicated a very low fertility for certified mental defectives . . . I have collected more rigorous data from three smaller rural communities. . . . Matched with comparable control individuals, the mentally deficient had issued 0.7 children per individual and the controls 3.7. . . . Reliable data on fertility trends for individuals with mental defects seem to show that effective fertility decreases with decreasing intellectual capacity" (10, p. 114). The decreased fertility of the mentally retarded has been also documented by other data supplied by Hallgren and Sjogren in a study of 25,000 people in southern Sweden (35).

Working with data over a period of forty years, Reed, Reed, and Palm studied the families of mentally inadequate individuals identified between 1910 and 1920 (67). Because of the care with which the early records were kept, it was possible to trace these Minnesota residents, some of whom were still alive and were available for the follow-up study. Generally speaking, the descendants were not as badly off as their progenitors. Galton's principle of filial regression was demonstrated, as the descendants turned out to be generally less severely retarded. Indeed, the multiple determinism of human genetics is demonstrated in these data since one of the descendants turned out to have served as U.S. congressman from Minnesota.

TABLE 2·2

RELATIVE FERTILITY OF A COMPLETE SAMPLE OF MENTAL
DEFECTIVES OF UNKNOWN ORIGIN FROM THREE
SWEDISH RURAL COMMUNITIES

	No. of Individuals	No. of Children	No. of Children per Individual	
54 Mental Defectives				
Extramatrimonial	54	8	0.15	
Intramatrimonial	7	32	4.60	0.7
108 Control Individuals				
Extramatrimonial	108	16	0.15	
Intramatrimonial	85	384	4.50	3.7

In a related paper Reed and Phillips framed some comments that are succinct and relevant to the whole issue of mental retardation and the familial incidence of the condition. They reported of one family: "The reproduction of the mentally deficient individuals in this family was not as great as might have been expected. . . . The IQ scores of the younger generation shared a regression toward the mean . . . the amount of social inadequacy is not as great as might have been expected" (66, p. 702).

Another study which gives interesting data is the one by Higgins, in which a large number of people belonging to the "Nam" family have been studied in Minnesota (37). This family shows considerable variability in the level of intelligence of its members. Some are below average in intelligence, while the over-all range is broad. Some fifteen hundred people were used in the investigation, and the intelligence level of the whole group is fairly normal.

The family whose members are generally mentally retarded has been a matter of historical as well as scientific interest. An example of this is the general sort of awareness concerning Goddard's work *The Kallikak Family.* Since its publication in 1912 the material has come to be known to many people. Unfortunately, many discussions of the Kallikaks are based on merely secondary sources, with the result that the research is known beyond the limits one might predict from its significance.

Goddard began his report by considering Deborah Kallikak and proceeded to investigate her numerous ancestors. While the intensity of the study is unquestioned, the concepts of mental retardation are quite ambiguous. Goddard used a blending of alcoholism, poverty, immorality, and "feeblemindedness" in such a way that evidence of one was used to infer the presence of another. The study is useful because it shows the lives of these wretched people and the impossible conditions under which they sometimes reared their families. Its scientific contribution to the study of mental retardation is modest.

The uncertainty which occurs when primitive conditions of life surround human behavior is understandable. Different cultural settings distort our evaluation of the way people live. An example of the way scholars have developed theories of behavior is given in the various writings of James Boswell. Burnett, a lawyer like Boswell, and, as a judge, later known as Lord Monboddo, believed that people living in primitive surroundings in the countries of the East were less than fully human in development. Such was the preoccupation of this amateur physical anthropologist with his ideas that he would interrupt accounts of travels to the strange lands of Asia to ask if the inhabitants had tails. When Johnson visited Scotland in 1773, Monboddo's search for physical evidence of a primitive branch of mankind was well known. Johnson was very much amused by a description of Monboddo, as he was then titled, as a "Judge *a posteriori.*" Such are the false starts which have made the scientific study of human nature a slowly developing discipline.

SUMMARY

In this chapter we have considered the personal and group reactions of families to mental retardation. The importance of mothers in the growth of their children has been discussed, and a sketch of a model to analyze mother and child interaction has been offered. A serious problem is that of counseling the family. A series of issues emphasizing content rather than techniques was discussed. Last of all, the facts and fictions of mentally retarded families were studied.

Placing the chapter on the family at the beginning of this work has been a deliberate move. While mental retardation poses challenges to teachers and physicians, it poses problems of infinite complexity to parents. Typically, mentally retarded children are studied because they are an educational problem, or a scientific enigma. To consider the entity in this light is to misconstrue its nature. Mental retardation is primarily a problem in human terms. If we would approach its study with the right set, we must see it as a people-centered problem from the beginning. Only by seeing how lives are affected can one move to the more segmented, truncated, aspects of the disorder with any sense of urgency.

This sense of urgency leads to the consideration of the problems in the remaining chapters. Mental retardation has many challenging technical problems to offer. As we go about the job of learning more about the condition, we can see the technical problems of etiology, instruction, diagnosis, and the like. Consideration of these must be detached and impartial. Yet this analysis is justified by the urge to do something, to contribute to the welfare of the people involved. In order to approach the issues of the following chapters in proper perspective, it is vital that we see the humanitarian core of the problem first.

BIBLIOGRAPHY

1. Adamson, W. C., *et al.*, "Separation Used to Help Parents Promote Growth of Their Retarded Child," *Soc. Work*, 1964, *9*, 60-67.

2. Altman, C., "Relationship between Maternal Attitudes and Child Personality Structure," *Am. J. Orthopsychiat.*, 1959, *28*, 160-169.

3. Altus, W. D., "Birth Order, Intelligence, and Adjustment," *Psych. Rep.*, 1959, *5*, 502.

4. Anastasi, A., "Intelligence and Family Size," *Psych. Bull.*, 1956, *53*, 187-209.

5. Aserlind, L., "An Investigation of Maternal Factors Related to the Acquisition of Verbal Skills of Infants in a Culturally Disadvantaged Population," unpublished Ph.D. dissertation, University of Wisconsin, 1963.

6. Behrens, M. L., "Child Rearing and the Character Structure of the Mother," *Ch. Dev.*, 1954, *25*, 225-238.

7. Benda, C. M., *et al.*, "Personality Factors in Mild Mental Retardation, Pt. I Family Background and Sociocultural Patterns," *Amer. J. Ment. Def.*, 1963, *68*, 24-40.

8. Bendig, A. W., "The Development of a Short Form of the Taylor Manifest Anxiety Scale," *J. Consult. Psych.*, 1956, *20*, 384.

9. Blodgett, H. E., "Helping Parents in the Community Setting," in *Counseling Parents of Children with Mental Handicaps*, Proceedings of the 33rd Conference of the Woods Schools, 1958.

10. Book, J. A., "Fertility Trends in Some Types of Mental Defects," *Eugen. Quart.*, 1959, *6*, 113-116.

11. Bossard, H. S., and Boll, S., "Child Behavior and the Empathic Complex," *Ch. Dev.*, 1957, *28*, 37-42.

12. Boyd, D., "Three Stages in the Growth of a Parent of a Mentally Retarded Child," *Am. J. Ment. Def.*, 1951, *55*, 608-611.

13. Brandon, M. W. G., "The Intellectual and Social Status of Children of Mental Defectives, I.," *J. Ment. Sci.*, 1957, *103*, 710-724.

14. Brill, K., and Joynson, M. G., "The Illegitimate Children of Mental Defectives; Summary of a Study," *Internat. Ch. Welf. Rev.*, 1954, *8*, 129-134.

15. Brown, F., "An Experimental Study of Parental Attitudes and Their Effect upon Child Adjustment," *Am. J. Orthopsychiat.*, 1942, *12*, 224-229.

16. Caldwell, B. M., Manley, E. J., and Seelye, B. J., "Factors Associated with Parental Reaction to a Clinic for Retarded Children," *Amer. J. Ment. Def.*, 1961, *65*, 590-594.

17. Carter, C. O., "Risk of Parents Who Have Had One Child with Down's Syndrome (Mongolism) Having Another Child Similarly Affected," *Lancet*, 1961, *2*, 785.

18. Centerwall, S. A., and Centerwall, W. R., "A Study of Children with Mongolism Reared in the Home Compared to Those Reared Away from the Home," *Pediat.*, 1960, *25*, 678-685.

19. Coleman, J. C., *Abnormal Psychology and Modern Life*, Scott, Foresman, 1950.

20. Doll, E. A., "Counseling Parents of Severely Mentally Retarded Children," *J. Clin. Psych.*, 1959, *9*, 114-117.

21. Downey, K. J., "Parental Interest in the Institutionalized Severely Mentally Retarded Child," *Soc. Prob.*, 1963, *11*, 186-193.

22. Drillien, C. M., and Wilkinson, E. M., "Mongolism: When Should Parents Be Told?" *Brit. Med. J.*, 1964, *2*, (5420): 1306-1307.

23. Farber, B., "The Effects of a Severely Retarded Child on Family Integration," *Mon. Soc. Res. Ch. Dev.*, 1959, No. 71.

24. _____, "Family Organization and Crisis: Maintenance of Integration in Families with a Severely Mentally Retarded Child," *Mon. Soc. Res. Ch. Dev.*, 1960, No. 75.

25. _____, "Perceptions of Crisis and Related Variables in the Impact of a Retarded Child on the Mother," *J. Hlth. Hum. Behav.*, 1960, *1*, 108-118.

26. _____, "Effects of a Severely Mentally Retarded Child on the Family," in Trapp, E. P., and Himelstein, P., (eds.) *Readings on the Exceptional Child*, Appleton, Century, Crofts, 1962.

27. _____, and Jenné, W. C., "Family Organization and Parent-Child Communication: Parents and Siblings of a Retarded Child," *Mon. Soc. Res. Child Devpm.*, 1963, No. 28.

28. _____, Jenné, W. G., and Toigo, R., "Family Crisis and the Decision to Institutionalize the Retarded Child," *C. E. C. Res. Mon.*, 1960, No. 1.

29. Fenichel, O., *The Psychoanalytic Theory of Neurosis*, Hogarth, London, 1946.

30. Forrer, G. R., "The Mother of a Defective Child," *Psychoan. Quart.*, 1959, *28*, 59-63.

31. Fromm-Reichman, F., *Principles of Intensive Psychotherapy*, Univ. of Chicago Press, 1950.

32. Goshen, C. E., "Mental Retardation and Neurotic Maternal Attitudes," *Arch. Gen. Psychiat.*, 1963, *9*, 168-174.

33. Grebler, A. M., "Parental Attitudes towards Mentally Retarded Children," *Am. J. Ment. Def.*, 1952, *56*, 475-483.

34. Haley, J., "Research on Family Patterns: An Instrument Measurement," *Fam. Proc.*, 1964, *3*, 41-65.

35. Hallgren, B., and Sjogren, T., "A Clinical and Genetico-Statistical Study of Schizophrenia and Low-Grade Mental Deficiency in a Large Swedish Rural Population," *Acta Psychiat. Neurol. Scand. Suppl.*, 1960, No. 140.

36. Herndon, C. N., "Intelligence in Family Groups in the Blue Ridge Mountains," *Eugen. Quart.*, 1954, *1*, 53-58.

37. Higgins, J. V., "A Study of Intelligence of the NAM Family in Minnesota," *Am. J. Ment. Def.*, 1959, *64*, 491-504.

38. Holt, K. S., "The Influence of a Retarded Child upon Family Limitation," *J. Ment. Def. Res.*, 1958, *2*, 28-34.

39. Hurley, J. R., "Maternal Attitudes and Children's Intelligence," *J. Clin. Psych.*, 1959, *15*, 291-292.

40. Jolly, D., "When Should the Seriously Retarded Infant be Institutionalized?" *Am. J. Ment. Def.*, 1953, *57*, 632-636.

41. Jones, E. E. and Thibaut, J. W., "Interaction Goals as Bases of Inference in Interpersonal Perception," in Tagiuri, R., and Petrullo, L., *Person Perception and Interpersonal Behavior*, Stanford U. Press, 1958.

42. Jordan, T. E., "Crucial Dimensions of Mother/Retarded Child Interaction," paper presented to the American Association on Mental Deficiency, Baltimore, 1960.

43. ———, *The Mentally Retarded*, first edition, Columbus, Charles E. Merrill Books, Inc., 1961.

44. ———, "Research on the Handicapped Child and the Family," *Merrill-Palmer Quart.*, 1962, *8*, 243-260.

45. ———, "Physical Disability in Children and Family Adjustment," *Rehab. Lit.*, 1963, *24*, 330-336.

46. Kanner, L., "Parents' Feelings about Retarded Children," *Am. J. Ment. Def.*, 1953, *57*, 375-383.

47. Kantor, J. R., "Preface to Interbehavioral Psychology," *Psych. Rec.*, 1942, *6*, 172-193.

48. Kelman, H. R., "Parent Guidance in a Clinic for Mentally Retarded Children," *Soc. Casework*, 1953, *34*, 441-445.

49. Kenney, E. T., "Ego Development and Authoritarianism in Four Groups of Mothers with Children who differ in I.Q. and School Adjustment," unpublished Ph.D. dissertation, Washington University, 1965.

50. Kirk, S. A., *Early Education of the Retarded*, U. of Illinois Press, 1958.

51. Klatskin, H., Jackson, E. B., and Wilkin, L., "The Influence of Degree of Flexibility in Maternal Child Care Practices on Early Childhood Behavior," *Am. J. Orthopsychiat.*, 1956, *26*, 79-93.

52. Klebanoff, L. B., "A Comparison of Parental Attitudes of Mothers of Schizophrenic, Brain Injured and Normal Children," Ph.D. dissertation, Boston University, 1957.

53. Kratter, F. G., "Negative and Positive Eugenic Programs for Mental Defectives," *J. Gen. Psych.*, 1960, *63*, 203-210.

54. Maccoby, E., and Gibbs, K., "Methods of Child Rearing in Two Social Classes," in Martin, W., and Stendler, G., *Readings in Child Development*, Harcourt, Brace, 1954.

55. McClelland, D., Rindlisbacher, A., and deCharms, R., "Religious and Other Sources of Parental Attitudes toward Independence Training," in McClelland, D., *Studies in Motivation*, New York, Appleton-Century-Crofts, 1955.

56. McFarland, M. B., and Reinhart, J. B., "The Development of Motherliness," *Children*, 1959, *6*, 48-52.

57. Meyer, H., "Problems Relative to the Acceptance and Reacceptance of the Institutionalized Child," *Arch. Pediat.*, 1956, *73*, 271-275.

58. Mickelson, P., "Can Mentally Deficient Parents be Helped to Give their Children Better Care?" *Am. J. Ment. Def.*, 1959, *53*, 516-534.

59. Morris, E. F., "Casework Training Needs for Counselling Parents of the Retarded," *Am. J. Ment. Def.*, 1955, *59*, 510-516.

60. Natterson, J. M., and Knudson, A. G., "Observations Concerning Fear of Death in Fatally Ill Children and Their Mothers," *Psychosomat. Med.,* 1960, *22,* 456-465.

61. Olshansky, S., "Chronic Sorrow: A Response to Having a Retarded Child," *Soc. Casewk.,* 1962, *43,* 190-193.

62. Patterson, L. L., "Some Pointers for Professionals," *Children,* 1956, *3,* 13-17.

63. Plutchik, R., and Kronovet, E., "Studies of Parent-Child Relations: A Critique," *J. Genet. Psych.,* 1959, *95,* 171-176.

64. Popp, C. E., Ingram, V., and Jordan, P. H. "Helping Parents Understand Their Mentally Handicapped Children" *Am. J. Ment. Def.,* 1954, *58,* 530-534.

65. Pringle, M. L. K., and Bossio, V., "A Study of Deprived Children, Part I, Intellectual, Emotional and Social Development," *Vita Humana,* 1958, *1,* 65-92.

66. Reed, E. W., and Phillips, V. P., "The Vale of Sidem Revisited," *Am. J. Ment. Def.,* 1959, *63,* 699-702.

67. Reed, S. C., Reed, E. W., and Palm, J. D., "Fertility and Intelligence among Families of the Mentally Deficient," *Eugen. Quart.,* 1954, *1,* 44-52.

68. Répond, A., "Les Réactions et Les Attitudes des Familles Envers Leurs Enfants Infirmes ou Anormaux," *Evolut. Psychiat.,* 1956, *17,* 317-330.

69. Richards, T. W., and Sands, R., "Mongoloid Children Living at Home," *Kennedy Child Study Center,* Santa Monica, California, 1963.

70. Rogers, C. R., *Client-Centered Therapy,* Boston, Houghton Mifflin, 1951.

71. Rosen, L., "Selected Aspects in the Development of the Mother's Understanding of Her Mentally Retarded Child," *Am. J. Ment. Def.,* 1955, *59,* 522-528.

72. Saenger, G., *Factors Influencing the Institutionalization of Mentally Retarded Individuals in New York City, Report:* New York State Interdepartmental Health Resources Board, 1960.

73. Saucier, J. F., "The Impact of the Prolonged Physical Illness of a Child upon the Family," McGill University, Quebec, 1963.

74. Schaefer, E. S., and Bell, R. Q., "Development of a Parental Attitude Research Instrument," *Ch. Devpm.,* 1958, *29,* 339-361.

75. ———, and Bayley, N., "Development of a Maternal Behavior Research Instrument," *J. Genet. Psych.,* 1959, *95,* 83-104.

76. Schipper, M. T., "The Child with Mongolism in the Home," *Pediat.,* 1959, *24,* 132-144.

77. Schonell, F., and Watts, B., "A First Survey of the Effects of a Subnormal Child on the Family Unit," *Am. J. Ment. Def.*, 1956, *61*, 210-219.

78. Sheimo, S. L., "Problems in Helping Parents of Mentally Defective and Handicapped Children," *Am. J. Ment. Def.*, 1951, *56*, 42-45.

79. Siegel, G., "Verbal Behavior of Retarded Children Assembled with Pre-Instructed Adults," in Schiefelbusch, R., (ed.) "Language Studies of Mentally Retarded Children," *J. Sp. Hear. Dis. Mon. Suppl.*, 1963, No. 10.

80. ———, and Harkins, J. P., "Verbal Behavior of Adults in Two Conditions with Institutionalized Retarded Children," in Schiefelbusch, R., (ed.) "Language Studies of Mentally Retarded Children," *J. Sp. Hear. Dis. Mon. Suppl.*, 1963, No. 10.

81. Skodak, M., and Skeels, H. M., "A Final Follow-Up Study of One-Hundred Adopted Children," *J. Genet. Psych.*, 1939, *75*, 85-125.

82. Stacey, C. L., and deMartino, M., *Counseling and Psychotherapy with the Mentally Retarded*, Chicago, The Free Press, 1958.

83. Standifer, F. R., "Parents Helping Parents," *Ment. Retard.*, 1964, *2*, 304-307.

84. Stein, Z. and Susser, M., "The Families of Dull Children: Parts II, III, and IV, A Classification for Predicting Careers," *Brit. J. Prev. Soc. Med.*, 1960, *14*, 83-88.

85. ———, "Families of Dull Children: Parts II, III, and IV," *J. Ment. Sci.*, 1960, *106*, 1296-1319.

86. Stevens, H. A., Sindberg, R. M., Morgan, J. R., and Glass, G. V., "A Study of an Extender Role for Professional Nurses—Pilot Phase," paper presented to American Association on Mental Deficiency, Great Lakes Region, 1963.

87. Stowe, M. M., "Parental Attitudes to Retardation," *Am. J. Ment. Def.*, 1948, *53*, 363-372.

88. Thibaut, J. W., and Kelley, H. H., *The Social Psychology of Groups*, New York, Wiley, 1959.

89. Uyeno, T., "Hereditary and Environmental Aspects of Dominant Behavior in the Albino Rat," *J. Comp. Physiol. Psych.*, 1960, *53*, 138-141.

90. Wakefield, R. A., "An Investigation of the Family Backgrounds of Educable Mentally Retarded Children in Special Classes," *Excep. Child.*, 1964, *31*, 143-147.

91. Walker, G. H., "Some Considerations of Parental Reactions to Institutionalization of Defective Children," *Am. J. Ment. Def.*, 1949, *54*, 108-114.

92. Windle, C., "Prognosis of Mental Subnormals," *Amer. J. Ment. Def. Mon. Suppl.*, 1962, *66*, No. 5.

93. Winterbottom, M., "The Relation of Childhood Training in Independence to Achievement Motivation," Ph.D. dissertation, University of Michigan, 1953.

94. Worchel, T. L., and Worchel, P., "The Parental Concept of the Mentally Retarded Child," *Amer. J. Ment. Def.*, 1961, *65*, 782-788.

95. Zuk, G. H., "Autistic Distortions in Parents of Retarded Children," *J. Consult. Psych.*, 1959, *23*, 171-176.

96. _____, "The Religious Factor and the Role of Guilt in Parental Acceptance of the Retarded Child," *Am. J. Ment. Def.*, 1959, *64*, 139-147.

97. _____, *et al.*, "Maternal Acceptance of Retarded Children: A Questionnaire Study of Attitudes and Religious Background," *Child Devpm.*, 1961, *32*, 525-540.

Chapter 3

RESIDENTIAL LIVING

When President Kennedy sent his message on mental illness and mental retardation to the Congress, he pointed out that there were at that time over 200,000 persons in residential agencies for the mentally retarded. Their care, at well below acceptable standards in many cases, required expenditure of six hundred million dollars annually. President Kennedy also pointed out that 126,000 babies are born retarded each year, children whose lives will be spent in residential institutions, in a significant number of cases. The enormous reality of the problem is further conveyed in the President's message by his telling remarks about a life of ". . . prolonged or permanent confinement in huge, unhappy mental hospitals . . . ," a phrase conveying the traditional picture of residential life, all too often still with us. Hopefully, there are signs that the situation is improving, and the President's message came at a time when many state governments were diverting energies into remedying the ills accumulated over the past one hundred years.

The present reality is that in every state of the union we find residential centers for the retarded. With exceptions they were founded before or around the turn of the century. They are relics of a time when social thought considered isolation the only practical measure, and carried it out in a mood of resigned pessimism. Very often pessimism led to limited programming and staffing, and social policy led to placing the institutions at great distances from the centers of population, often on land donated by private charity. With changes in the economy and population growth came increasing enrollments. The institutions expanded and per capita costs declined, a degree of efficiency paralleled in education as the industrial efficiency movement permeated all branches of society. In all fairness, the industrial efficiency movement made feasible the greatest efficiency at the least cost. Unhappily, the translation into social policy de-emphasized "greatest efficiency" in favor of "the least cost." The result was the development of large institutions whose humanitarian functions were all but lost, except in the minds of the dedicated persons caring for the inmates. Indeed, such was the remarkable state of public philosophy up to about 1950 that it was possible to find state programs which expended funds on the inmates of penal institutions at twice the rate for the mentally retarded; the vicious were treated better than the deserving.

Currently we are in a period of comparative enlightenment. Public money, while never easy to obtain, is channeled into improving existing institutions, and new residential centers are being established. The reforms of the last two decades have made inroads into the accumulated ills of previous years, and the level of child care and programming is generally rising. Since there will continue to be a clientele for residential institutions, a knowledge of typical practices in residential institutions is invaluable in a broad consideration of mental retardation. One which immediately commands attention is the size of the populations in residential institutions. In 1965, Scheerenberger conducted a census of 138 state institutions (56). His data reflect the census for late 1964; at that time there were 192,493 persons receiving care, which is about 3 per cent of the retarded persons in the United States. Thirty-six per cent of the institutions reported overcrowding, while a few, being new institutions, had yet to receive patients. The population was approximately balanced by sex, 55 per cent males and 45 per cent females. Eighty-two per cent were below IQ 50. The median age was around nineteen; only 26 per cent of the population were more than thirty years of age. The needs of the residents were served by over 76,000 workers.

Types of Institutions

In general, people think of one type of institution when they consider residential settings. They recall large state agencies which in some cases are massive, nineteenth-century structures built, at the time, at a strategic distance from large towns, but now largely surrounded by the encroachment of residential areas and suburbs. The other kind which comes most easily to mind is the agency placed, as with the state university, at a point beyond that which might lead to contamination of more than a hamlet or so. By virtue of the rustic setting, many residential institutions have a high degree of self-sufficiency, and substantial portions of retarded persons can be diverted into useful labor. Current innovations in planning consist of less geographical isolation and more small institutions. In Illinois, this trend is evident, and it is accompanied by innovation in scope. Not merely are the new facilities small, they are also designed to serve both non-resident and resident retarded persons. In 1964 the American Association on Mental Deficiency asserted that enrollments under one thousand were desirable for even the institutions serving multiple purposes.

Another type of residential program is the center established by religious bodies who see the care of the handicapped as an activity within their scope for charitable reasons. Accepting children of their own religious persuasion primarily, but not excluding others, they often parallel the state agencies. That is, they accept children who need residential care, but the criteria for admission may differ slightly. They may not be able to care for totally dependent children or for all age groups, and they may not have sufficient staff or funds to operate twelve months in the year. Their contribution to the total program of residential service is easily overlooked, but once examined it is not usually forgotten.

A third type of agency is the private institution which operates on the basis of fees. Residential settings of this type include small operations, sometimes conducted because the need is great and sometimes because desperate parents will pay high fees. On the other hand, there are other agencies dependent on fees which are run as non-profit enterprises. Some of these are national in scope, having several branches in different parts of the country. They have excellent reputations and provide good services. This kind of agency is likely to grow despite the high cost of operation. It is possible that legislation may allow maintenance costs to be deducted for income tax purposes, freeing funds for expenditure at the discretion of parents. For example, Louisiana grants an exemption of $1,000 on the amount of income taxed by the state. This kind of tolerance for the burden imposed on parents who must seek residential care for their children may be extended in the future by other states.

A last form of residential care for retarded children is the use of foster homes. Such homes are normal in that they are considered adequate by the welfare agencies who are responsible for the children. Usually there are not enough foster homes for children free from disabilities, and it follows that the number available to retarded children is probably smaller. Nevertheless, foster home placement for retarded children exists as we shall see in Chapter 6, and it indicates the high sense of charity that people possess. That is, there are people who take retarded children into their homes and do so without regard for the small grants of money that public welfare agencies usually make (30). This commendable service usually goes unnoticed and is as meritorious in its own way as the more publicized contributions made by scientists. We can hope that this kind of service will one day receive recognition now given to professional workers here and overseas. While numerically small, foster homes are valuable because of the warmth and love they can give to children previously living in depriving homes.

Staff Functions

One way to convey the complexity of residential institutions is to consider the range of occupations that constitute the work force. Usually the agency within the institution with which parents and community groups have commerce is the department of *social service*. The staff are, ideally, fully trained social workers. Their liaison role with extramural groups calls on their training in the use of community resources. More specifically, their case work training allows them to develop materials in the form of social histories and supplementary data; such materials are gathered during the preliminary work on retarded persons who are referred for possible placement, and are used to decide if a child should be admitted to the institution. The findings of social service personnel are generally examined by other specialists, since pre-admission evaluation of children needs to be made from more than one professional point of view. Another important function of social service personnel is maintaining liaison with parents after children have been admitted. Visits by parents to the institution and periodic returns to the home by inmates are negotiated by departments of social service. Discharge from the institution and the concomitant problems of personal adjustment to the family and community are negotiated by departments of social service, as are the unofficial absences which arise when inmates wander, or decide that they simply prefer to run away. In the more fortunate circumstances, social service workers conduct individual and group guidance activities aimed at improving personal and social adjustment. Such service may be rendered to parents as they attempt to cope with the reality problems their retarded dependents present. In many instances the coordination of services to individual clients and their families is handled through social service. The case worker may seem to do little directly for inmates—as opposed to attendants whose work has face validity—but the complexity of intramural care can be brought to fruition only by coordination of ward care, family care, and training. In many respects the social service agency contributes to the reality of efficient service and protective care. In recent years, social workers have considered mental retardation in their professional deliberations and have introduced it into their curricula. In this respect they have been ahead of most professions dealing with a broad spectrum of human problems (2).

Special Education. Some institutions are designed for specific levels of retardation, for example educable children, while others may be designed for trainable youngsters. It follows that the activities which educators conduct vary from institution to institution. In some cases there may be programming for all levels, including the totally dependent, and for all ages, even the very old. Generally, teachers carry on the work at the heart of the activities and rehabilitation programs. That is, they provide the stimulation of a general nature which the institutions offer to as many young people as possible; also, they provide the specific stimulation or skills and knowledge on which any attempt at rehabilitation must hinge. Usually, the education staff sees children for much of the day, and generally carries on an approximation of the functions of day school special classes. Clearly, the level of abilities with which special teachers work is below that usually found in school programs. The activities for trainable children are fairly similar, when numbers permit. Our best evidence, gathered by Cain & Levine, suggests that special education cannot combat the depressing effect of institutional living (5).

Special teachers have a function which is not usually stressed in community programs; they provide an opportunity for evaluation of children in a context other than the ward or day room. Behaviors may be followed in a close manner through all the waking hours, and leads arising from observation in the cottage can be evaluated in the different context of the classroom. For example, emotional development frequently receives setbacks after visits from parents and trips home. The pervasiveness of regressive behavior may be appraised by teachers and reported to child care workers, psychologists, and so forth.

Speech and Hearing Specialists. As Chapters 5, 9 and various other works (57) indicate, the author considers language a vital form of behavior within which mental retardation may be studied. The reasons for this conviction are better explained at length, but it is interesting to observe the degree of support the proposition has received from the corpus of studies conducted by Schlanger and others. Currently, specialists teach language to retarded children and have a role in the program of institutions which supports other professional activities and particularly augments the contributions of special education teachers. While speech and hearing workers conduct hearing examinations and evaluate speech, they also do a good deal of clinical teaching. They stimulate language in pre-verbal children, and facilitate the improvement of articulation, which is both an end in itself and a means through which other helping professions can contribute to children's development. The major change in thinking about retarded children has been the shift from pessimism to selective optimism. Speech and hearing workers have contributed to the optimistic picture by a shift from their traditional aversion to retarded children to acceptance of the problems retardation poses to the professions.

Attendants. While many occupations are represented in the work force of residential agencies, the least trained group, the attendants, is usually the largest (67). This is understandable because residential care is conducted twenty-four hours a day for years on end. Accordingly, staff must be available at all times for close supervision of the actions of the residents. The attendants in a cottage or on a ward are the persons who carry out the reality of service. They direct bathing and toileting, for example, an activity which is time consuming and requires close supervision. All manner of personal needs from fastening buttons to counting heads fall within the assigned functions of attendants. When supervision of feeding, blowing noses, and dressing are incorporated, the scope of attendant to responsibilities becomes clear. In fact, the philosophy of an institution is transmitted to the residents through the minute by minute actions of attendants, and only to a lesser extent or indirectly by professional staff.

One of the more welcome trends in residential programming has been recognition of this reality. Cleland's studies (8) and Bensberg's work (3) have considered the problems of attendants—their selection, their training, and their behavior. Observation of ward activities indicates very clearly that study of this issue is well chosen. In fact, the role of *attendant* amounts to that of parent-surrogate; that is, the nurturing functions of family life are present in residential living only if they are consciously introduced into attendant behavior by administrators. Much attendant behavior is not programmed, and the result is that the development of children may be a hit-or-miss affair. That is, the vital nurturing experiences which retarded children need may depend on the accident of supervision by a nurture-prone attendant rather than a punitive-authoritarian figure. Such an attendant is one whose definition of self and of his job stresses child nurturance. It does not follow that all attendants perceive that their role is best described as child care aide, as Illinois titles the position. Also, it does not follow that the attendant population necessarily shares the nurture and development philosophy of a progressive superintendent. The reasons are many, but prominent among them is the economic reality of entry into the position. Most attendants are ill-paid, poorly educated, and come to the job for diverse reasons. As the remuneration for attendant positions raises from state to state, so the caliber of personnel fluctuates. In some places, administrators cannot afford to scrutinize applicants too closely; while in others, a pool of persons may exist and competition for appointments may develop. It follows that attendants with limited education, lower class backgrounds, and authoritarian values (27) project their beliefs into child care, while better favored attendants do the same thing, although the processes of interaction may produce more desirable outcomes.

An acceptable residential agency is in many ways a middle-class entity. Those responsible for its operations in theory, the professionals, tend to have a homogeneous set of beliefs about mental retardation, cleanliness, discipline, and so forth. However, they don't bathe children, although they may stipulate when bathing shall take place. In the last analysis, child-care may be a lower-class phenomenon because attendants translate middle-class goals, bathing and toileting, into reality through their own actions and standards of performance (35).

It follows that the training of attendants is not an idealization of the role, or a response to civil service statutes. It is the device through which a vital segment of the work force, amounting to 50 per cent in many institutions according to McDowell (36), and Windle (68), accomplishes the program goals set by professionals. While administrators set objectives for child care, it is the aides who decide which behavior on wards and in day-rooms contravenes proper standards. If being "seen but not heard" is a criterion of acceptable behavior cherished at home by an aide, it will be applied on the job. If quiet is maintained at the price of withdrawal and rocking by residents, aides may be satisfied, but administrators are not. However, the reality is that aides are more important than administrators in giving vitality to the long- and short-range goals of residential living.

In recent years training programs for aides have appeared. A 1964 survey by Parnicky and Ziegler (44) indicated that most institutions, but not all, had training programs, most of which were compulsory and were conducted during the working day. As public money becomes more available, we may expect to see attendant training become more efficient. It should do so through (a) the development of larger pools of applicants attracted by better salaries; (b) less turnover due to better salaries and more rewarding programming; (c) development of more personal satisfaction as attendant positions acquire better status; and (d) development of alternatives to the dead-end quality positions now projected to attendants with aspirations about promotion and development.

Physicians. Traditionally, residential facilities have been served by physicians in two ways; first through the typical assignment of administrative responsibility to a person holding a medical degree. This tradition had its origins in the medical concept of mental retardation and in the high sense of concern that profession once entertained about mental retardation. The second pattern of service by physicians has been the more defensible connection of concern for the health of inmates. Institutional populations have more developmental anomalies than community residents, and the contribution of physicians has often set the stage for the work of other professions. It is virtually impossible to educate a malnourished child or to begin a program of gross motor activity with one who is obese. It is in residential populations that the contribution of physicians is perhaps most clear; in other settings (private practice for example) the physician's contribution through counseling is invaluable, but it is a contribution matched by other personnel. In the case of residential populations, it is often mandatory that the therapeutic regimen prescribed by physicians be accomplished, so that other professions may make their contribution.

Psychologists. The role of psychologists has evolved over the years, and the change in the contribution of these specialists has paralleled evolution of thought about retardation. Classification of retarded persons with a view to proper placement has generally been the role assigned to psychologists. Within recent years, attention has shifted from classification to more dynamic considerations. In consort with social workers and physicians, accurate perception of retarded persons can be developed and understood in the context of community and family issues.

Recent developments have modified the static contribution of psychologists. One has been the shift from measuring instruments to concepts, for example from Binet scales to adaptive behavior. Another has been a more basic change of responsibility; it is a change from diagnostic considerations to work on programming. It is exemplified in work on operant conditioning applied to shaping the behavior of adolescent retardates (51) and in the development of training programs for residents with some potential for work in selected industrial settings (51, 59).

Administrators.   Having considered the discrete professions, it is appropriate to comment on the organization of services. This is an aspect of residential life that is easily overlooked. The professions make their contributions only through organization, and it is as necessary to residential life as the invisible staff who prepare food and supply heat and power.

In the past, administrators were usually physicians. Times change and the decline of physicians as administrators in general hospitals is beginning to be paralleled in residential centers for the retarded. By coincidence this trend is paralleled by a decline in the formulation of mental retardation as a medical problem. As the social nature of the issue has been developed, the value of non-medical personnel as administrators has emerged. Today, persons with training in social work, education, and so forth, are assuming the responsibility for residential agencies.

Below the chief executive, organization is usually by function. That is, administration is handled by dividing services into those of a supportive nature—medical and nursing services, education, recreation, and rehabilitation—and those concerned with direct care—cottage life, ward activities, and so forth. Specific details naturally vary from agency to agency, but the general patterns are consistent.

Professional Organization.   Apart from discrete contributions within professional boundaries, we may consider briefly the programming of services within the full perspective of institutional life. Generally speaking, line organization flows from a chief executive to subordinates in charge of broad functions, e.g., cottage life, education, and others.

Recently we have seen attempts to build formal organizations by rational means. The anthropologist Orzack studied the staff organization at the Central Colony in Wisconsin for two years (41). His analyses disclose that new institutions provide every opportunity for developing effective patterns of administrative behavior and child care. It seems that this period of time has a limit, and then bureaucracy—in the non-invidious sense of the word—begins to restrict the ease with which new patterns of behavior can be changed easily.

The Choice of Residential Living

Perhaps mental retardation becomes a problem in human lives most poignantly when parents begin to perceive that residential living may be a suitable strategy for the care of a retarded child. There are many ways in which the strategy of residential living may arise; in some families problems of child-care may make the choice seem perfectly clear from the beginning; this choice is also made by well-educated parents (43). In such cases the problem of placing a child shifts to the issues of finding a suitable place and then enduring the passage of time until a bed is available. In the case of the exceptional family, financial resources can bring solutions comparatively soon; more typical families must wait several years until there is room in public institutions. Even then, costs are not avoided since clothing and a fractional contribution to the cost of maintenance may be required. Also, visiting may involve considerable expense because of the remoteness of the institution.

The elective pattern of institutionalizing may arise also after many years have passed; parents perceive that the welfare of their child may be in jeopardy when they are no longer young enough to provide close supervision. In such cases the problem has two aspects; the first is the dilemma of the parents. The second is separation of, for example, a teenager moved from a supportive home—sometimes called "defamilization." Fifteen or sixteen years of careful training may have produced a person attuned to the role of youngest child, a typical role even in families with younger children. Such a degree of accommodation on the part of a retarded adolescent and his family may be the product of many years of training. One learns his family role, and it may present serious problems when residential living is begun. Some of the difficulty is obviously that met by the young person who now faces a degree of rejection. A retarded youngster facing residential living after family life has no reality factor to relate to his separation from the family circle. Even at an early age children do not adapt easily to the artificiality of residential life. It is with difficulty that children are trained to see institutional life as the greater part of their existence; older children face the task of shedding a social role acquired with difficulty and acquiring a very different one. Such children are not always the most retarded; moderate retardation ($<$ IQ 50) compounded by orthopedic or convulsive problems may make residential life appropriate for a young person who has been used to a richer ambience. Understandably, private institutions may be loath to accept the task of socialization which successful residential living requires. They may be reluctant to begin a process with an adolescent which is more easily accomplished with a younger child. Given the choice, private institutions are slow to take on adolescents, though they are not entirely averse to it.

We can begin to see that selection of residential living by parents creates as many problems as it solves. Our values tell us that children belong at home, and that is because living at home is best for all concerned. It does not always follow that parents find residential living a perfect answer since the choice has the negative, if incorrect, connotation of child-rejection. Concern about what "they" will do can be partially allayed by visits, but the non-factual element can plague and persist. Occasionally, admission can be gained to a residential agency which serves a selected age range. In such cases current planning may carry a child to age twenty-one, but no further. A second strategy may then be necessary. On the other hand, some residential agencies accept retarded persons in infancy and may well have a senior citizen in his eighties on the rolls. In this last case the initial act of choosing residential living may have few loose ends. Generally, we find that some parents maintain contact with institutions through the years while others find residential living a legal form of abandonment.

A point of concern is selection of the optimal point in time and development to begin residential living. In some respects the choice is settled by the reality of competition for admission, which requires several years of waiting. However, planning is sometimes possible and the issues shift. They may be formulated, as *first*, the point in child development when growth towards maximum achievement can be optimized despite the change from home to institution; *second*, the point at which a change will minimally disrupt whatever gains have been made because of limitations in the institution. Both points are based on three findings: (1) Children living in institutions and families tend to have different patterns of development. (2) A variety of studies, those of Stedman & Eichorn (62), Centerwall & Centerwall (6), and Kugel & Reque (31) show the value of home life, while others, noticeably those of Schlanger (58), Richards & Sands (49), and Zigler and Williams (70) indicate that residential living adversely affects development. (Lest the issue be oversimplified, recognize that the reason for institutionalizing some, but not other, children of comparable retardation may affect these findings.) (3) A third type of finding is that, in theory, institutional living can be quite enriching, provided one has access to an unusual pattern, or when children have a history of exposure to a substandard care (28).

The choice of residential living still leaves some options at the discretion of the family. Briefly, they may maintain their child-care role, but indirectly, through the residential agency; they may, on the other hand, lose all contact with the resident by design or by erosion of interest with the passage of the years. Loss of contact can obviously come about through the death of parents, and brothers and sisters, with their own immediate families to care for, may not choose to maintain and strengthen contacts made fragile by time. Downey's analysis of Chicago families has revealed some elements which are correlates of high and low interest in their children residing in two Illinois institutions (13, 14). Only about one-fifth of nearly seventy ecological and personal traits were significantly different in the families. The number of years the parents have been married, the mother's age, and educational attainment were significant; on the other hand, social class and marital integration were not related, and religious values had a role which varied over the years.

Admission to Residential Living

On the face of it, retarded persons enter residential living because they are retarded. However, the matter is a little more complex because there are changes in the patterns of entry from time to time. Goldstein examined the statistics on enrollment in public institutions which, as he pointed out, account for 95 per cent of all residential provisions (22). Goldstein's findings were based on data for the years between 1904 and 1952 and showed a trend to lower chronological age at the time of first admission. The data all indicated that while severe cases of retardation remained a minority, their proportion in institutional populations was rising. Goldstein also found that the proportion of high grade retardation had dropped so that it was approximately equal to the admission rate for moderately retarded persons. Complementary data based on census figures plus Public Health figures were gathered by Sabagh & Windle (53). They found an increase in the rate of placement in institutions among children and a decrease among adolescents and adults. Males were more commonly admitted than females. A third study, by Patton & Weinstein, looked at the rates of entry at the residential facilities operated by the State of New York (46). Between 1950 and 1958 the enrollment in the six state facilities grew from 18,066 persons to 21,712. This is an increase of 20 per cent; which occurred mainly in the first five years considered. In general the picture is much like that given by Goldstein, and by Sabagh & Windle.

In addition to differences in the ages and degrees of severity, there are differences in the backgrounds from which entrants come. A series of papers from the Pacific State Hospital have contributed to our knowledge of this matter (*14, 54, 63*). Sabagh *et al.*, have found that a disproportionate number of resident retarded persons come from the Negro and Mexican minority groups (*54*). They have also found lower educational and occupational backgrounds in their population, although the finding did not occur with the most seriously retarded. Lower-class whites contributed disproportionately to the admissions at Pacific State Hospital. Churchill has analyzed sex differences in admissions (*7*). Tarjan *et al.*, have observed that there are differences in ages at admission which are consistent within diagnostic categories (*63*). Familials tend to begin residential living in adolescence, while children with visible problems, Down's disease, microcephaly and hydrocephaly, enter at a much earlier age (*43*). In general, severe cases were admitted sooner than mild cases. Saenger analyzed the pre-admission status of retarded individuals between six and twenty-four years of age (*55*). He found the rate of institutionalization was ten times greater for persons in the IQ range 20–49 than for persons above IQ 50. As with the Pacific Colony studies, Negro and Latin minorities were overly represented when compared to white Catholic and Protestant groups. The smallest rate of entry into residential life was found among Jewish retarded youngsters. This last finding is similar to that of Farber, Jenné, and Toigo, who reported that high social status Jewish families were not generally willing to place children in residential facilities (*18*).

In 1965 the Illinois State Department of Mental Hygiene published an examination of the individuals on the waiting lists for admission at the Dixon and Lincoln centers (*66*). This important study contained both findings and recommendations on 1,442 persons, 993 were males, and the remainder, 499 subjects, were females. Eighty-four per cent of the subjects were below the age eighteen years; the median age for males was eight years, for females six years, with a median age of eight years for all subjects. About half the subjects came from Cook County (Chicago), and about the same number came from downstate.

Findings were that (1) most of the classifiable subjects in the age group 6-11 years were in the IQ range below thirty-five ($\frac{272}{402}$), while a majority of the age group 12-17 years were above that level ($\frac{146}{228}$); (2) 44 per cent of the applicants had one or more physical handicaps; (3) 68 per cent of the applicants were not in school; (4) 48.3 per cent were living with their parents; (5) 80 per cent of the children at least six years old were toilet trained; (6) 80 per cent of the children at least six years old displayed serious behavior problems; the proportions were roughly comparable at all levels of retardation, ranging from 52 per cent to 68 per cent; (7) uncontrollable behavior was a common problem seen in the least retarded, while emotional stress was more commonly seen as a problem dictating residential care in the seriously retarded; (8) incomes of families with children on the waiting list were below the Illinois average, and the rate of family disorganization was above average.

A third approach to institutional entrance is found when we analyze behavior prior to entry. It is generally agreed that acting out behavior can lead to prompt commitment. This precipitating element has been reported by Tarjan et al. (63), Sabagh et al. (54), and Saenger (55). In particular, sexual offenses lead to swift and certain banishment to residential agencies. When we put together the various elements, we find the probability of institutionalization rises steeply. A Negro, lower-class child found in acts deemed sexual or destructive will find himself in a public institution very quickly; this observation is corroborated in Henderson's work (24). It appears that in many cases the antecedents to commitment are very different. In some instances the degree of retardation may be mild and secondary to a particular class of behavior. Institutionalization then becomes an act with connotations of concern for the welfare of others. In other cases, entry into residential life is an attempt to help the child, usually one who is seriously retarded.

A variant pattern of entry into residential life is re-commitment, the return to institutional life after a period of community and family experience. When the situation arises it usually has clear reasons. For example, high-grade retardates with work potentials may fail for reasons quite divorced from intellectual abilities and work habits. When a youngster has been returned to an originally adverse mode of life, that is, circumstances of crime and social disorganization, it is highly probable that he will run afoul of authority in some form. In such cases the discharged resident may be treated like his normal associates unless his former status is revealed. Should his residential background be revealed, the probabilities rise that commitment will appeal to courts as a legitimate mode of banishment. In this case re-commitment may be fortuitous. On the other hand, there is the reality of hostile retarded youngsters whose personal traits make friction with the community quite predictable because of outbursts while in residence. British studies indicate that residents with a history of acting out behavior have a high probability of re-commitment. According to Tong and McKay, a pattern of aggression while in residence, and a history of escapes, make a return to residential living most probable (65).

In many cases it is not easy to describe precisely what the optimal agency for retarded persons is. Many facilities are oriented to one disease category, which may be quite unreasonable because retarded persons requiring residential care may be burdened with other problems. Mental illness is not unknown among the retarded, and it is an exercise in fine discrimination to say which is the primary or secondary state. Also, there have been institutions for epileptics in the past, and their relevance to retardation is not easily handled in practice, although it may be in theory. There are the cerebral palsied whose retardation may be compounded by orthopedic problems, and then there are the delinquents. Last of all, we should recognize that retarded persons can live long enough to become geriatric problems. Clearly, it is not enough to plan residential facilities for persons deemed "retarded"; that is only the beginning. The best hope lies in our current commitment to small units; within that value system lies the best hope of providing for the heterogeneity of secondary, but no less critical, characteristics found routinely in retarded persons. The strategy is to develop units geared to the various configurations of disability and allow their staffs to develop expertise within better defined patterns of programming and care.

Leaving Residential Living

There was a time, not too long ago, when residential living was a pattern with fixed properties. It was stable and the turnover was small; it was dreary and the arrangement was custodial; it was permanent and most commitments terminated in death. As one writer has expressed it, the residential population was like a stagnant pool; very little new flow entered it, and very little left. This pattern has changed in several ways.

To begin with there has been a change in administrative philosophy in favor of community living as a worthy goal which is practical in some cases. Translated into programming we have seen increasing emphasis on industrial training, and in Great Britain and the United States, for example, there have been many successful programs, leading to discharge of retarded persons. Another change has been recognition that institutional care may be a suitable pattern of living for a brief time. That point of view appears in the development of institutions with specific age restrictions or with clear rehabilitation purposes. In 1962, Noone examined the pattern of enrollment at the State Institution at Laurel, Maryland (40). He found that over a period of time 582 entries were not quite balanced by 353 releases. The increase was greatest in cases of severe retardation, and the decrease of patients was greatest along mild cases. The patients were generally white males under age ten.

Another change has come through recognition that not all residents have been properly placed. There have been children committed to residential agencies because they were neglected and rejected. An institution, even one for the retarded, was thought better than the circumstances in which the child was found. Discharge may then take the form of entry into another more suitable agency, or return to the community until some other disposition can be made.

Not all discharges are of the same type; in some instances residents go home for holidays, which are usually of a prescribed length and are arranged formally. Residents are sometimes placed in foster homes, and in rare cases in half-way houses, hostels to which persons return after working within the community. Another pattern is care in foster homes, an arrangement which has the value of presenting a semblance of family life, although the reason may be a lack of space in a residential setting.

It is appropriate to take note of unofficial as well as official departures. On occasion residents wander away or simply run away, but such trips are usually brief. Failure to return from visits to home and community are more serious. According to Windle (68), the longest unofficial departures are usually made by females, but no other associations, e.g., with age, IQ, or length of residence, seem significant.

In the case of persons being returned to community and family life officially, the questions of successful and unsuccessful placement arise. As with all persons who have been taught to be good (i.e., conforming) members of a regimented group, the transition to independent living is not automatic. There are decisions which people have to face for the first time. The "someone" who provides a change of linen, clean clothes, and food is now the ex-resident himself, a person who previously took these things for granted. Persons of normal intelligence and maturity do not find their return to secular or civilian life easy, and persons with less than adequate intelligence may fail to develop patterns of independent living. Analogous study of the post-hospital careers of persons treated for mental illness indicates that family expectations play a critical role in determining subsequent adjustment (60). In cases where institutional placement has been seen as a legal form of abandonment, post-hospital adjustment is probably not very good and undoubtedly leads to re-commitment. In the case of entry into agencies explicitly designed to serve a restricted age range, families may have evolved to the point that family care and supervision may not be easy.

Obviously, success and failure may depend on personal properties of residents, as well as the milieus they subsequently enter. According to Shafter (59), residential facilities can predict by objective means the inmates most likely or least likely to effect successful vocational adjustment after discharge. Of sixty-six possible traits, he concluded that about a dozen were discriminatory. Generally speaking, they amounted to a picture of traits that make any person an acceptable worker; they included benign patterns of behavior toward people and a conforming attitude toward job tasks.

Cohen's analysis of unsuccessful job placements of fifty-seven young men and women revealed that failure was often non-vocational and was due to unsuccessful adjustment to community life (9). In some instances employers reported poor attitudes toward work, and used terms such as "lazy" and "vulgar"; Cohen felt that community attitudes played a critical role in the effectiveness of attempts to discharge residents. Sloan used more dynamic factors based on Rorschach protocols in his attempt to predict post-discharge success in the community (61). Using fifteen matched pairs, he applied seven criteria suggested by Beck, factors commonly used as serving categories. Sloan concluded that he could not distinguish the successful from the unsuccessful on the basis of Rorschach signs.

The Social System

So far the material presented has been descriptive; it has conveyed the realities and generalities of resident populations, and the agencies that serve them. There is a supplementary point of view which may now be introduced; it is the consideration of a resident population as a social system, an assembly of human beings whose relationships to one another constitute the connective tissue of organic social life. Regarded in this light, retarded persons in residence can be said to have the social attributes we speedily apply to Trobriand Islanders, and more slowly recognize in Middletown and Elmtown. A relatively small group of writers (appropriately, social scientists) have used them to cast light on the behavior of retarded persons (15, 16, 17, 23, 35, 39, 54, 66). This is a contribution which has begun to yield valuable insights and will assuredly yield more. At a time when retardation is commonly and mistakenly formulated within the limited data of biological science, it is well to consider the value of phenomena from the social sciences.

Role. Each of us has a role or, more accurately, a number of roles. As we move through the routines of the day, we may be successively indulgent father or mother, competitive worker, jaded commuter, and, once more, benevolent parent. There is more than a role title involved here; each role has an explicit set of attitudes and functions which people acquire and shed, and which may be contradictory at selected points in the day. Being a retarded person in residence can be profitably understood as a series of allied roles. This means that, with variations and with several degrees of ease, a resident acts in accordance with what is expected of him (as he perceives it) and in accordance with what he feels is appropriate. As with all roles some have high, others low, status. It follows that a residential agency has a role expectation for a retarded person; the role emerges from presumptions about the capacities of the person and from the nature of the organization. Role expectations of others have traditionally limited the repertoire of suitable behaviors. That is, we have usually felt that the diagnosis of retardation eliminated as possible and desirable a range of behaviors. Retarded persons were supposed to be "sick" (this in itself a role of benign infantilism in the minds of most convalescents) and to be incapable of self-care and independence. In the context of residential life retarded persons are generally expected to be compliant, to be lacking in guile, and to be generally amenable to blandishments of all types. Attacks of initiative tend to subvert traditional concepts of ward management, and they are usually extinguished, in the Skinnerian sense, whenever possible. Our presuppositions generally consider persons in "mental hospitals" to be of low status. We also tend to ascribe a similar status to those who work with them. (It may be sheer coincidence that we hear of "teachers of the gifted," but also of "retarded teachers").

Establishment of residential living as a life style usually means abandonment of one role (e.g., the "youngest child," commonly found in family life) and acquisition of another role, "resident patient." Commonly, the agency does all it can to orient the new entrant, but there are role transitions only the inmate can make for himself. At this point we may borrow from Goffman's stimulating work (21) and observe that acquisition of the new role and perception of its low status occurs ritually in many social organizations, for example, the army, prisons, and convents. Certain compulsory acts of an ultimately beneficial nature may be experienced. These include bathing, issuance of a distinctive garb, and isolation for a brief but probably denigrating period of time. With this experience older retardates begin to perceive the restrictions imposed on them, and to grasp the amount of fate and power control attendants and others exert. For older, brighter adolescents the entry may begin the process of orientation to other inmates as persons in whose eyes status may rise and fall, as opposed to the fixed status more typically inferred from the restrictions on one's mobility. In this situation, constructions of one's own role may be perceived as the consequence of forced detention, and perception of the role *inmate* as one who is incarcerated for unjust reasons. Out of the welter of intended and fortuitous cues to appropriate behavior can emerge a role more consonant with the benevolent intentions of the authorities. Exposed to residential living from an early age, residents who need considerable personal care, e.g., children with convulsive disorders, may perceive themselves not as prisoners but as patients. They may see themselves as worthy objects of others' attentions and as the recipients of care for medical rather than punitive reasons. In such a state of affairs attendants are probably perceived benignly, that is, as nurturing figures rather than as punitive and restricting figures. In the majority of cases the polarization just presented is less than accurate; most inmates of institutions for the retarded probably fall somewhere between these two extremes, and probably alternate as the routines of residential living modify personal ambitions and expectations. As with family life there are times when the needs of all inhibit the behavior of some; in such situations young people, normal and retarded, resident and non-resident, tend to behave as institutional demands support or thwart personal preferences.

Two social processes structuring the role of retarded persons which have been discussed by Edgerton and Sabagh (16) are *mortification* and *aggrandizement*. Mortification is the social process of questioning autonomy of action and self-concept; the process consists of acts which devalue the status a person has enjoyed and usually leads to feelings of self-doubt and uncertainty about status and role. Aggrandizement is the opposite process, the act of increasing the value ascribed to himself. The two concepts apply to most *total institutions*, as Goffman (21) terms them, and seem to apply to residential agencies for the retarded. Mortification occurs when the new resident perceives that he is in an institution and that he is expected to obey the injunctions of the staff. He undergoes the rites of initiation described in the previous paragraph and may end up feeling quite depressed and understandably apprehensive about sterilization and other punitive acts which the grapevine conveys (1, 16). Subsequently the resident of an institution for the retarded will find means to develop more self-supporting, aggrandizing perceptions of his situation. Edgerton and Sabagh feel these steps include: (1) the favorable comparisons that the resident can make with the most seriously retarded inmates, (2) support for his self-serving story of previous adequacy from the peer group, and (3) perception of approval for conventional behavior coming from agency staff. Possibilities beyond those given by Edgerton and Sabagh are: (1) the opportunity to participate in community related rehabilitation and training programs, (2) the occasional licit relationship with the opposite sex at recreational activities, and (3) liaison with the family through visits and off-campus leave. Edgerton and Sabagh observed that persons who have been successful at aggrandizement include being judged a good risk for community living.

According to Dentler and Mackler (12), social pressure in the form of attendants' attempts to control the behavior of new residents affects sociometric status. Between the first and second months, a group of cottage residents moved from a sociometric structure of forty mutualities, toward a structure containing three mutual ties. Expressing the sociometric changes in descriptive terms, Dentler and Mackler remarked that sociometric status in the cottage they studied was related to individuals' compliance with behavior norms set for them. Their analysis of compliance is revealing; they feel that constriction of affect and interpersonal behavior develops in the form of withdrawal. Concomitant changes are declines in language, social development, and level of intellectual functioning. The author has observed essentially the same social phenomenon and is inclined to consider a limited repertoire of means for attaining accommodation within an imposed social structure one of the features of the behavioral syndrome we call mental retardation.

Apart from the external structuring of role there is the self-perceptive aspect, the element of wearing the role which results in either comfort, support and warmth or, to extend the metaphor, in irritation and discomfort. On the face of it, it seems improbable that any but the more severely retarded would automatically accept their status and roles on the basis of institutional initiative. Links with the community are generally maintained by thorough contact with relatives, and in the case of residents with potentials for education and rehabilitation, systematic attempts are made to make eventual community living with its own roles a probable outcome. In both cases television is a sustained link with community and family life, and it conveys explicit information on the roles that young people play. Understandably, retarded persons in residence attempt to incorporate facets of community role playing into their own daily behavior by imitation of idealized roles (39). Of course some inmates are more able to meet the role expectations which they and their peers set. It follows that some are more successful at this than others and that the more effective constitute models for the other residents. Edgerton (15) has described such an *élite* within the Pacific State Hospital, a group of twenty-five boys and twenty-six girls. A history of law violations is found in Edgerton's group, and they tend to have a working knowledge of questionable patterns of behavior, and to qualify partially by establishing credibility as "tough" and "sharp." Among older residents an economic equivalent can be observed, and the entrepreneur who displays initiative may be tolerated by staff. Although such services as car washing for money may be contrary to policy, they are frequently encountered. At times such service may be slow, as in the case of a long-time resident who insisted on clean water. He would immerse his wash cloth twice and then walk a hundred yards to refill his bucket. The relevance of this incident lies in staff tolerance and tacit approval for an admittedly deviant but high-status role. In the analysis of car washing at Pacific State Hospital, Edgerton, Tarjan and Dingman (17) found that the simple economies of the service appealed to long-term staff, while newer staff initially perceived it as beneficial to the inmate-entrepreneur.

CHILD CARE THROUGH RESIDENTIAL LIVING

As with special classes, institutions have beneficial and harmful results. From observation the author is inclined to see the differential effects as consistent and emerging from social class considerations. The social elements are those which affect children prior to residential living and which affect them after they enter the institution.

We may begin by recalling that residential agencies are usually middle class, professional in theoretical values. That is because the persons who make policy usually come from that stratum of society. But we may recall that face-to-face care of residents is conducted by attendants whose social class origins are usually lower. Their child-rearing values are not, in general, modified by training, and they use the techniques of control which are natural in their own milieu. Translated into ward practice or cottage life, the result is often depression of language, as attendants misjudge quiet for control, and suppress affect, leading children with limited non-verbal resources to drift into phantasy or rock on their chairs. Children from lower-class homes may find nothing new in enforced immobility and the frequent stress on suppressing noise. Children from clearly depriving and punitive homes may find the entire experience beneficial, because someone, however harried, cares. Others, from middle-class homes, may find the comparative impersonality of group care and group manipulation harmful, because their previously welcomed noise and spontaneous verbalizations are now extinguished. In such cases the theoretically middle class agency becomes what its attendants and aides are; the higher their education, the more likely they are to tolerate a non-disruptive degree of activity. The poorer the background, the more punitive they may be. The socialization process becomes what the attendants make it, and the social class orientation of the institution reflects the values of the attendants who put policy into practice, and who are the institution vis-à-vis the inmates. It may seem that there is a middle class bias in these remarks, and there is. Our best social policy probably lies in recognition that the social criteria used in assessing mental retardation are generally middle class, and that we have traditional terms—subcultural, culturally deprived—to describe social behavior in which class origins are explicitly non-middle class. A gambit is to employ an attendant of as high a level as possible and to make explicit, through compulsory training, the child-care role the person is expected to assume. Having found such people it is imperative that we keep them, although this is not easy for many reasons, prominent among which are the limits to promotion, salaries, and status (25). These problems, in turn, may arise from the failure to see socialization of patients as the prime responsibility of the lowest level of staff, and a failure to shift their role from custodian-keeper-warden to therapeutic figure. A keeper does not deserve as much salary as a child-care worker, and only training can break the vicious circle of marginally desirable people seeking an undesirable role. Only an upgraded position with quasi-formal training will attract people from middle class backgrounds. When people with middle class child-rearing values and a nurturing concept of their roles are numerous, we may expect to see residental facilities become ameliorative in practice as well as in theory. At that time their custodial responsibility will be augmented by their concern for developing potentialities which would otherwise pass unnoticed.

SUMMARY

In this chapter we have examined the major issues that arise in a study of residential living. There are several kinds of residential agencies in which retarded children live. We have seen that the selection of residential living, as opposed to community and home living, is an issue laden with social and emotional complications. Ecological factors, apart from the biological degree of defect, influence admission to residential living and a number of personal and behavioral traits affect discharge. Increasingly, residential agencies are examined as cultural units by sociologists and anthropologists. Careful analysis indicates that the effects of residential living on child development may be understood by study of the personnel who care for these children.

BIBLIOGRAPHY

1. Abel, T., "Moral Judgments among Subnormals," *J. Abnorm. Soc. Psych.*, 1941, *36*, 378-392.

2. Begab, M., *The Mentally Retarded Child—A Guide to Services of Social Agencies*, U. S. Dept. of Health, Education, and Welfare, Washington, D. C., 1963.

3. Bensberg, G., (ed.) *Recreation for the Mentally Retarded: A Handbook for Ward Personnel*, Southern Regional Educational Board, Atlanta, Ga., 1964.

4. Berkson, G., "Stereotyped Movements of Mental Defectives. V. Ward Behavior and its Relation to an Experimental Task," *Amer. J. Ment. Def.*, 1964, *69*, 253-264.

5. Cain, L. F., and Levine, S., "Effects of Community and Institutional School Programs on Trainable Mentally Retarded Children," *CEC Res. Mon. Series B*, No. B-1, 1963.

6. Centerwall, S. A., and Centerwall, W. R., "A Study of Children with Mongolism Reared in the Home Compared to Those Reared Away from Home," *Pediat.*, 1960, *25*, 678-685.

7. Churchill, L., "Sex Differences Among Mildly Retarded Admissions to a Hospital for the Mentally Retarded," *Amer. J. Ment. Def.*, 1964, *69*, 269-276.

8. Cleland, C. C., "Natural versus Systematic Selection of Attendants: Intra-Institutional Administrative Problems," *Amer. J. Ment. Def.*, 1964, *69*, 354-359.

9. Cohen, J. S., "An Analysis of Vocational Failures of Mental Retardates Placed in the Community after a Period of Institutionalization," *Amer. J. Ment. Def.*, 1960, *65*, 371-375.

10. Dentler, R., and Mackler, B., "The Socialization of Retarded Children in an Institution," *J. Hlth. Hum. Behav.*, 1961, *2*, 243-251.

11. _____, "Mental Ability and Sociometric Status Among Retarded Children," *Psych. Bull.*, 1962, *59*, 273-283.

12. _____, "Effects on Sociometric Status of Institutional Pressure to Adjust Among Retarded Children," *Brit. J. Soc. Clin. Psych.*, 1964, *3*, 81-89.

13. Downey, K. J., "Parental Interest in the Institutionalized Severely Mentally Retarded Child," *Soc. Prob.*, 1963, *11*, 186-193.

14. _____, "Parental Interest in the Institutionalized Mentally Retarded Child," unpublished Ph.D. dissertation, University of Illinois, 1962.

15. Edgerton, R. B., "A Patient Elite: Ethnography in a Hospital for the Mentally Retarded," *Amer. J. Ment. Def.*, 1963, *68*, 372-385.

16. ———, and Sabagh, G., "From Mortification to Aggrandizement: Changing Self-Concepts in the Careers of the Mentally Retarded," *Psychiat.*, 1962, *25*, 263-272.

17. ———, Tarjan, G., and Dingman, H. F., "Free Enterprise in a Captive Society," *Amer. J. Ment. Def.*, 1961, *66*, 35-41.

18. Farber, B., Jenne, W. C., and Toigo, R., "Family Crisis and the Decision to Institutionalize the Retarded Child," *C. E. C. Res. Mon.*, 1960, No. 1.

19. ———, and Marden, P., "High Brow versus Low Grade Status Among Institutionalized Mentally Retarded Boys," *Soc. Prob.*, 1961, *8*, 300-312.

20. Gallagher, E. B., and Albert, R. S., "The Gelbdorf Affair—An Examination of Institutional Dilemmas in a Progressive Mental Hospital," *Psychiat.*, 1961, *23*, 221-227.

21. Goffman, E., *Asylums: Essays on the Social Situation of Mental Patients and Other Inmates*, Aldine Publishing Co., Chicago, 1962.

22. Goldstein, H., "Population Trends in U. S. Public Institutions for the Mentally Deficient," *Amer. J. Ment. Def.*, 1959, *63*, 599-604.

23. Guskin, S., "Social Psychologies of Mental Deficiency," in Ellis, N., (ed.) *Handbook of Research on Mental Retardation*, McGraw Hill, 1963.

24. Henderson, R. A., "Factors in Commitment of Educable Mentally Handicapped Children to Illinois State Schools," unpublished Ph.D. dissertation, University of Illinois, 1957.

25. Kaplon, D., "The High Grade Moron—A Study of Institutional Admissions over a Ten Year Period," *Proc. Amer. Assoc. Ment. Def.*, 1935, *40*, 69-91.

26. Kaufman, M. E., "Group Psychotherapy in Preparation for the Return of Mental Defectives from Institution to Community," *Ment. Ret.*, 1963, *1*, 276-280.

27. Kimbrell, D. L., and Blanchard, L. G., "Some Psycho-Social Determinants of Employed and Discharged Ward Attendants in Institutions for Mental Defectives," *Amer. J. Ment. Def.*, 1964, *69*, 220-224.

28. Kirk, S. A., *Early Education for the Mentally Retarded*, University of Illinois Press, 1958.

29. Krishef, C. H., Reynolds, M. C., and Stunkard, C. L., "A Study of Factors Relating to Post-Institutional Adjustment," *Minn. Welfare*, 1959, *11*, 5-15.

30. Kuenzel, M., "Social Status of Foster Families Engaged in Community Care and Training of Mentally Deficient Children," *Amer. J. Ment. Def.*, 1939, *44*, 244-253.

31. Kugel, R. B., and Reque, D., "A Comparison of Mongoloid Children," *J. Amer. Med. Assoc.*, 1961, *175*, 959-961.

32. Lewis, W. D., "The Effect of an Institution Environment upon the Verbal Development of Imbecile Children, I: Verbal Intelligence," *J. Ment. Def. Res.*, 1959, *3*, 122-128.

33. Lyle, J. G., "A Study of the Verbal Ability of Imbecile Children," unpublished Ph.D. dissertation, University of London, 1959.

34. ———, "Environmentally Produced Retardation—Institution and Pre-Institution Influences," *J. Abnorm. Soc. Psychol.*, 1964, *69*, 329-332.

35. MacAndrew, C., and Edgerton, R., "The Everyday Life of Institutionalized 'Idiots'," *Hum. Org.*, 1964, *23*, 312-318.

36. McDowell, F. E., "Role Playing and Discussion as Training Methods for Changing Role Definitions of Attendants for Institutionalized Mental Retardates," unpublished dissertation, Peabody College, 1963.

37. Maney, A. A., Pace, R., and Morrison, D. F., "A Factor Analytic Study of the Need for Institutionalization: Problems and Populations for Program Development," *Amer. J. Ment. Def.*, 1964, *69*, 372-384.

38. Mayo, L., (chmn.) "A Proposed Program for National Action to Combat Mental Retardation," *The President's Panel on Mental Retardation*, 1962.

39. Miles, A. E., "Some Aspects of Culture Among Subnormal Hospital Patients," *Brit. J. Med. Psych.*, 1965, *38*, 171-176.

40. Noone, J. J., "A Study of the Commitments and Departures from an Institution for the Mentally Retarded," unpublished dissertation, University of Illinois, 1957.

41. Orzack, L. H., "Role Implications of Change in a New Organization," paper presented to the Fifth World Congress of Sociology, 1962.

42. Oudenne, W., "Development of a Cottage Staffing Ratio: A Result of a Practicum Method of Training for Administrative Positions," *Ment. Retard.*, 1963, *1*, 370-374.

43. Olshanksy, S., and Schonfeld, J., "Institutionalization of Pre-School Retardates," *Ment. Ret.*, 1964, *2*, 109-115.

44. Parnicky, J., and Ziegler, R., "Attendant Training—A National Survey," *Ment. Retard.*, 1964, *2*, 76-82.

45. Pasamanick, B., (ed.) "Standards for State Residential Institutions for the Mentally Retarded," *Amer. J. Ment. Def. Mon. Suppl.*, No. 4, 1964.

46. Patton, R. E., and Weinstein, A. S., "Changing Characteristics of the Population in the New York State Schools for Mental Defectives," *Amer. J. Ment. Def.*, 1960, *64*, 625-635.

47. Pisapia, M., "Mental Retardation in the Social Work Curriculum," *Ment. Retard.*, 1964, *2*, 294-298.

48. Pocs, O., "Community Participation of Mothers with Mentally Retarded Children," unpublished master's thesis, University of Illinois, 1960.

49. Richards, T. W., and Sands, R., "Mongoloid Children Living at Home: Interim Report," Kennedy Child Study Center, Santa Monica, Calif., 1963.

50. Ringness, T. A., "Self-Concept of Children of Low, Average and High Intelligence," *Amer. J. Ment. Def.*, 1961, *65*, 453-461.

51. Roswell-Harris, D., "Industrial Training for the Mentally Subnormal in a Hospital Setting," *J. Ment. Subnorm.*, 1963, *9*, 1-5.

52. Sabagh, G., and Edgerton, R. B., "Sterilized Mental Defectives Look at Eugenic Sterilization," *Eugen. Quart.*, 1962, *9*, 213-222.

53. _____, and Windle, C., "Recent Trends in Institutionalization Ratio of Mental Defectives in the United States," *Amer. J. Ment. Def.*, 1960, *64*, 618-624.

54. _____, *et al.*, "Social Class and Ethnic Status of Patients Admitted to a State Hospital for the Retarded," *Pac. Sociol. Rev.*, 1959, *2*, 76-80.

55. Saenger, G., *Factors Influencing the Institutionalization of Mentally Retarded Individuals in New York City: A Report*, New York State Interdepartmental Health Resources Board, Albany, N. Y., 1960.

56. Scheerenberger, R. C., "A Current Census of State Institutions for the Mentally Retarded," *Ment. Retard.*, 1965, *3*, 4-6.

57. Schiefelbusch, R. L., and Smith, J. O., (eds.) *Research in Speech and Hearing for Mentally Retarded Children*, U. S. Office of Education Project F 010, 1964.

58. Schlanger, B. B., "Environmental Influences on the Verbal Output of Mentally Retarded Children," *J. Speech Hear. Dis.*, 1954, *19*, 339-343.

59. Shafter, A. J., "Criteria for Selecting Institutionalized Mental Defectives for Vocational Placement," *Amer. J. Ment. Def.*, 1957, *61*, 599-616.

60. Simmons, O. G., and Freeman, H. E., "Familial Expectations and Post Hospital Performance of Mental Patients," *Hum. Relat.*, 1959, *12*, 233-241.

61. Sloan, W., "Prediction of External Adjustment of Mental Defectives by Use of the Rorschach Test," *J. Consult. Psych.*, 1948, *12*, 303-309.

62. Stedman, D., and Eichorn, D., "A Comparison of the Growth and Development of Institutionalized and Home-Reared Mongoloids during Infancy and Childhood," *Amer. J. Ment. Def.*, 1964, *69*, 391-401.

63. Tarjan, G., *et al.*, "Effectiveness of Hospital Release Programs," *Amer. J. Ment. Def.*, 1960, *64*, 609-617.

64. Tizard, J., "Residential Care of Mentally Handicapped Children," *Brit. Med. J.* 1960, *1*, 1041-1046.

65. Tong, J. E., and MacKay, G. W., "A Statistical Follow-Up of Mental Defectives of Dangerous or Violent Propensities," *Brit. J. Delinq.*, 1959, *9*, 276-289.

66. *The Waiting List: A Study of the Mentally Retarded*, Illinois State Department of Mental Hygiene, Springfield, Ill., 1965.

67. Wells, F. L., "The State School as a Social System," *J. Psychol*, 1938, 5 119-124.

68. Windle, C., "An Explanatory Study of Unauthorized Absences from Pacific State Hospital," *Trng. Schl. Bull.*, 1959, 55, 73-75.

69. ———, "Prognosis of Mental Subnormals," *Amer. J. Ment. Def. Mon. Suppl. No. 5*, 1962.

70. Zigler, E., and Williams, J., "Institutionalization and the Effectiveness of Social Reinforcement: A Three-Year Follow-Up Study," *J. Abnorm. Soc. Psych.*, 1963, 66, 197-205.

Chapter 4

CHARACTERISTICS OF THE MENTALLY RETARDED

Having considered the problem of mental retardation as a social issue in the previous chapter, we may now focus our attention a little more precisely on the mentally retarded individual. We will pay particular attention to how he acts, how he thinks, and we will attempt to identify any attributes that set him apart from his associates and friends who are not retarded.

A very appealing and fairly obvious way to begin is to consider the retarded "in his natural habitat." Specifically, we could start by talking about what individuals do and, by means of anecdotes, sketch a character type or a personality type. This would be informative and even entertaining. On the other hand, the information would be limited and would not allow us to generalize or extrapolate. A way of assessing any method of investigating human beings is to ask if it helps to predict human behavior. By this standard a more calculated approach to behavior is necessary. To put it another way, we should view behavior self-consciously when attempting to give a rational account of it; it is important to work from an established point of view, holding to some rationale for explaining one's analysis.

THEORIES OF BEHAVIOR

There have been many attempts to give a comprehensive account of human nature. There is the Marxist analysis of human nature which views man specifically as a social being, an economic creature. Such a point of view attempts to give a comprehensive account of man and of the entire social order. It predicts a series of events and attempts to shape them towards predetermined ends. Less global accounts of the human lot have been attempted since Marx. Freud was a student of one segment of behavior, the inter- and intra-personal character of behavior. Freudian thought is an analysis of man as an irrational creature. According to Freud, adult behavior is traceable to early experiences which motivate daily actions.

Both these points of view have recently been applied to the study of mental retardation. In the previous chapter, Forrer's formulation of the behavior of a mother was mentioned. That paper was based on a contemporary formulation of Freud's work. Current Marxist science has a concern for the handicapped, and relevant issues are pursued in the U.S.S.R. The use of "defectology" as a construct is necessary in contemporary Soviet science, which must be consonant with Marxism at all times.

As a contrast to the broad issues of Freud and Marx, both of whom were trying to present comprehensive models, we can consider some more limited attempts to study human behavior. Let us consider some of the conceptual systems of the behavioral sciences and of psychology in particular.

A significant problem for students of human behavior is *motivation*. This is the issue that arises when one asks why people act as they do. It is approached in the scientific literature through positions like that of Murray. Murray believed that much of human behavior is motivated by a system of *needs* and *presses*. Both are constructs that link the individual with his surroundings. Murray lists several sets of needs and defines these by concrete dispositions which he usually finds reflected in stories that people tell. His technique consists of showing pictures to people and asking them to narrate stories which the pictures could illustrate. Themes tend to emerge consistently in a series of stories, and these relate (sometimes generally, sometimes precisely) to the motivational state of the person telling the story.

More recent studies are those initiated by McClelland, who has set himself the more circumscribed task of viewing just a portion of the motivation spectrum. Working from the premise that thematic materials give insight into specific motives, he has considered the motivation of achievement behavior and affiliative behavior. A number of studies have developed McClelland's postulates, and since this is a current, emerging point of view, we may expect more developments. One example is the Jordan and deCharms paper (41), which applied basic motivational considerations to the mentally retarded. This paper will be discussed in detail a little later.

One other basic, sophisticated point of view needs to be considered. As in the studies of McClelland and Murray, this point of view is not a theory of behavior in the retarded, but one that takes a broader view of how people act and how they develop and change. There have been few developments in the understanding of human nature as penetrating as the work of Jean Piaget, the Swiss psychologist. His work, now extended over some thirty years, is at once amazingly simple in its approach and equally complex in its analyses. Piaget has been a sophisticated eavesdropper, a shrewd playmate, a penetrating logician; virtually all of his experiments have dealt with how children think (60). The basic studies have been surrounded by a supplementary series of papers in which people try to describe what Piaget thinks. Berlyne has recently summarized some of Piaget's contributions to children's development (11). Woodward has applied Piaget's ideas on sensory-motor development to mental retardation and found them valid and helpful (85).

Systematic positions on human behavior are to be found in Benoit's papers, derived from the writings of Hebb (8), (9), and in Hutt and Gibby's attention to psychodynamic formulations in understanding the retarded child (34).

Having suggested that there are some systematic positions one might assume in examining the behavior of retardates, we encounter a dilemma. There is the careful use of a conceptual position with limited data to support it on the one hand, and the mass of research literature which can be loosely classed as generally empirical on the other.

In analyzing the behavior of the retarded in this chapter, we shall let the established data of a generally behavioral sort constitute both the theoretical position and the relevant data. In some instances, the studies will take a systematic position—for example, some of the studies in learning; in other cases, the studies will have no precise orientation, but will have an implicit empirical set towards the issues. The author believes that mental retardation is largely an empirical problem.

THE SEVERITY OF MENTAL RETARDATION

To characterize the retardate in general, we must first know whether retardation is usually slight or severe. One might rephrase the issue by asking, "How retarded are retarded individuals?"

Generally speaking, most mentally retarded individuals are more like their fellows than unlike them. People acquire their genetic endowment through both parents, and most have a variety of attributes that come from a variety of ancestors. The generality of this contributing background was noted in Chapter 2 and in the Reed, Reed, and Palm study where it is stated that the offspring of defective individuals tend to be a little closer to normal than their parents. The principle'of filial regression, as Galton named it, tends towards homogeneity of intellect in the population.

Looking at the issue a little more closely, we may consider those people defined in a population as retarded. Here again, while there are individual cases of severe retardation, the vast majority of defectives are not acutely different from the rest of mankind. There are, for example, so many more school provisions for educables than for ineducables; there are so many more children who can learn a modest amount of academic material and acquire minimal vocational skills than there are totally dependent human beings. The numerous studies reporting a decrease in the known cases of retardation in the post-school period are further proof of this observation. In the group of eighty retarded persons in Iceland studied by Helgason, three-fourths were "morons," to use the investigator's words (33). The remaining twenty-one cases were "imbeciles" (16/80), while five were profoundly retarded.

Another way of looking at the problem is to examine the figures on the distribution of IQ's in a university clinic population shown in Figure 4·1.

There are, of course, some questions about the validity of such figures, but they usually tend to reflect the population of retardates as a whole.

An examination of these data reveals 99 cases in the IQ interval 48-78, out of 212 in the total group below IQ 78. Roughly 48 per cent of this population is in the educable range; the proportion below IQ 48 is larger than usual, reflecting this particular clinic's slightly deviant par-

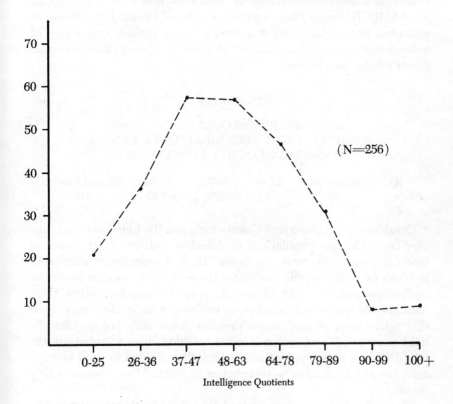

Figure 4·1

Distribution of IQ's in a Clinic Population

(N=256)

Intelligence Quotients

ent population. Additional information of a slightly different nature but essentially relevant has come from a large scale survey, the Kauai Pregnancy Study (6). This study is now reporting information through a number of scientific outlets and in 1963 provided figures on the proportions below a cut-off score of IQ 80. Five per cent of the children studied were below IQ 80; however, only 32 per cent of the total were below IQ 75 and only 18 per cent were below IQ 70. The actual rise of the proportions is not relevant at the moment, although it is slightly unusual; what is relevant is that the greater proportion of the children were in the mildly retarded group, as opposed to the general tendency to view retardation as a term with fixed connotations of severity. The Onondaga County Survey, which has been mentioned previously, shows in Table 4·1 that about 1,400 cases, or about 50 per cent of the subjects, were between IQ 50 and IQ 89. Only 186 were in the intervals below 49. If one confines the analysis to those subjects below IQ 74, there is better than a three-to-one ratio in favor of retardates being what is described educationally as "educable" and what is defined by the AAMD Technical Planning Project as Level IV, mild retardation of measured intelligence. This is a level which permits a fair degree of independent living and acquisition of some vocational skills, with sufficient careful preparation.

TABLE 4·1

IQ SCORE BY FREQUENCY, N = 2,085
(DERIVED FROM TECHNICAL DATA REPORT,
ONONDAGA COUNTY SURVEY) (87)

IQ.	Under 25	25-49	50-74	75-89	90 and over
N.	47	139	636	749	514

Considering the Onondaga County data and the university data, one may conclude that populations of defective individuals are quite as heterogeneous as the total population. There are significant differences in levels of ability among retardates themselves. A member of the retardate population is not necessarily severely retarded. While these data are not quite as illustrative as one might hope, they do suggest that retardation, at least in the samples given, may just as likely be mild as severe. To answer our initial question "how retarded are the retarded?" we may say, typically, sufficiently retarded to need society's care, but not necessarily so retarded as to preclude an attempt to help them.

There are, of course, some retardates whose inadequacies are compounded by other handicaps. In a follow-up to the Onondaga County study, Trippe and others looked at what they called the "School-Excluded Mentally Retarded Child" (81). Of the eighty-three children they examined, a large proportion presented additional problems of severe motor handicaps, visual disorders, speech disorders, deafness, epilepsy, and a number of other conditions. Such multiple handicapping is far more common than is usually realized. The presence of more than one handicap presents not so much an additive disorder, but rather an exponential decrease in level of functioning, rendering the child more handicapped than we usually recognize.

On the whole, where mental retardation is the prime concern, the facts would indicate that the level of intelligence in a population of retardates is sufficient to justify attempts to educate and train them.

AGE AND RETARDATION

We have seen that variability in severity is an important aspect of the behaviors we call mental retardation. The condition expresses itself in degree from person to person; it also expresses itself by age in any large sample of the population. This, as we shall see, drastically reduces the value of formulating the condition as a biological state. Fluctuations of incidence by age can only be explained in a biological model of the condition, by saying one can acquire and lose mental retardation as one does infectious diseases. The fact is, of course, that the criterion series rather than the person is the key to understanding fluctuations in incidence by age.

In infancy evaluations are largely limited to study of developmental errors and sensory-motor maturity. This criterion series understandably excludes linguistic behavior and the socio-occupational behaviors which are crucial indices for adequacy in later years. The shifts in criteria produce estimates which vary as infants meet and fail to meet the criteria relevant at one time but not at another. Behavior deemed inadequate is more common in the middle years of childhood. Essen-Möller found the highest incidence rates between ages ten and fourteen in a southern Swedish population (25). Malzberg's data shown in Table 4·2 indicate that the age group CA 10-14 shows roughly comparable proportions of children diagnosed retarded or borderline. Under age five the borderline cases are less evident (4.3%) when compared with mental defectives (15.3%). In the later teen years, the proportions in Malzberg's data continue the balance found in the early teens.

TABLE 4·2

NUMBER AND PERCENTAGE OF CASES OF
MENTAL RETARDATION AND BORDERLINE RETARDATION
(Adapted from Malzberg) (56)

Age	Mental Defectives		Borderline		Total	
	N	%	N	%	N	%
Under 5	131	15.3	8	4.3	139	13.3
5-9	346	40.5	90	48.1	436	41.8
10-14	271	31.7	69	36.9	340	32.6
15-19	89	10.4	17	9.1	106	10.2
•	•	•	•	•	•	•
•	•	•	•	•	•	•
•	•	•	•	•	•	•
	855	100	187	100	1042	100

Of course, in the adult years the incidence of retardation reflects the emphasis on independent living and vocational competence, both of which can occur in radically different social contexts. Behavior which is adequate in a non-competitive rural area may be grossly inadequate in other circumstances.

In later years old age complicates the picture of behavior in all people regardless of their intellectual endowment during their early years. Gifted as well as normal people experience a decline in their powers of concentration due to biological changes. Since mentally retarded persons can enjoy a comparatively long span of life, they too become caught up in the problems of old age. Most residential centers have an inmate of advanced years, and the larger institutions may have a considerable number of persons in their seventies and a few over eighty. An assembly of mature and older persons presents a number of interesting questions if only because retardation is commonly viewed as a problem of childhood. We might speculate on the possibility of a reduced discrepancy between normal and retarded persons in middle and later years since life functions are conducted through social roles rather than intellectual powers.

The outcome of fluctuations by age is of course a rather cautious approach to considering retardation. Instead of the "it" presumed in biological models to have several modes of behavioral expression, the matter assumes a more chameleon-like nature. When one looks at behavior by age, the arbitrary quality of definition emerges and the necessity to examine criterion series becomes inescapable. It is then a short jump to the issues raised in Chapter 1, concerning the range of alternative formulations of retardation. Age emerges as a fascinating source of variation in rates of incidence for the behavior we call retardation.

Actually, much of our knowlege of older retarded persons is anecdotal, and only a small amount of descriptive materials exists. Bell and Zubek tested and retested, after five years, groups of retarded persons in their twenties, thirties, forties, and fifties (4). Wechsler full scale IQ's generally showed gains ranging from 9.1 points for the youngest subjects to 4.4 points for the oldest. Verbal scale gains were more homogeneous, while performance gains were heterogeneous. An interesting speculation about mental growth advanced from their data by Bell and Zubek is that mental growth of retarded persons may continue for a period of time longer than that encountered in normals.

In addition to growth, there is the problem of decline among retarded persons. Thompson examined the matter by assembling a battery of ten tests and then administering them to 137 persons (78). The finding relevant to this discussion was a drop in functioning occurring at about age thirty; a levelling-off process was encountered which may persist for a number of years. A slightly different approach to the study of decline was conducted on a comparable population by Kaplan (45). A test-retest technique was applied to sixty-six persons who had been residents of two California institutions for a long time. The interval between administrations of the Stanford-Binet scale averaged fifteen years ($\overline{M}$ = 14.95 yrs.); the first scale was administered at about age forty-one, and the decline in mental age found at the second examination was 6.65 months. The matter of decline in mental functions of mentally retarded persons is subject to a host of influences, and we may hope that more attention will be paid to the course of intellectual growth and decline.

A final aspect of age which should be raised is the matter of mortality. Among the seriously retarded, intellectual limitations are simply one element in a configuration of biological defects. The consequence is that mortality can be high (44). About 8 per cent of patient turnover in a hospital in northern Ireland in one year was due to deaths (57). The cerebral palsy syndrome can increase the mortality rate up to thirty times and even a mild degree, according to Schlesinger, Allaway, and Peltin, expands the mortality rate fivefold (68). Kaplan's data is now a quarter of a century old (44); his analysis showed that about one in seven and one in fourteen persons, respectively, survived to age fifty among persons he termed *imbeciles* and *idiots*. We must recognize that there have been advances in medical care, but a discrepancy in life expectation still exists. In the mid sixties, Helgason felt that the general mortality rate for the retarded was twice the typical rate (33).

SOCIAL COMPETENCE AND MENTAL RETARDATION

An important issue in considering the characteristics of mentally retarded individuals is the way in which they behave in relation to other people. Popular myth would have us believe that the retarded are amusing people whose behavior is unfailingly entertaining and who are a legitimate source of fun and a justifiable target for ridicule. Traditionally, "the fool" has been fair game for all. In this age of sensitive and articulate minorities there is reason to believe, however, that even the retarded deserve our respect.

To study the interpersonal relations of the retarded seriously, we must first examine the role that intelligence plays in establishing relationships between people. Looked at in this light, the retardate's social relations are part of the larger issue of social relations in general.

Some three or four decades ago Almack looked at the role of intelligence level in the selection of associates (1). He found that children tend to select playmates of the same level of mental maturity. The correlation coefficient between the mental ages of children selected to attend a party and the mental ages of the hosts was uniformly significant. A slightly less significant relationship was obtained beween IQ's, which are, of course, indicants of the velocity or rate of mental growth.

Bonney expanded on this issue by considering the relationship between social success and several variables, one of which was IQ. Correlation coefficients obtained between the social status scores and IQ's in the three grade levels under consideration gave the following results: third, + .34 ± .09 (N=48); fourth, + .31 ± .06 (N=81); fifth, + .45 ± .05 (N=100) (14, p. 34).

These data warrant the generalization that children do respond to the intellectual characteristics of their associates. Those children whose mental maturity approximates that of their associates will be on terms of intimacy with them, leaving those whose intelligence is dissimilar unaccepted, if not actually rejected.

A related issue emerged several years ago when people, eager to see retarded youngsters happy, objected to special class placement for them. The grounds were that special class placement would jeopardize their social relations by isolating them from their presumed friends and associates. Johnson looked at this issue of the social status of the retardate in the regular classroom and in two papers shed considerable light where previously there had been mostly heat (38) (39). In the paper published jointly by Johnson and Kirk (39), the issue was approached sociometrically. Twenty-five classrooms from grade one to grade five were used. Each classroom had at least one child with a Binet IQ below 69, and the total population of children was 689. The authors report:

1. Only 5.13 per cent of the mentally handicapped were classified as stars as compared to 19.45 of the typical group. There were, comparatively, more than three times as many stars in the typical group than there were in the mentally handicapped group.

2. Over 69.23 per cent of the mentally handicapped group were classified as isolates as compared to 39.00 per cent of the typical group. Thus we see that over two-thirds of the mentally handicapped children's names had not been mentioned or were mentioned so few times as being sought as a friend that they were classified as being isolates. The incidence of isolation among the children in the typical group was only about one-half that for the children in the mentally handicapped group.

3. The differences in the social position of the children within the mentally handicapped and typical groups were even more obvious when the data on rejectees are examined. Only 4.4 per cent of the children in the typical group were classified as rejectees as compared to 46.15 per cent of the children in the mentally handicapped group. There were, comparatively, over ten times as many rejectees among the mentally-handicapped children as there were among the typical children (39, p. 67).

In view of these findings, special class placement would not precipitate a cleavage between the retardate and his fellows; this cleavage exists whether the retardate is in school or not. One might go so far as to say that the special class, with its greater homogeneity of intellectual level, would provide a positive basis for friendships between the retardate and his classmates. Because they occupy the same intellectual level, he would be more likely to accept his classmates and to be accepted by them.

It may also be noted that among retarded populations in hospitals, social life is by no means non-existent. Typically, any group of human beings, with the exception of the severely retarded and withdrawn, will profit from association with their peers. In fact, many of the characteristics shown by the retarded and found objectionable by school authorities are at least partially the consequence of being deprived of the opportunity to associate with other children and thus to grow proportionately.

Porter, Collins, and McIver have extended the study of social and personality traits through the use of *The Children's Personality Questionnaire* (61). The CPQ scale developed by Porter and Cattel was administered to a total of 329 boys and girls with a mean IQ around 65. Data from independent studies of two sub-populations were consistent at several points for boys and for girls. Boys emerged as emotionally immature, depressed, and reserved (to cite the first three findings), while girls were excitable, impatient, and unrestrained. The investigators felt that sex differences were quite marked. They also observed there were personality patterns they could characterize as typical, and they noted that the component traits within the patterns were generally less than desirable and acceptable.

A comprehensive study of the social adjustment of the retarded was made by Saenger under the auspices of the State of New York (64). This study differs in two interesting ways; first, it deals with severely retarded adults, and second, it considers their community experiences. In describing interaction within the family, Saenger pointed out:

"One half of all parents interviewed felt that the retarded related well, were easy to get along with, presented no problem (47 per cent). Somewhat more than one out of every four considered the relationship as essentially good. There were occasional slight problems, none of them serious. Excessive demands for attention, passive clinging to the mother, which tend to be typical for children around the fifth and sixth year of age, were most frequently mentioned" (64, p. 84).

Looking at the specific activities that the severely retarded undertake in the family circle, Saenger reported the following data on how the individual passes his time (See Table 4·3). Perhaps the significant item in these data is the small percentage of "inactive" behaviors. These severely retarded individuals tend to pursue a pattern of activities similar to that of a small child and to enter into activities with others in the home to a similar extent.

TABLE 4·3

ACTIVITIES OF THE SEVERELY RETARDED AT HOME
(64, p. 88)

Solitary Activities

Looks at TV, listens to radio	97%
Looks at books, papers, magazines	63%
Plays with toys, dolls	13%
Sewing, embroidery	15%
Other solitary activities	30%

Social Activities

Plays or talks with parents	18%
Plays or talks with siblings	20%
Plays or talks with visitors	34%

Considered Inactive by Parents

"Stays by himself, does nothing"	20%
"Just follows me around"	7%
Number of cases	347

A vital part of Saenger's data is the material on community activity. Table 4·4 suggests that the adult with an IQ of 40-50 is not completely helpless. Eighty per cent can operate to some extent outside the home; the majority are effective within the neighborhood, and a small percentage, 21 per cent, can move about within the community.

TABLE 4·4

EXTENT OF TRAVEL (*64*, p. 102)

Never goes anywhere 20%
Can walk to corner, same block............................... 10%
Can walk same street or immediate neighborhood................ 35%
Can take bus, subway in familiar area........................ 14%
Can take bus, subway, anywhere.............................. 21%
Can ask for directions....................................... 70%
Can read street signs 18%

Number of cases.. 348

Interpersonal relationships are a two-way affair; they are a matter of give and take. It is important, therefore, to consider how the neighbors view the retarded. Generally speaking, one of the hazards that families with retarded children face is a reduction in their social activities (See Farber, "The Impact of a Severely Retarded Child on Family Integration") and a severing of their contacts with friends outside the home. Table 4·5 shows the feelings that neighbors develop towards the family of the retardate with a breakdown by socio-economic status. On the whole, there is reason to suggest that the retarded enjoy a fair degree of acceptance and that the number of rejections, while a function of decreasing socio-economic status, is fairly low; it is probably comparable to that of some intellectually adequate human beings.

TABLE 4·5

TYPE OF NEIGHBORHOOD AND EXPRESSIONS OF HOSTILITY
BY NEIGHBORS AND THEIR CHILDREN (*64*, p. 115)

| | | Socio-Economic Status | | |
Reaction of Neighbors	Total	Low	Med. Low	Med. High	High
Predominantly hostile, unsympathetic	5%	9%	4%	4%	2%
Children unfriendly	8%	9%	14%	2%	2%
Number of cases	348	87	115	82	48

The relationship between the retarded individual and his normal fellows is a marginal one. He operates at a disadvantage because the choice of companions is significantly related to intellectual ability. Since he is not fully accepted in the regular classroom as a desirable associate, special classes may help him. When the retardate is beyond school age, and even when he is seriously retarded, he interacts to some degree with members of the family and with the neighbors. Rejection occurs here and is related to socio-economic considerations, but it is not total.

ADAPTIVE BEHAVIOR

Over the past several years there has been an increase in concern about the extent to which narrowly cognitive formulations of mental retardation accurately convey variability of performance routinely encountered in persons of limited intellect. In particular, attention has centered on the social process and the extent to which individuals with low IQ's were able to conduct their affairs effectively. The Heber monograph of the American Association on Mental Deficiency called attention to what is now referred to as adaptive behavior. Subsequently, Leland and the Parsons (Kansas) group have applied a good deal of energy to the issue (50, 51). As it now stands, we have several matters which constitute the intellectual complex, *adaptive behavior*. First, *empirically*, we find that IQ scores for most retarded persons simply do not describe the level of operant and social behavior in retarded persons. A minority who are profoundly retarded seem to function at a level consonant with their psychometric ratings, according to the work of MacAndrew and Edgerton (52). Second, *taxonomically*, the Parsons group have focused on five behavioral domains, (1) independent functioning, (2) individual responsibility, (3) social responsibility, (4) civic responsibility, and (5) economic responsibility (50); the last two are relevant for adolescents and adults. Third, *categorically*, a system of *Levels*, paralleling the *AAMD* levels for cognitive retardation, has been assayed, and treatment and training objectives have been formulated for each level. Fourth, *psychometrically*, tests have been suggested which may be used in the assessment of level of adaptive behavior. The Vineland is a probable source of information, but Leland's opinion is that clinical judgment is a prime resource in the absence of more suitable tests.

The probability is that clinicians will want to examine overt behavior as far as possible. Such a process is use of *measures*, as opposed to the use of *indicants*, (Stevens, 1951), terms which are devices held to be correlates of the behavior *sub judice*. Indicants are handy, tests for example, but they present problems in validity which are not disposed of by their titles. A test of adaptive behavior, an indicant, may have high reliability, but validity remains a persistent problem for all but the credulous.

Fifth, *conceptually*, the lack of instruments is not without its advantages. It presents us with the opportunity to think about the concept of adaptive behavior. At this point the term "adaptive behavior" has a polished quality which is rhetorical rather than substantive. People committed to study of the matter employ it with a tentativeness that uninformed persons should emulate. By this we mean that theoreticians are convinced there are domains of behavior which we need to incorporate into our formulations of mental retardation. The exact nature of those domains has not been expressed fully as yet. As Leland put it, we need to explore this dimension (51); we need to establish the boundaries which distinguish it from intellectual operations on the one hand and from low-order habits on the other. Jastak's factor, *reality perceptions,* which is described on page 126 may be useful in exploring adaptive behavior. It will be a slow process, however, and we can hope that people will not read into the construct a degree of precision which we have yet to develop. Fundamentally, the present concern for adaptive behavior is strategic. It is a nuclear concept which can clarify the complex of behaviors we call mental retardation. It conveys a reality-centered concern for how retarded people function above and beyond their performance on indicative scales of intelligence. We may hope to see conceptual-empirical exploration lead to the development of indicative instruments—but, hopefully, not before conceptual refinements fully justify instrumentation and popular application.

AMBIGUITIES IN BEHAVIOR

Most people have a set of principles which they apply to behavior. They can, for example, perceive when a friend or relative is upset; they can identify inconsistencies within behavior patterns. This sensitivity usually takes the form of noting incongruities, errors of behavior, and deviations of a subtle kind. Regardless of how disparate the items of behavior are, they are usually put in the pigeon-hole "odd."

The significance of this reaction is that our sensitivities to unusual behavior are ordinarily adequate but few of us know what to do with this behavior other than call it "odd." We perceive that a child's behavior is unusual, but the initial sensitivity does not guarantee subsequent skill in analyzing the problems.

Children can show many behavioral disturbances and an experienced teacher or a concerned parent can be relied on to recognize that "something" is wrong. The antecedent conditions, or the causes, may be infinite and subtle. In many cases, far too many cases, a judgment of mental retardation is reached by a parent or a teacher who jumps to a conclusion without pausing to consider other explanations of deviant behavior. Since in this chapter we are directly concerned with behavior, we may reasonably pay attention to the complex of problems children present. We may reasonably attempt to sort out behavior originating in intellectual deficit from equally perplexing behavior due to other conditions. Obviously, a precise analysis of the nature of atypical behavior determines what one does or does not do for a child. In some cases treatment may be possible; in others it may not be. Only when one has considered the range of explanations for behavior can one make rational decisions about the disposition of people's problems.

A common source of uncertainty is the behavior of the child who does not learn to read or who makes uncertain progress in reading. Probably nothing leads to a more rash, intemperate judgment of mental retardation as often as this.

Considering the complexity of reading, it is remarkable that so many children do learn to read. Nevertheless, when we find a child whose reading progress is poor, we tend to view this failure as reflecting the child's mental maturity rather than the difficulty of the task, or the adequacy of the instruction.

Even when the problem is viewed in a more sophisticated fashion, it is still possible to make grave errors in evaluating the child. Perhaps the best measure of school aptitude is the Stanford-Binet; it has a rational place in the evaluation of learning problems. Unfortunately, however, not enough attention is paid to its limitations. Given a child with reading problems, the Stanford-Binet may be the wrong test, yielding a false picture of mental retardation. Bond and Fay have called attention to this issue (13). They have pointed out the effects of reading skill on performance on the Stanford-Binet. In their paper, which deserves wider attention, they have shown that this scale, which is our best measure of school-aptitude (intelligence), is itself highly vulnerable to levels of school performance. A circular process results when low-school achievement in reading is measured by a test which is itself sensitive to low achievement in reading. Low reading skill lowers the test score, leading to a low mental age. Poor reading is then attributed to low capacity, a truly vicious circle.

While deploring the illogic of this situation, it is wise to keep in mind the sensible comment on testing by Hartogs in 1948; he contended that it was no longer possible to consider that an appraisal of a child's intellectual status was entirely valid when it merely consisted of statements about the MA and IQ (32).

Other causes of problem behavior in children which can be easily misdiagnosed as mental retardation are sensory disorders and the effects of ethnic and cultural differences in child-rearing and value orientation. Children whose behavior reflects these differences may not perceive goals that others value as important to themselves. De-emphasis of competition and de-emphasis of independence-training can lead to uninterested and unmotivated behavior, which is misleading to all but the perceptive student of behavior patterns. Only a careful, detailed study may reveal the important determinants of behavior.

Ambiguities in behavior patterns have led to a discussion of what is termed *pseudofeeblemindedness*. Among others, Arthur (3), Benton (10), and Kratter (48) have looked at this problem.

Benton points out that there are two meanings of the word *pseudofeeblemindedness*. On the one hand, the term may refer to a mistaken diagnosis; on the other, it may refer to behavior which is correctly attributed to mental retardation but which is the result of unusual etiological factors or antecedent conditions. He feels these two uses are mutually exclusive.

Kratter has emphasized the role of emotional nurture in mental development. Using the work of Goldfarb and Spitz, he has discussed ego-development under conditions of emotional deprivation. Kratter also sees the acute problem of psychotic and psychosis-like states as simulators of mental retardation. He points out in this regard: "Before including (these) mentally reduced psychotics, whose social and intellectual withdrawal symptoms commenced during their early childhood or adolescence, into the group of mentally defective persons, one ought to emphasize their resultant mental retardation differing in aetiology from all those customarily referred to as mental defectives, be they of endogenous or exogenous origin" (48, p. 415).

Kratter also calls attention to other clinical syndromes, having a variety of causative factors, which simulate mental retardation. He points to Heller's disease, lead encephalopathy, and the group of disorders which DeSanctis called *dementia praecocissima,* also associated with early years.

Perhaps the best contributions to distinguishing between the behavior patterns have come from Kanner. He has called our attention to the baffling syndrome called the "autistic state" (43). This is a condition that well illustrates Hertzogs' dictum previously mentioned. In this behavior pattern the child has minimal contact with other human beings and appears unresponsive, mute, preoccupied, and withdrawn. To illustrate the demands which this condition places on diagnostic skills, one such case seen by the author had been treated successively as a problem of (1) delayed speech, (2) hearing loss, (3) mental retardation, and (4) unsociability. Treatment ranging from playing records, which the child ignored, to making loud noises intended to "jar" him out of his withdrawal had been markedly ineffective. In all fairness, even when the condition had been eventually diagnosed as an autistic state, improvement was no greater. The prognosis for this condition is poor, as Bender has pointed out (7).

Pasamanick has discussed sociocultural retardation which he feels numerically far more important than genetically determined retardation (59). He views this condition as preventable and as society's responsibility.

A paper by Bruner, while not specifically on mental retardation, has called attention to the role of growing up in a stimulating setting (15). Following some of Hebb's work, Bruner has argued that an early non-stimulating environment produces an adult with functionally limited ability. The author has pointed out that ineffectiveness of the individual's performance constitutes his mental retardation, and that the empirical, phenomenal use of the term need not imply anything about etiology or the future course of the disorder (40).

This point of view encourages more flexibility in our expectations of the retardate. Such flexibility is necessary if one is to incorporate the series of papers by the Clarkes in England into one's concept of mental retardation (19), (20). It may be useful to reiterate this matter of flexibility, since the many patterns of behavior which atypical children show must be considered carefully. Rigid formulations are inconsistent with the varied behavior patterns that retardates manifest.

Jastak has spoken to this point in discussing the endogenous slow learner (36). Using a factorial technique, he isolated five independent personality variables and several sub-components:

(1) Intellectual endowment, a general factor affecting all abilities defined as the capacity for personality integration.

(2) Language polarity, a dynamic group factor which determines the person's capacity for literacy and cultural assimilation.

(3) Reality perceptions, a group dynamic, which affects the practical judgment and reasoning of a person, his outlook upon life, his approach to people, to the physical world, and the flow of daily events.

(4) Motivation, a group factor, which tells us something about the self-control, the perseverance, and frustration tolerance of the subject.

(5) Psychosomatic efficiency, a clustering dynamic, associated with the ease with which physical energy is mobilized and applied to situations demanding the smooth and graceful expression of motor resources (36, p. 271).

Working with this inductively derived schema, he reports no two identical constellations in his sample of thousands of cases. He concludes by referring to slow learners not as people with a fixed, stereotyped pattern of behavior but as "certain people with certain attitudes and personalities who fail to learn certain types of skills at certain periods of their lives, in certain places, and in response to certain people" (36, p. 274).

THE RETARDED AS A THREAT TO OTHERS

Many people believe that the retarded are a threat to the safety of others. It is not unknown, of course, for the retarded to commit crimes against people and property, but this issue is not as great as many people imagine.

Saenger has given us a picture of the seriously retarded adult. He emerges as a fairly tractable human being, usually confining his activities to home and the neighborhood, and finding his satisfactions in watching TV and other innocuous pursuits.

Less severely retarded individuals commit acts which may be criminal and hostile. Such a case once occurred in a large city, with considerable attention being paid to the fact that the offender was previously an inmate of a state school for the retarded (65). The crime, murder committed while stealing a purse, can be fruitfully analyzed by recalling Grigg's words:

> . . . it may be postulated that an adult of IQ 50-60 does not have capacity for adequate foresight, and thus often reacts to the momentary situation. . . . He appears impulsive not so much because of emotional make-up, but because it is his nature to react to the present with little ability to project his act either to the past or to the future (30, p. 374).

A relevant consideration is how the retarded react to frustration. Human beings react by channeling their energies in one of three ways according to Rosenzweig. They respond *impunitively*, which is to say, without any great display of feeling; they may turn their feelings inward, an *intropunitive* reaction; or they may turn their feelings outward, reacting *extropunitively*. Portnoy and Stacey used the Rosenzweig P-F Test on sixty retardates and found them mostly extropunitive in direction and ego-defensive in mechanism (62). This is a generalization, but it is generally substantiated by the work of Angelino & Shedd (2).

In those cases where the delinquent retarded are in an institution, a number of questions arise. The regular hospital or state school does not operate on a total security basis, nor does the penal institution seem an appropriate place for the retarded. Several writers have called attention to the problems which the defective delinquent presents in the setting of a hospital (35), (58), (77), (82).

CHARACTERISTICS BY SYNDROME

While we acknowledge that the mentally retarded are individuals and that they therefore differ from one another, we also recognize that there are some consistent groupings of physical, neurological, and psychological attributes. This is the basis of the clinical entities we know today. For example, *mongolism* is the term applied to human beings who manifest a high proportion of about two dozen "signs." Few possess all of them, and some are shared with other syndromes. As an individual's constellation of traits coincides with that of others, we develop the specific entities encountered in the study of disease. A word of caution before continuing: most syndromes are drawn with a fine hand. They tend to emerge in the literature as mutually exclusive, clearly delineated patterns. When attempting to find this precision in the children, workers often find a blurring of the marked distinctions. We find that the "classic cases" exist only in the literature; one might go so far as to say that the children simply have not bothered to study the textbooks. They develop symptoms that are not as easy to classify as we might suppose.

The Brain-Injury Syndrome

Strauss has developed an entity which describes the behavior and characteristics of youngsters who have received some sort of injury to an originally intact brain (76). He describes the child who has suffered a brain injury as an *exogenous* child, as opposed to an *endogenous* child whose limitations were inherent in his earliest development. The brain-injured child is described by Strauss in these words: "In our researches we have so far differentiated the following basic deviations in the mental make-up of brain-injured children:

(a) disturbances in perception,

(b) disturbances in concept formation (thinking and reasoning),

(c) disturbances in language,

(d) disturbances in emotional behavior" (76, p. 714).

Apart from these conceptual formulations, there have been studies on the psychological growth of brain-injured children. Probably because of the greater frustrating and non-rewarding experiences they have undergone, brain-injured retarded children have less motivation towards achievement. They show less desire to compete with a standard of excellence and feel less impelled to associate with other youngsters. Tolman and Johnson have demonstrated that such characteristics tend to be affected by the length of time that retardates have spent in a residential setting (80).

Satter and Cassel reported data on tactual-kinesthetic localization in organic brain-damaged children and other groups of children. They reported that brain-damaged children made greater errors in their localizations than children whose retardation was psychogenic or due to familial causes (67).

In examining the social development of different kinds of retardates, Cassel and Riggs used the Vineland Social Maturity Scale (17). This instrument is used to investigate several aspects of social development. The retarded were those whose difficulties were familial, organic, or unknown in etiology. There were sixty cases ranging in IQ from 40-76. The organics differed from the other two groups by being relatively inadequate in all areas.

A series of interesting studies have been reported by Pasamanick and others since around 1954; in these studies they relate various degrees of brain injury to such conditions as cerebral palsy, epilepsy, mental deficiency, learning difficulties, and behavior disorders. A basic paper in this series described a "Syndrome of Minimal Cerebral Damage in Infants" (59). It is the thesis of this paper that the presence of "minor but clearly defined deviations from the normal neurological and behavioral development patterns, usually with more or less complete compensation by 15 to 18 months of age" can have sequels in the form of neuropsychiatric disorders later in childhood.

Phenylketonuria

One of the disorders that is receiving considerable attention is phenylketonuria, a disorder described in more detail in Chapter 8. While the disorder is rare, it has become the occasion of much outstanding research. Phenylketonuria has been discovered and a treatment suggested in a matter of a few decades.

Kratter has reported data on the psychological characteristics of a group of phenylketonurics. He reported that eleven of twelve cases showed a high degree of activity and were quite distractable. They were mischievous and had a short span of attention. Their interest in their surroundings was also short-lived (47).

Gonadal Immaturity

Berman and his associates have given an account of a group of boys whom they describe as showing gonadal immaturity (*12*). The traits they identified in these boys were shyness and reluctance to speak, lack of sociability, timidity, and withdrawing tendencies. The authors reported, for example, that the boys were afraid of the physical examination but did not protest. This study is discussed later since the boys were subjected to a therapy with interesting results.

Down's Disease

There are few syndromes in mental deficiency that elicit stereotypes of behavior as quickly as Down's disease (mongolism). The mongoloid child is held to be universally cheerful, cooperative, placid, and a joy to raise. That such is not the case has been at least partially substantiated by Silverstein (*69*). We have, therefore, ample reason for reiterating the point that mongoloid children come in all shapes and sizes, range from placid to irritable, and can be as demanding as any other child. Interestingly, the degree of mongolism, i.e., the number of stigmata, does not predict the degree of retardation, (*37*), (*42*). It may well be that the chromosomal error depresses growth below the previously established and uniquely individual potential of each individual. Chromosomal error may be used to develop finer distinctions about the behavior of mongoloid children. As we shall see in Chapters 7 and 8, mongolism is associated with two chromosomal mechanisms, *trisomy* and *translocation*. Gibson and Pozsonyi have examined twenty-one characteristics in ten examples of each chromosomal error (*27*). Variability of development and behavior was not extreme, but there were differences. For example, translocation mongolism was associated with passivity. Under stress, trisomic children were more active.

The attributes of mongoloids are clearly worthy of investigation. Assessing intellectual level, Wunsch studied seventy-seven mongoloids; he found that about 66 per cent of them were moderately retarded and that about 20 per cent were severely retarded (*86*). Examining sixty-four adult patients with Down's disease, Sternlicht and Wanderer found a mean IQ of 24, and a mean MA of 3.5 years (*75*). Ellis and Beechley matched groups of mongoloid and non-mongoloid retardates by age, sex, and IQ, and found that the mongoloids were less emotionally disturbed than the non-mongoloids (*24*).

An interesting behavioral study of mongoloids was reported by Durling and Benda (*22*). Table 4 · 6 shows some pertinent data about the intellectual growth of mongoloids, the tendency for growth to continue beyond the normal point in age for a large group of them.

TABLE 4·6

CHRONOLOGICAL AGE AT PEAK OF INTELLECTUAL
GROWTH (22)

Age Peak of Deviation	Mongoloid	Familial
Below 16 yrs.	16%	32%
Around 18 yrs.	35%	42%
20-37 yrs.	48%	26%

As the authors point out: "There are a few peculiarities of the mongoloid mental growth which seem significant. There is first the great irregularity of progress and the differences in the speed of development rate . . ." (22, p. 579). The data seem to indicate that intellectual growth in this entity is quite different both from normals and from other retardates. Data provided by Ross show that the growth curve within the period of intellectual maturation is similar to that found in normals (63).

Still another source of variation in the behavior of mongoloid children is the environment in which their behavior is shaped. The physical properties such as weight and height are generally unaffected in a unique way; however, social development and language tend to be reduced when children grow in residential agencies rather than at home. McNeill has examined several facets of growth in mongoloid children, some of whom lived at the Lincoln and Dixon agencies in Illinois (55). He found that developmental ages were generally higher in biological growth, with language and social development next, but still ahead of mental maturity. Mongoloid children reared at home differed from those at Lincoln and Dixon because their language and social attainment were slightly more advanced, in the ordinal sense.

INVESTIGATIONS OF COGNITIVE PROCESSES

An area of investigation which has begun to attract attention is the attempt to understand the cognitive processes of retarded individuals. This tendency is useful since more psychological studies place the locus of investigation outside the individual; it is quite important to study intra-individual characteristics too.

Working with significantly retarded individuals in England, Tizard and Loos evaluated their ability to comprehend the problems in the Minnesota Spatial Relations Test. The authors demonstrated the phenomenon of learning sets, but also made some interesting comments about what they hold to be untapped resources for learning even in seriously retarded individuals (79).

Gothberg studied the concept of time in retarded children and reported: (1) that the concept of time was related to mental age, (2) that the mentally retarded child has a limited grasp of time sequence, of time in an historical sense, and (3) that children below a mental age of five years can do little with time concepts (26). We shall refer to this interesting study in another connection a little later.

From time to time workers report the results of projective tests on retarded samples. Among the studies which may be mentioned is that of Chambers and Hamblin, who reported that familial defectives produce fewer *M*'s—human movement responses—than organic defectives. Chambers and Hamblin interpret this as indicating a restricted "inner life" (18). Another study relating to the cognitive processes using projective material is that of Beier and associates who gave the Thematic Apperception Test to forty female defectives. They reported a striking similarity to the thematic content of non-retarded adolescents. "The defective adolescent is as concerned about parent relationships, morality, aggression, love, as is the normal adolescent" (5, p. 589). Jordan and deCharms found the length of stories told by retardates sufficient for content analysis (41).

An issue of a more technical nature is the process of concept formation in the retardate. Here again, there are several studies which merit attention. Stacey and Portnoy studied concept-formation by means of object sorting (73). They reported conceptual levels ranging from *abstract-symbolic* to what they identify as *functionally fabulated*. In each case they derived their formulations from the way the subject approached the task.

An interesting group of studies has used language either as a dependent variable or as a mediating variable. Winthrop has reported differences in vocabulary using the concreteness and abstractness of the responses of eighty-one retardates (84). He suggests that cases of organic brain damage may be more stimulus-bound than idiopathic and familial cases.

Recently there have been developments of Osgood's work in language, applying the formulations to the cerebral palsied and the retarded. In particular, Kirk and McCarthy have operationalized or reified the linguistic processes described by Osgood. At the same time, Wepman has developed an inductive model of cognitive process based on his work with aphasics. Both of these innovations are pursued more fully in Chapter 5.

Griffith, Spitz, and Lipman have speculated on the role of common mediators when retardates attempt to identify a similarity among several objects (29). Their findings are an extension of a previous paper (28) and are interesting:

> The present study attempted to cast light on the relationship between concept formation and the availability of mediators. A group of retarded subjects, and an equal MA group of nine-year-old normals, were given an abstraction task in which they had to discover a similarity among three words. In a separate session, the stimulus words were presented to determine the number in each triad, defined in terms of an acceptable abstraction.
>
> Although the percentage of abstractions attained generally increased as the number of words defined in common with a possible abstraction increased, the nature of the relationship varied among groups. Retardates and normal seven-year-olds were not very successful in concept attainment unless they had the opportunity to match words on the basis of their eliciting a common immediate associate, i.e., unless they defined at least two words in terms of an acceptable abstraction (29, p. 250).

A relevant group of studies has concerned the visual modality in retardates. Using good experimental techniques, several writers have developed material about visual cognitive phenomena.

McMurray has presented two papers of interest; in one he has demonstrated a difference in the perception of reversals by exogenous and endogenous retardates (54). His samples are small but reflect careful selection and matching of subjects. Another paper analyzed rigidity in thinking by means of the Wisconsin card-sorting test. McMurray presents evidence showing that endogenous defectives can shift more easily than exogenous defectives from one principle to another in sorting cards. They also showed less perseveration in their thinking (53).

Spitz and his associates have presented several studies which analyze sensory illusory phenomena. Interestingly, these authors have chosen to investigate vision, and they seem to have been quite willing to come to grips with the neural basis of this phenomenon. Spitz reported a difference in the amount of inspection time required by a group of adolescent retardates before reporting perception of the spiral aftereffect (70). Spitz and Blackman exposed normals and retardates to a reversible visual material, which precipitates an aftereffect (71). They found that the retarded had less capacity for perceiving visual aftereffects, took longer to develop them, and took longer to erase them. The retarded also showed greater rigidity on the measure of reversibility.

In another paper, Spitz and Blackman reported on the Mueller-Lyer illusion in retardates and normals (72). Their findings were that subjects of average intelligence did not perceive a significantly larger illusion. Since satiation is held to account for the neural basis of the process, it is interesting that satiating S's, both normal and retarded, saw a significantly larger illusion; also, satiating retardates saw a significantly larger illusion than non-satiating retardates.

An interesting comparison is that of all degrees of intelligence from the institutionalized retardate to the superior college student on a common task. Leibowitz and associates have demonstrated the role of intelligence level in perception in such a range of abilities (49). Ninety-eight subjects in four groups were asked to compare a disk on a turntable at various angles to the line of vision with one of a graded series of ellipses. The results substantiate the judgment that intelligence plays a role in such perceptions.

In summarizing these studies on intra-individual cognitive processes in retardates, two conclusions seem appropriate. The first is a general comment to the effect that this area of study has precise conceptual problems to offer and that the problems are pursued carefully. The second is that formulations on the nature of mental deficiency are adequate only insofar as they recognize the significant intra-individual characteristics of retardates. Their cognitive processes are different and can be experimentally demonstrated to be so. This has implications for how and what they may be taught under varying conditions.

FUNCTIONAL ACHIEVEMENTS OF THE MENTALLY RETARDED

Having considered some empirical but non-applied studies on the behavioral attributes of retardates, we may now consider some of the data on the level of functioning which retardates can reach.

A study by Capobianco investigated arithmetic achievement in exogenous and endogenous retardates (16). He found that on three quantitative tests there was no significant difference between groups. Using three qualitative indices, the investigator found insignificant differences. The endogenous S's were found to function slightly below MA level on three quantitative tests. The exogenous S's worked closer to the level established for their mean MA.

Looking at the matter of reading, we may consider the monograph by Dunn (21). Dunn has compared the reading processes of boys of the same mental age; one group was mentally retarded, the other was normal. The subjects in this study were twenty retardates and thirty normals. Some of the results were as follows:

1. Silent and oral reading tasks were performed more effectively by the normals.

2. The retardates' reading errors included more difficulty with vowels, more omissions, and inadequate responses to more words.

3. The normals used context clues more effectively.

4. The normals had fewer visual problems.

5. In their teachers' judgment, the retardates were less well adjusted.

Jordan and deCharms reported data on achievement in language in retardates exposed to a special class curriculum and in retardates who were in regular classes because no special classes had been available (41). Closely matching the S's, they reported a significant difference in academic achievement in favor of achievement in the mentally retarded who had been in regular classes.

Another study of the retarded summarized investigations of speech and language. Harrison presented the findings of several studies, some of which were as follows:

1. There is considerable immaturity in the speech of retardates.

2. Their auditory memory spans are short.

3. Retarded children can profit from early and intensive speech therapy.

4. Institutionalized children have a lower language output.

5. Retardates generally use little abstract language (31).

Harrison reported a number of significant omissions in the studies. There had been little research with mentally retarded children on:

1. The effect of perceptual dysfunction on speech and language development.

2. Development of abstract and conceptual thinking.

3. Scales for diagnosis and for evaluation of growth in speech and language.

4. Analysis of speech and language performance as part of the differential diagnostic process.

5. Methods and techniques of value in the developmental language and therapeutic speech programs.

6. Language and speech development during the pre-school period.

A relevant matter is the competence retarded persons maintain in the tool skills of reading and number. Stein, Susser, and Lunzer examined these skills in retarded persons who had been out of British schools for some time and were in their middle twenties (74). Those attending special schools were more literate, while one third of those who did not attend special schools remained illiterate. Special schooling did not leave persons below IQ 65 with a greater number facility in their later years, according to the investigators.

Turning to other aspects of life, we must remember that the retarded are capable of learning skills, although their intrinsic rational limitations do emerge fairly quickly. Sarason has described a girl diagnosed as a "garden-variety defective" who was capable of doing a number of the duties of a laboratory technician (66). He reported over ten skills she could command with an IQ of 70. Whitney has given a list of occupations that border-line defectives have performed (83). Boys, for example, may work as baker's helpers, bus-boys, deckhands, grocery clerks, jockeys, hospital orderlies, and theatre ushers; girls may work as beauty shop attendants, commercial laundry workers, maids, waitresses, and store clerks. In recent years, the variety of jobs young retardates may handle has expanded remarkably.

In a study to which we have referred previously, Saenger has pointed out some of the occupations filled by seriously retarded adults (64). Eighty-five per cent of his working sample worked in the community: 52 per cent in private industry; 17 per cent "on his own," which is surprising; 6 per cent employed in the business of a friend or relative; and 10 per cent in their parents' business. This working group formed 27 per cent of the subjects studied by Saenger. The majority of those working were employed as messengers or in making deliveries (36 per cent).

Lest this seem too sanguine a picture, it is worth pointing out that the total group studied by Saenger was not really successful in earning a living; those who did work did not earn a great deal of money. Usually one finds gross errors in judgment in people with low IQ's, and Saenger's group were all between 40 and 50 in IQ.

SUMMARY

This chapter has described the characteristics of mentally retarded individuals. For the most part, the studies have been drawn from the literature of the behavioral sciences. The attempt has been to rely on data which have been established empirically rather than by reminiscence. By and large, the result has been to draw a cautious but valid picture of how the retarded act.

A negative sort of comment emerges; one cannot fail to be impressed by the gaps in the empirical knowledge of how mentally retarded people behave. Perhaps the dialogue in mental retardation has stayed at the level of reminiscence by people of extensive experience too long. The alternative is to gather information and to develop new knowledge deliberately through scientific investigation. An example of this point of view is the activity current in the field of learning phenomena. There, standard constructs and hypotheses are being applied with retarded persons acting as subjects. Ellis's work presents a good deal of valuable information which illustrates the value of rigorous investigation (23).

A relevant point is the lack of programming in research. In areas such as learning there are a few consistent contributors. Their studies are important because they produce new information. They are important also because they emerge from a self-conscious theoretical position.

This much seems clear; the retarded present a picture of dysfunction in which many aspects of behavior are involved at least to some extent. The retarded person has a limited grasp of abstractions. He does not have the capacity to foresee all the consequences of his actions. He has potential for a limited group of occupations. He is not inherently dangerous, but his presence may be disturbing to others. He has the capacity to profit from our attempts to help him.

BIBLIOGRAPHY

1. Almack, J. C., "The Influence of Intelligence on the Selection of Associates," *Sch. & Soc.*, 1922, *16*, 529-30.

2. Angelino, H. A., and Shedd, C. L., "A Study of the Reactions to Frustration of a Group of Mentally Retarded Children as Measured by the Rosenzweig Picture-Frustration Study," *Psych. Newsletter*, 1956, *8*, 49-54.

3. Arthur, G., "Pseudofeeblemindedness," *Am. J. Ment. Def.*, 1947, *52*, 137-142.

4. Bell, A., and Zubek, T. P., "The Effect of Age on the Intellectual Performance of Mental Defectives," *J. Gerontol.*, 1960, *15*, 285-295.

5. Beier, E. G., Gorlow, L., and Stacey, C. L., "The Fantasy Life of the Mental Defective," *Am. J. Ment. Def.*, 1951, *55*, 582-589.

6. Bierman, J. L., "The Community Impact of Handicaps of Prenatal Origin," *Pub. Hlth. Rep.*, 1963, *78*, 839-855.

7. Bender, L., 'Childhood Schizophrenia," *Nerv. Ch.*, 1942, *2*, 138-140.

8. Benoit, E. P., "Relevance of Hebb's Theory of the Organization of Behavior to Educational Research on the Mentally Retarded," *Am. J. Ment. Def.*, 1957, *61*, 497-507.

9. _____, "Towards a New Definition of Mental Retardation," *Am. J. Ment. Def.*, 1959, *63*, 559-565.

10. Benton, A. L., "The Concept of Pseudofeeblemindedness," *A. M. A. Arch. Neurol., Psychiat.*, 1956, *75*, 379-388.

11. Berlyne, D. E., "Recent Developments in Piaget's Work," *Brit. J. Educ. Psych.*, 1957, *27*, 1-12.

12. Berman, H. H., Albert-Gasorek, K. E., and Reiss, M., "Gonadal Immaturity as an Etiological Factor in Some Forms of Mental Deficiency and Its Therapy," *Dis. Nerv. Syst. Monog. Suppl.*, 1959, *20*, 3-7.

13. Bond, G. L., and Fay, L. F., "A Comparison of the Performance of Good and Poor Readers on the Individual Items of the Stanford-Binet Scale, Forms L and M," *J. Educ. Res.*, 1950, *43*, 475-479.

14. Bonney, M. E., "Relationship between Social Success, Family Size, Socio-Economic Home Background, and Intelligence Among School Children in Grades III to V," *Sociometry*, 1944, *7*, 26-39.

15. Bruner, J. S., "The Cognitive Consequences of Early Sensory Deprivation," *Psychosomat. Med.*, 1959, *21*, 89-95.

16. Capobianco, R. J., "Quantitative and Qualitative Analyses of Endogenous and Exogenous Boys on Arithmetic Achievement," *Mon. Soc. Res. Ch. Dev.*, 1954, No. 58.

17. Cassel, M. E., and Riggs, M. M., "Comparison of Three Etiological Groups of Mentally Retarded Children on the Vineland Social Maturity Scale," *Am. J. Ment. Def.*, 1953, *58*, 162-169.

18. Chambers, G. S., and Hamblin, R. C., "Rorschach 'Inner Life' Capacity of Imbeciles under Varied Conditions," *Am. J. Ment. Def.*, 1957, *62*, 88-95.

19. Clarke, A. D. B., and Clarke, A. M., "Cognitive Changes in the Feebleminded," *Brit. J. Psych.*, 1954, *45*, 173-179.

20. _____, and Reiman, S., "Cognitive and Social Changes in the Feebleminded—Three Further Studies," *Brit. J. Psych.*, 1958, *49*, 144-157.

21. Dunn, L. M., "A Comparison of the Reading Processes of Mentally Retarded and Normal Boys of the Same Mental Age," *Mon. Soc. Res. Ch. Dev.*, 1954, No. 58.

22. Durling, D., and Benda, C. E., "Mental Growth Curves in Untreated Institutionalized Mongoloid Patients," *Am. J. Ment. Def.*, 1952, *56*, 578-588.

23. Ellis, N. (ed.), *Handbook of Mental Deficiency*, McGraw-Hill, 1963.

24. Ellis, A., and Beechley, R. M., "A Comparison of Matched Groups of Mongoloid and Non-Mongoloid Feebleminded Children," *Am. J. Ment. Def.*, 1950, *54*, 464-468.

25. Essen-Möller, E., "Individual Traits and Morbidity in a Swedish Rural Population," *Acta Psychiat. Scand. Suppl., 100,* 1956.

26. Gothberg, L., "The Mentally Defective Child's Understanding of Time," *Am. J. Ment. Def.,* 1949, 53, 441-455.

27. Gibson, D., and Pozsonyi, J., "Morphological and Behavioral Consequences of Chromosome Sub-type in Mongolism," *Amer. J. Ment. Def.,* 1965, 69, 801-804.

28. Griffith, B. C., and Spitz, H. H., "Some Relationships between Abstraction and Word Meaning in Retarded Adolescents," *Am. J. Ment. Def.,* 1958, 63, 247-251.

29. _____, and Lipman, R. E., "Verbal Mediation and Concept Formation in Retarded Adolescents," *J. Exp. Psych.,* 1959, 58, 247-251.

30. Grigg, A. E., "Criminal Behavior of Mentally Retarded Adults," *Am. J. Ment. Def.,* 1948, 52, 370-374.

31. Harrison, S., "A Review of Research in Speech and Language Development of the Mentally Retarded Child," *Am. J. Ment. Def.,* 1958, 63, 236-240.

32. Hartogs, R., "The Pseudofeebleminded Child and Adolescent in Court," *Nerv. Ch.,* 1948, 7, 425-431.

33. Helgason, T., "Epidemiology of Mental Disorders in Iceland," *Acta Psychiat. Scand. Suppl.,* 1964, No. 173.

34. Hutt, M., and Gibby, R. G., *The Mentally Retarded Child,* Allyn and Bacon, 1958.

35. Ireland, E. C., "The Female Defective Delinquent," *Am. J. Ment. Def.,* 1947, 52, 63-70.

36. Jastak, J., "The Endogenous Slow-Learner," *Am. J. Ment. Def.,* 1950, 55, 269-274.

37. Johnson, C. D., and Barnett, C. D., "Relationship of Physical Stigmata to Intellectual Status of Mongoloids," *Amer. J. Ment. Def.,* 1961, 66, 435-437.

38. Johnson, G. O., "A Study of Social Position of Mentally Handicapped Children in Regular Grades," *Am. J. Ment. Def.,* 1950, 55, 60-89.

39. _____, and Kirk, S. A., "Are Mentally Handicapped Children Segregated in the Regular Grades?" *Excep. Ch.,* 1950, 17, 65-68.

40. Jordan, T. E., "Towards More Effective Use of the Term 'Mental Retardation,' " *Am. J. Ment. Def.,* 1958, 63, 15-16.

41. _____, and deCharms, R., "The Achievement Motive in Normal and Mentally Retarded Children," *Am. J. Ment. Def.,* 1959, 64, 457-466.

42. Kääriäinen, R., and Dingman, H. F., "The Relation of the Degree of Mongolism to the Degree of Subnormality," *Amer. J. Ment. Defic.,* 1961, 66, 438-443.

43. Kanner, L., and Lesser, L. I., "Early Infantile Autism," *Pediat. Clin. N. Am.*, 1958, *5*, 711-730.

44. Kaplan, O., "Life Expectancy of Low Grade Mental Defectives," *Psych. Rec.*, 1940, *3*, 295-300.

45. _____, "Mental Decline in Older Morons," *Amer. J. Ment. Def.*, 1943, *47*, 277-285.

46. Knobloch, H., and Pasamanick, B., "Syndrome of Minimal Cerebral Damage in Infancy," *J. Am. Med. Assn.*, 1959, *170*, 1384-1387.

47. Kratter, F. E., "The Physiognomic, Psychometric, Behavioral, and Neurological Aspects of Phenylketonuria," *J. Ment. Sc.*, 1959, *105*, 421-427.

48. _____, "The Pseudo-Mental-Deficiency Syndrome," *J. Ment. Sc.*, 1959, *105*, 406-420.

49. Leibowitz, H., Waskow, I., Loeffler, N., and Glaser, F., "Intelligence Level as a Variable in the Perception of Shape," *Quart. J. Exp. Psych.*, 1959, *11*, 108-112.

50. Leland, H., "Some Thoughts on the Current Status of Adaptive Behavior," *Ment. Retard.*, 1964, *2*, 171-176.

51. Leland, H. (ed.), *Conference on Measurement of Adaptive Behavior*, Parsons State Hospital and Training Center, Parsons, Kansas, 1964.

52. MacAndrew, C., and Edgerton, R., "IQ and the Social Competence of the Profoundly Retarded," *Amer. J. Ment. Def.*, 1964, *69*, 385-390.

53. McMurray, J. G., "Rigidity in Conceptual Thinking in Exogenous and Endogenous Mentally Retarded Children," *J. Consult. Psych.*, 1954, *18*, 366-370.

54. _____, "Visual Perception in Exogenous and Endogenous Mentally Retarded Children," *Am. J. Ment. Def.*, 1954, *58*, 659-663.

55. McNeill, W. D. D., "Development Patterns of Mongoloid Children: A Study of Certain Aspects of their Growth and Development," unpublished Ph.D. dissertation, University of Illinois, 1954.

56. Malzberg, B., "Some Characteristics of Mental Defectives Examined by the Child Guidance Clinics of the New York State Department of Mental Hygiene," *Am. J. Ment. Def.*, 1952, *56*, 510-518.

57. Nelson, W. M. C., "An Analysis of the Reasons for Discharge from a Special Care (Mental Deficiency) Hospital," *Acta Psychiat. Scand.*, 1964, *40*, 50-64.

58. Paddle, K. C. L., "Some Observations on the High Grade Unstable Mental Defective," *Am. J. Ment. Def.*, 1947, *51*, 654-659.

59. Pasamanick, B., "Research on the Influence of Sociocultural Variables upon Organic Factors in Mental Retardation," Woods Schools Conference, 1959.

60. Piaget, J., and Inhelder, B., "Diagnosis of Mental Operations and Theory of Intelligence," *Am. J. Ment. Def.*, 1947, *51*, 401-406.

61. Porter, R. B., Collins, J. L., and McIver, M. R., "A Comparative Investigation of the Personality of Educable Mentally Retarded Children and Those of a Norm Group of Children," *Excep. Child.*, 1965, *31*, 457-463.

62. Portnoy, B., and Stacey, C. L., "A Comparative Study of Negro and White Sub-Normals on the Children's Form of the Rosenzweig P-F Test," *Am. J. Ment. Def.*, 1954, 59, 272-278.

63. Ross, R. T., "The Mental Growth of Mongoloid Defectives," *Amer. J. Ment. Defic.*, 1962, *66*, 736-738.

64. Saenger, G., *The Adjustment of Severely Retarded Adults in the Community, Report;* New York State Interdepartmental Health Resources Board, 1957.

65. *St. Louis Post-Dispatch,* December 4, 1959.

66. Sarason, S., *Psychological Problems in Mental Deficiency,* 2d ed., Harper & Row, Publishers, 1953.

67. Satter, G., and Cassel, R. H., "Tactual-Kinesthetic Localization in the Mentally Retarded," *Am. J. Ment. Def.*, 1955, 59, 652-657.

68. Schlesinger, E. R., Allaway, N. C., and Peltin, S., "Survivorship in Cerebral Palsy," *Amer. J. Publ. Hlth.*, 1959, *49*, 343-349.

69. Silverstein, A. B., "An Empirical Test of the Mongoloid Stereotype," *Amer. J. Ment. Def.*, 1964, *68*, 493-497.

70. Spitz, H. S., 'Neural Satiation in the Spiral Aftereffect and Similar Movement Aftereffects," *Percept. Mot. Skills*, 1958, *8*, 207-213.

71. _____, and Blackman, L. S., "A Comparison of Mental Retardates and Normals on Visual Figural Aftereffects and Reversible Figures," *J. Abn. & Soc. Psych.*, 1959, *58*, 105-110.

72. _____, "The Mueller-Lyer Illusion in Retardates and Normals," *Percept. Motor Skills*, 1958, *8*, 219-225.

73. Stacey, C. L., and Portnoy, B., "A Study of Concept Formation by Means of the Object-Sorting Test with Subnormals," *Am. J. Ment. Def.*, 1951, *56*, 169-179.

74. Stein, Z., Susser, M., and Lunzer, E. A., "Reading, Reckoning, and Special Schooling Among the Mentally Handicapped," *Lancet*, 1960, 305-307.

75. Sternlicht, M., and Wanderer, Z. W., "Nature of Institutionalized Adult Mongoloid Intelligence," *Amer. J. Ment. Def.*, 1962, 67, 301-302.

76. Strauss, A. A., "The Education of the Brain Injured Child," *Am. J. Ment. Def.*, 1952, *56*, 712-718.

77. Tarjan, G., "The Psychopathic Delinquent and the Custodian," *Am. J. Ment. Def.*, 1949, *53*, 477-485.

78. Thompson, C. W., "Decline in Limit of Performance Among Adult Morons," *Amer. J. Psychol.*, 1951, *64*, 203-215.

79. Tizard, J., and Loos, F. M., "The Learning of a Spatial Relations Test by Adult Imbeciles," *Am. J. Ment. Def.*, 1955, *59*, 85-90.

80. Tolman, N. G., and Johnson, A. P., "Need for Achievement as Related to Brain Injury in Mentally Retarded Children," *Am. J. Ment. Def.*, 1958, *62*, 692-697.

81. Trippe, M. J., *et al.*, "The School-Excluded Mentally Retarded Child," *Am. J. Ment. Def.*, 1959, *63*, 1005-1009.

82. Westwell, A. E., "The Defective Delinquent," *Am. J. Ment. Def.*, 1951, *56*, 283-289.

83. Whitney, E. A., "A Pathetic Type—The Borderline Defective," *J. Ch. Psychiat.*, 1951, *2*, 176-186.

84. Winthrop, H., "Relative Variability with Visually Mediated Vocabulary Among the Retarded," *Psych. Rep.*, 1959, *5*, 318.

85. Woodward, M., "The Behavior of Idiots Interpreted by Piaget's Theory of Sensori-Motor Development," *Brit. J. Ed. Psych.*, 1959, *29*, 60-71.

86. Wunsch, W. L., "Some Characteristics of Mongoloids Evaluated in a Clinic for Children with Retarded Mental Development," *Am. J. Ment. Def.*, 1958, *62*, 122-130.

87. _____, *A Special Census of Suspected Referral Mental Retardation, Onondaga County, New York; Technical Data Report*, State Dept. of Mental Hygiene, Syracuse, N. Y., 1955.

Chapter 5

LANGUAGE

It is a half century since the pioneers in the study of mental retardation, Binet and Simon, first called attention to the central place language occupied in their formulation of mental retardation. Writing in *Mentally Defective Children,* they used written communication as the nucleus of traits they found in children at the *imbecile* level, and oral communication as the nucleus of traits they found in children at (to use their now out-dated terminology once more) the *idiot* level (8). The central role they gave to language has been largely ignored in the subsequent fifty years. In one of those errors of emphasis in which scholarship and science abound, study of mental retardation gave way to the technical problem of measurement at the expense of the higher order considerations. In the decade before 1910 people had turned to scientific management and its preoccupation with the cult of efficiency. This emphasis on the study of people through science and

143

technology was to prove a curse in many ways; but in the training of school administrators at the time the work of the Galbreaths and others, with its technological flavor, undoubtedly made Goddard's translation of the Binet-Simon scale appear the all-purpose tool for formulating and measuring the problems of retardation. In retrospect it seems that pre-occupation with measurement of retardates' behavior was analogous to concentrating study of fevers around the thermometer. In any case, the measurement aspect of Binet and Simon's work was stressed at the expense of their interest in language. Had that idiom prevailed rather than the mental measurement theme, our knowledge of mental retardation might be more advanced than it is. In this chapter we will consider language and mental retardation, repeating the basic but neglected theme first introduced by Binet and Simon.

The Nature of Language

Categorical Aspects: In the broadest terms *language* means the range of processes through which people communicate with other people. At times the communication may be indirect; at other times it may not involve the actual presence of another person. In each instance, however, there is an abstract, identical component which enables people to convey the intangibles of thought and to reformulate the realities with which they live. In more specific terms, language may be represented by a series of behaviors, a number of human acts which are commonly encountered in everyday experiences.

Speaking is perhaps the most obvious type of linguistic behavior. It is the unique function of man as it emerges from the biological level of human nature as an expression of a comparatively advanced nervous system; it emerges also as an otherwise ineffable expression of the experiences of men in the course of their lives. In certain human beings, speaking conveys expressive style and gives clues to their natures and temperaments. This unique and idiosyncratic property of language is exploited in the investigations of literature, psychology, and psychiatry.

Listening is no less a practical example of language behavior, despite the lack of simple observables. It is a modality with properties all too often unappreciated. Through the act of listening a child can be heir to the entire tradition of the human race; more concretely, he can acquire the information on which to base rational acts and to achieve the paramount end of education—the realization of individuality. Secondarily, listening allows one to acquire the information necessary for the practical procedure of relating to one's neighbors and earning a living. It is the medium by which children are guided from the earliest years and by which the subtleties of educational processes are conveyed.

Reading is, of course, the language behavior which most fully admits people to the commonwealth of ideas. By acquiring the ability to grasp meaning in a form not dependent on the presence of another person, children acquire the greater ability to see the world in many ways and through the eyes of many people. Readers are independent people, and through that property they participate still more in education's goal of liberated intelligence and full development of individuality.

Writing also advances independence; it does so by adding the ability to convey ideas to skill at receiving them. The congruence of the two acts gives children a sense of adequacy and provides adults with the minimal literacy needed to survive in a society with little place for the unskilled in its economic processes.

Thinking, however, constitutes the language process, *par excellence.* It is the ultimate gift of man that he can formulate reality in more than the sensory form by which it first impinges on his consciousness. By using verbal symbols, the bricks and mortar of language, people can formulate reality in alternate ways; they can use different words to discover new realities in the primordium of sensory experience. Stripped of facility at formulating reality by linguistic means, man would probably lose a unique survival skill.

Summarizing, we may observe that language is several behaviors which are routine in the normal experiences of living. One might go so far as to say that their development is what makes living normal; that is, the several language behaviors described are acts which are vital to personal and social development. Failure to grow in patterns of language behavior can be a form of maldevelopment and hence a self-defining type of abnormal behavior.

So far, language has appeared as a matter of behaviors, directly and indirectly observable processes. However, language is more than that; it is a process which should be analyzed in other ways. (See Figure 5·1). In addition to (1) *behaviors,* language has (2) *directions,* (3)

Figure 5·1

Aspects of Language

Behaviors	speaking	listening	reading	writing	thinking
Direction	expressive	receptive	receptive	expressive	autistic
Locus	outer	inner	inner	outer	inner
Form	oral	oral	graphic	graphic	neural

locus, and (4) *forms.* These last properties are elements which convey structure and allow us to be explicit in the discussion of language. The (2) *directions* of language are the ways in which language relates the inner reality of reflection to external considerations. For example, much language behavior is expressive in direction, as people convey their thoughts to others by writing and talking. Conversely, allowing others to talk at or to us and permitting their thoughts to influence us by means of the printed page is to describe language behaviors which are passive in direction. There is a third form, the direction, or a lack of it conceivably, by which language behavior relates to oneself alone. Piaget has used the work *autistic* to describe language behavior of young children—often spoken rather than merely self-contained—which has the self as active and passive referents. The word is invoked because it seems no other is needed, although the usage here is not intended to convey the complexity described in *Language and Thought in the Child* (77).

(3) *Locus* is another way of categorizing language behaviors. It is the site at which language has its effect. Most language has an outer locus since it is employed in the business of living with one's fellows and in formulating the realities which the everyday world presents. On the other hand, language has an inner locus, the process of thinking. Not all the behaviors of mankind relate to others. As Piaget has shown, normal development includes a self-centered phase, one in which even oral language is not used solely as a device for communication. In addition to this temporary condition, there is the prior and subsequent process of inner language, the processes of thought which guide all but the most impulsive or reflexive behavior. Language with an inner locus is not well understood. To be sure, we can peep into the inner linguistic stream, as it were, by mirrors, when we use free association and projective tests. However, these operate at a fairly sophisticated level and are not immune to a host of invalidating influences. Getting at language in a more immediate way is possible only through introspection, a process notoriously difficult to handle. Psychoanalytic theory refers to the *primary process* in thought, the conceptual-linguistic stream we encounter in dreams, and in the words of schizophrenics. Following the ideas of Rapaport, inner language is the process of manipulating drive-reducing representations of memory (79). It should be kept in mind that the primary process may be glimpsed in non-objective art, a process in which drives may well spring forth without resort to the structure which secondary process in thinking renders intelligible. The literary work of James Joyce, whose medium was words above all, is perhaps all the more formidable if no less incomprehensible because of its attempt to capitalize on the primary process at the bottom of language.

Finally, (4) *form* is a category of language. The obvious form is *oral*, the process of talking in which we take ideas in our minds and use them to shape a stream of vibrated air passing through the articulators. Hopefully more than sound and fury, oral language is the basic medium by which the affairs of mankind from education to business are transacted. The graphic form of language is the written word. Its subtlety is often missed because it can seem too close to drawings and therefore (as in ideographs) simply another visual representation of reality. However, in occidental languages words are representatives of sounds, and the visual form gives no hint of the reality to which it alludes. Graphic language, be it Palmer-style writing or Braille, has meaning only when verbal associations of an intangible or tangible nature are acquired. There is no short cut to the meaning of graphic language except through the mind of man. It follows that learning to write and read are all the more remarkable since they are skills acquired before the mind has attained full development. The connections between this observation and the sustained immaturity of the retarded may be used as an object of endless speculation.

Summarizing, we may turn to Figure 5·1 again. Language has been described by means of four categories: (1) *behaviors*, (2) *directions*, (3) *locus*, and (4) *form*. To this over-all categorical approach we can add an analytic presentation, consisting of elements of language which can be profitably studied in discrete ways.

Analytic aspects: The smallest element in language is probably the *phoneme* or speech sound. This is the unit sometimes represented graphically by two letters, as the last sound in the word *cough*, or more routinely by one, as the first sound in the word *fun*. Phonemes have been studied in detail by Irwin and his associates (*34, 35*), and we shall consider application of this work to language development by normal and retarded children a little later. Assemblies of phenomes constitute words, and vocabulary constitutes a vital component of language to which attention has been given profitably; for example, linguists speak of *types*, meaning different words in a person's vocabulary. Assemblies of words are linked together by structure, and the result is the element in language we call *syntax*. Words are changed by means of grammar, and *morphology* is the general term for the mutations which words experience. Generally speaking, the language of primitive people is complex in many ways and stands in great contrast to the comparative simplicity of English.

In addition to the structure of language we may mention analytic elements which have been contrived for purposes of investigation and analysis. There are many ways in which individual words may be combined; among them is the adjective/verb ratio introduced from German to English by Boder (*12*), and subsequently little used. The ratio of different words to samples, *types* to *tokens*, (TTR) has been employed (22). Osgood has analyzed meaning or words by means of a series of polarized adjectives (hot-cold, etc.) in the *semantic differential* technique (74). Recently the syntax of language has been studied by Wepman and his associates with a view to classifying aphasias (36). In addition, there are the considerable bodies of work on philology and communication theory which study language from an entirely different point of view. These highly specialized disciplines serve to indicate the scope of the domain we call language. In recent years there seems to have been some connection established between the communication specialists and the functionalists who study patterns of speech. As yet, philologists and the students of oral speech seem to have made little progress in finding needed strategies in their reciprocal studies of language. As a final observation on the variety of language, it is interesting to note that an influential movement in contemporary philosophy, loosely termed "the Oxford School," is committed to the analysis of verbal, i.e., linguistic propositions.

Acquisition of Language—Description

Having briefly considered language, we may next examine the process of language development in children. It is a remarkable thing to see the growth of children over a period of a few years, and language growth is a useful example because it is at once readily observable and proportionately baffling. The baffling part arises from the things we do not know. For example, categorization of stages of growth is quite straightforward. We can sample language at intervals of two months, as Irwin has done, and build a picture of consecutive stages. However, stages are contrived by the investigator's technique, and we do not know how one gets from one stage to another; nor, indeed, do we know in a detailed way what vectors advance growth. As we shall see subsequently, our knowledge of negative factors is more detailed.

We may begin consideration of language acquisition by considering children at birth. If all has gone well, gestation will have developed a six-to eight-pound baby whose nervous system at birth functions primarily as an automatic monitoring device. Little direction of behavior emerges from the cerebral cortex, and body processes are largely self-regulating. In addition to routine body functions, the skeletal muscles work, and babies produce cries or sounds as air is expelled from the lungs via the larynx and mouth. The senses work well, although perception tends to be diffused, and behavior is controlled in the most direct way, that is, without recourse to the mediating processes of thought, memory, and volition.

Phonemes. Newborn infants spontaneously make noises and have a repertoire of phonemes or speech sounds which expands in the succeeding years. Babies who are less than two months old may produce seven phonemes according to Irwin (35), and the ensuing months may see development of twenty-seven phonemes by the age of two and a half years. During this period vowels are more common than consonants. Not all the speech sounds produced are employed in mature speech; for example, the click produced by the raising and lowering the tongue is used in only the Xhosa group of languages as far as we know. Other speech sounds which a given child's language requires may not be present for several years. The result is that some phonemes are generally not fully available to children in the first few years of life, while others are available, but are not used in the native tongue a child may employ. This means that a degree of misarticulation is understandable and normal in all young children. We find, as we might expect, that children have individual patterns of phonemic growth within a generalized state of progression towards maturity. In general, girls seem to grow in articulation at the same rate as boys from age thirty months to sixty-six months, according to Poole (78), while consistency between the sexes is reported in children of kindergarten age by Winitz (110). According to Poole, about two-thirds of the sounds used in children's conversation are correctly articulated by age four and a half years. By 3-5 years, *b, p, m, w,* and *h,* are usually articulated correctly; at 4-5 years, *d, t, n, g, k, ng,* and *y,* are correctly produced. Sounds which are correctly pronounced by seven and a half years are *z, s, r, th,* (78). Poole believed that at the age of eight "articulation maturity" was reached, a figure generally corroborated by Templin (104). These data should not be used for normative purposes to the exclusion of Metraux's on vowels, but they convey well the developmental sequence which phonemic development presents (64).

Vocabulary. During the second trimester of infancy, babies put strings of phonemes together quite frequently, and are occasionally startled to find they are receiving more attention than usual. Certain combinations of phonemes probably feel good and taste better to babies; if the random group of phonemes happens to be the Lapp word for father or mother or food, and the child is a Lapplander, certain swift and positive events follow.[1] Eventually, aggregates of phonemes

---

[1] The choice of Lapp is not accidental. The language is considered comparatively impoverished, meaning heavy value is placed on the limited number of words. Basque is said to contain few abstractions, and single words may function as entire sentences. The research possibilities for comparative studies are intriguing in the two languages and English.

are produced voluntarily by babies and we call them words. Shirley's babies had a median age of sixty weeks when they used their first word although one out of four had begun at forty-seven weeks. Nouns are the first items in children's oral vocabularies, and these are followed by verbs. With maturity come the finer details of syntax: the adjectives, prepositions and adverbs. McCarthy's data show that from eighteen months on the proportion of nouns and verbs combined drops from 63 per cent of all words until, by age fifty-four months, it is down to 44 per cent (53). According to Carroll subsequent growth is hard to assess for methodological reasons, but he believes that vocabularies of children are probably larger than we suspect (15). In an excellent commentary on language, which should be more widely known, A. F. Watts summarized a number of studies of vocabulary development (108). He felt that the average child entering an English school at age five probably had a vocabulary of 2,000 words, and that it would amount to 4,000 words within two or three years. Subsequently, it would grow by about 700 words a year, so that it would amount to 8,000 or 10,000 words by age fourteen. Running all through the acquisition of words is a qualitative increment. As children's vocabularies mature they acquire abstract words, items they cannot comprehend in their early years. Generally speaking the abstract property of words is not well handled until about age six, under typical circumstances.

Sentences. The growth of sentences under normal conditions begins earlier than we realize. For instance, the first "word" used by a child may well represent an object, but it may have connotations an older child would convey with a sentence. Accordingly, we may say that one-word sentences are the usual first stage, and that increasing maturity, experience, and motivation produce longer sentences. Data gathered by McCarthy describing sentence length of children from eighteen to fifty-four months at half yearly intervals shows a mean semi-annual increment of .9 words, or about two words each year (54). At eighteen months the mean sentence length was 1.2 words, and at fifty-four months the mean sentence length was 4.6 words. It is appropriate to point out that the length of sentences is more than a simple way of describing states of growth in young children. Sentence length and its variant, mean length of response (MLR), has turned out to be a valuable measure of language. Mrs. Nice first described sentences by length, namely: (1) single words, (2) early sentences, (3) 3-4 words, and (4) 6-8 words, in 1925 (69). She concluded that sentence length was the best single criterion of linguistic growth, an observation many people have since agreed with. (97, 98, 113).

Acquisition of Language—Explanations

In an age when objectivity is more prized than honesty as a scholarly goal, we are inclined to be easily misled by accounts of phenomena which contain masses of evidence. Language acquistion is no exception to this state of affairs. More explicitly, we have a number of descriptions of growth in language by children—for example, those by McCarthy (53), Metraux (64), and Templin (104)—but what we lack and do not expect these excellent studies to provide, is explanation in addition to description. To know what x number of words of such and such a type may be found in children is not the same, nor as valuable, as knowing why change takes place over a period of time. Put another way, it is helpful and practical to know the stage of language development we may anticipate, but it is more helpful to understand the process by which a child moves from one stage to another. Such information is not currently available for practical reasons. Any human attribute develops in a structure of three factors. First, there is the (1) *ontological* consideration or fixed properties of a person. Eye color, for example, is not likely to be easily changed, nor is the pattern of the finger prints; on the other hand, a large number of human properties, of which language is a prime example, are (2) *functional,* meaning their development is not fixed, but the very opposite. Producing their variable situation is the class of (3) *ecological* elements, the situational factors and circumstances of life which influence all but the small class of (1) *ontological* traits. To understand why language development takes place is to grapple with unmeasurable potentials under a variety of personal circumstances. To have a comprehensive explanation of language growth, as opposed to a description, would require several developments, none of which is really available. We would need to know the amount of variability of development determined by ontological factors, which, in turn, would require specification of more or less immutable human traits. Also, we would require an account of how situational factors alter a mutable trait. For language development, which is most complex, the nature of an explanation would be a set of detailed propositions concerning multiple causes and effects, an issue scarcely touched today by a detailed proposition on any single cause and effect.

Scholarship being the challenging thing it is, some investigators have made overtures to the problem, and we may expect to see these efforts followed by better specification in the future. We may now briefly consider some of the current explanations of how language development takes place.

1. *Mowrer* has proposed that talking has to be taught, as opposed to expectations that it will unfold automatically with the passage of time. Hearing words, he indicates, leads to perception of positive values and rewards. Words become associated with parents, who, in turn, connote "food, fun, and friendly companionship" (67). Having experienced this pleasant state of affairs, the baby "jollies" himself along by recalling the noises he has heard and their pleasant associations, and by conjuring them up for himself by reproducing the noises. The noises, or words, are now rewarding because of their associations; they are *autistic* because they refer to the self, rather than to other people. In other words, their first employment is noncommunicative but, rather, self-satisfying. Language development occurs because words are reinforced through identification with parents.

2. *Myklebust* has suggested that early language development begins with the mechanisms of identification, internalization, and assimilation. (68). (1) *Inner* language is the first process to appear, probably developing in the first eight months of life. During this period babies are grasping the meaning of experiences. From eight to twelve months (2) *receptive* language is probably emphasized as children perceive the meaning of words addressed to them. Subsequently, (3) *expressive* language emerges as familiarity with people, experiences and words have been assimilated. The progression leads to production of words which have a communicative intent.

3. *Skinner* wrote a book entitled *Verbal Behavior* (95). This work does not deal with the broad aspects of language but with verbal behavior defined mostly through the methodology of experimental manipulation. The bulk of the work consists of a discussion of common forms of verbal behavior using neologisms such as *mand* and *tact*, and so forth. Skinner's position is that verbal behavior is emitted much like motor behavior, that is, through the elements of stimulus, response, and reinforcement. In an appendix, he alludes to a hungry baby and a mother describing the act of nursing as a behavior resulting from discriminant learning by the mother. A reciprocal explanation of child behavior is given, indicating that the baby's vocalization is also shaped. The Dutch linguist Siertsema has commented that Skinner slights the intrinsic pleasure of imitation which infants experience. He feels that external reinforcement is less important than Skinner does, and seems to be closer to Mowrer in his concern for the self-pleasing aspect of early vocalization through identification (92).

4. A fourth possibility exists, not as an explanation but as a sketch of an explanation drawn from several sources. It is probable that breadth could be added to our comments on language acquisition by consider-

ing not children alone but mothers and their children as the basis for comments. We could start with the two-person group alluded to in Chapter 2, and assess the strategies of mother and child as they interact. The basic unit might be verbal behavior under contingent circumstances. Actual application of small-group theory to language and retarded persons has been reported by Siegel (*90*), and Siegel and Harkins (*91*). The paradigm is that advocated in the 1961 edition of this work, and it is to be hoped that the two-person group will be applied to shed light on language acquisition by small children interacting with their mothers.

Negative Influences on Language

A little earlier in this chapter it was observed that language growth is not a process of *unfolding*, with all the connotations of inevitability and naturalness that term conveys. Viewed more realistically as a function which is (1) acquired and (2) intimately dependent on external influences, we can appreciate the extent to which language may not develop along expected lines. While being acquired, language can be deflected at any point in the process. Structured as it is by circumstance, language growth can be influenced by accidents and by adverse experiences of all sorts. The result is that a number of factors can interfere with a process, the complexity of which can be aptly conveyed by consulting McCarthy (*54*). She listed 126 language-oriented behaviors drawn from eight studies of the first three years of life. Many of the behaviors McCarthy described are interrelated, with the result that disturbance of one can have implications for the development of others.

In the preceding discussion of how language is acquired, a number of terms appeared which are relevant to the discussion of negative influences on language.

(1) *Identification* suggests that speech develops because human relationships and needs are becoming important to infants. It follows that the social context in which children grow can affect the growth of language adversely. The Iowa studies showed us that orphanages of a type we hope are gone forever could depress the linguistic attainment of perfectly normal children. The lack of sustained, warm contacts with adults is a depressant, and it places the burden of stimulation on other children. As Wolfensberger, Mein, and O'Connor have shown, groups of people in closed societies develop large core vocabularies, words which account for most conversations, and therefore a good deal of cognitive stimulation (*111*). Identification in that sense means overwhelming identification with other immature persons. It can have a more basic meaning when it is applied to intimacy with

adults in the earliest months. Identification can mean stimulation from parents, a process which normally starts right after birth. When circumstances lead to isolation of infants, their linguistic development is arrested, apart from the psychiatric effects on ego-formation. The occasional newspaper report of a child discovered in a locked room is clear evidence. Less intense but equally sustained deprivation can leave children physically intact but unequal to the expectations of linguistic attainment which elementary schools hold. The "low IQ" children from slums are perhaps the clearest example of this situation.

(2) *Sensory development* underlies language growth. Loss of hearing acuity in the speech range leads to serious interference with the normal processes of developing speech. The initial stage of speech development is quite passive. Infants absorb stimulation from the world around them and are capable of discriminating between familiar and unfamiliar sounds at an early age. Further, infants can discriminate familiar and meaningless sounds, doors being closed quietly, for example, from such meaningful sounds as the clink of a bottle. Being forms of communication, gestures or grunts convey what can be observed in the first few months of life, long before words appear. Mild hearing loss can have a serious effect on language; profound hearing loss is proportionately more serious. Complicating the situation is the probability that hearing loss will go undetected for years.

(3) *The need* to speak is a factor which normally advances speech development. Granted a sense of identification and intact senses, there must still be some gain to be realized by using words. If less demanding forms of communication, gestures or grunts, can convey what children have in mind, it is normal to rely on them. Parents, in their eagerness, may inhibit speaking because the need is simply not there. Asking children to choose food, and then naming everything on the table, does not help children, although it can be more convenient for parents. Need may be expressed in another way. Children are usually rewarded, or reinforced, for attempts at speech. The reward becomes highly desirable, and children's speech can become instrumental behavior leading to reinforcement by parents in the form of expressions of love. As Skinner has pointed out, verbal operants typically specify their own reinforcement. The need to speak is the same as the need to be rewarded with praise and affection. The absence of rewards for speaking is quite clear in non-verbal homes, and the need to speak is proportionately inhibited. The difficulties this can produce are endless. School is a linguistic culture and it seems strange indeed to children

from non-oral homes or from those segments of society which have as their *ethos* a non-verbal ambiance.

(4) Emotional disturbance in children tends to confound language development or to depress it. In severe forms of emotional disturbance language is consistently affected and mutism is not uncommon. Here again, the connection can be oversimplified; being disturbed is in some conditions a matter of perceiving reality in a distorted way. The medium by which we see the world is a set of lenses composed of values, experience, and the concepts which we have developed. To a considerable extent linguistic symbols are the device for codifying these three elements. In that sense linguistic disturbance is caused by psychiatric problems; but we can also say, in another sense, the linguistic disturbance *is* the emotional disturbance. This last formulation is parallel to mental retardation and language, a relationship to be discussed shortly. From this point on, the connection between language and retardation will grow a little closer. A link is the basis in physical development for defective language. In some cases of mental retardation, intellectual limitations are only one component of a broad spectrum of limitations. Developmental failure going back to the early period of gestation produces structural anomalies which preclude development of normal speech. (1) *Cleft palate* consists of an opening in the roof of the mouth which produces an incomplete oral cavity. The result is that the breath stream cannot be molded correctly by the normal process of raising the tongue to the roof of the mouth or to the ridge just behind the front teeth. On occasion the defect extends to the lip, producing a more radical fissure. (2) *Cerebral palsy,* often thought to be due to birth injury, is found in children whose gestational and perinatal histories are normal; in such cases developmental failure is probably the source. It produces mild to severe disturbances of muscular control which affect voluntary direction of the muscles used in speaking. The tongue, for example, simply cannot be raised in some cases, with a corresponding loss of articulation proficiency. (3) *Minimal brain injury,* a rather inexact term, accounts for symbolic disturbances of language. In some cases aphasia is produced, while in others delayed language development is a symptom. The evidence tends to be ambiguous on the effects of some forms of developmental error. For example, the author has found language comparatively normal in children with adverse early developmental histories (37). In those cases mental retardation and learning problems were quite common. (4) *Mental retardation* is a cause of poor language development. This is not the redundant remark it might seem, particularly in a book on mental retardation, because the connec-

tion between the two constructs is quite tricky. Looked at in one way, mental retardation is quite distinct from language, and therefore cause and effect relations can be implied when a high incidence of speech defects is found. Looked at another way, mental retardation is low language skill; that is, verbal items predominate in many tests of intelligence, and low IQ is an expression of low verbal performance. In that sense the two are inseparable. We may now turn to consideration of the relationship between mental retardation and language disorders in greater detail.

Incidence

Descriptive studies are generally not considered as significant as experimental studies in the current climate of science. There are good reasons for this, mainly because descriptions tend to be repetitive and to differ only in minor ways. The result is that most fields of scholarship which use empirical techniques currently avoid gathering mere descriptions of the populations they study. Language in the mentally retarded may be considered an exception to the generalization just given because linguistic studies of retarded persons have been slighted and our grasp of the facts is less than complete. Description has much to tell us at this point and we may use it profitably to explore retardation.

Generally speaking, a group of retarded children will include some with good speech and syntax, and it will include many with poor speech and syntax. However, it is well to recall that retarded persons do not fit stereotypes any better than non-retarded persons. Accordingly, a single, all-encompassing statement about the language of the retarded is not possible, and should be replaced by several statements, each attuned to the severity of retardation, age, and circumstances of life. As yet we have an incomplete list, although the discrete entries on the list may be quite accurate.

Kennedy compared the incidence of speech disorders in 308 retarded persons below IQ 69 with the incidence in a control group of 106 controls (42). She found a higher incidence in the retarded SS, 42 per cent, than in the controls, 30 per cent. Fifty-three per cent of 1,000 educable children were described by Steinman, Grossman, and Reece as speech defective (100). An incidence of 66 per cent was described by Sirkin and Lyons in their study of speech defects in 2,522 institutional subjects (94). A figure of 66 per cent has been given by Gens (26), which also is close to the percentage given by Schlanger and Gottsleben (88), but different from a report of 94 per cent given by Tarjan et al. (103). Mathews surveyed the literature on incidence in the middle of the decade 1950–60 and found even greater disparity, reporting incidence figures between 5 and 79 per cent (*59*). These figures are quite inconsistent—and quite accurate. That is because the populations are different, and investigators are likely to use different standards to assess the language proficiency of their subjects. The figures, as they stand, are accurate descriptions which we supplement with additional comments on severity.

The commonsense expectation that retardation and language disorders are more closely related in the case of seriously handicapped persons is supported by the facts. Among the mildly retarded a fairly high incidence of language disorders is found for several years, but maturity operates as a source of improvement. The result is that mildly retarded persons generally have fairly good speech by the time adolescence has been reached, although their early language status was poor (*84*).

Mild retardation. Among children in the mildly retarded range of severity (IQ 50-70) delay in talking is common (*29*); a mean age of 34 months for producing the first word was reported by Karlin and Strazzulla, who found a correspondingly delayed age for sentence usage of 89 months (*40*). Among children growing at this rate of mental development, articulation problems are found, and they occur in combination with other language problems, disorders of rhythm and voice, for example. According to Wilson's analysis of 225 special-class children, freedom from speech defects was associated with the borderline and near borderline levels of ability (*109*). Conversely, Donovan found "severe speech defects" in 8 per cent of two thousand educable children (*19*). Mutism, the absence of speech, is rare in children who are mildly retarded; Karlin and Kennedy found mutism in a number of cases of retardation, but found none in those whose intelligence quotient was in the fifty to seventy range (*39*).

Moderate retardation. The children just described constitute the majority of retarded persons. Only about 15 per cent fall below IQ fifty, and among them are 10 per cent (of the total) who are generally described as moderately retarded (IQ 30-50). This is a substantial group of people and their problems are not as light as the word *moderate* might suggest. Language is an area of behavior which is affected in several ways. First of all, freedom from speech defects is uncommon, and defective speech is likely. Lubman's account of speech in one hundred and fifty persons below IQ 50 reported acceptable speech in only twenty-six (*48*). In a study previously referred to, Sirkin and Lyons found defective speech in 74 per cent of the moderately retarded persons in their large population (*94*). Wolfensberger, Mein, and O'Connor have indicated in their studies of retarded persons that poor speech does not seem to be connected with a reduction in language output (111). Schlanger has corroborated this finding in an anecdote (86). He analyzed the speech of residents of the Training School at Vineland and described the language of a girl with an intelligence quotient of thirty-eight as "almost complete garrulousness." Analyzing the types of speech difficulty encountered in thirty-two moderately retarded persons, Karlin and Kennedy found only one example of good speech, while there were seven mute individuals, and twenty-four others with at least some degree of defective speech (39). In addition to describing language disorders at this level of retardation, by giving types of speech error, it is wise to keep in mind the probability of more fundamental problems. Specifically, language tends, at best, to have a stereotyped quality; that is, expressions are often used in a monotonous way. The exchange of pleasantries with professional personnel can lead to routine exchanges whose inflexible form tends to mask a basic impoverishment of thought. To be sure, this applies to people of normal intelligence, but their use of stereotyped language is usually insightful. In the case of moderately retarded persons, conceptual impoverishment tends to be present at all times.

Severe retardation. There is a point at which our descriptions of high intelligence start to lose their clarity because of defects in our units of measurement. This is also the case when we consider severe retardation, a degree usually conveyed by psychometric ratings below IQ 30 or 20. Among persons whose intellectual defects are great, a variety of problems occur, and linguistic deficit may be related to motor and neural deficiencies, apart from limitations imposed by limited ability to deal with abstractions. The linguistic status of severely retarded persons, regardless of mechanisms, tends to be primitive. Mutism is common and primitive levels of language development such as babbling and jabbering are frequent. The explanation lies in the general finding that onset of speech is related to intelligence; the obverse of this is that delay is also related to intelligence and the finding is all the more reliable in the extreme case (47). However, the absence of speech in severely retarded persons is not a single state; discriminations are possible between various kinds of mutism. It is possible for mutism to be an absolute thing; that is, the absence of language means an absence of all interest in expression, all ability to communicate, and so forth. This is not always the case and some severely retarded persons wish to communicate but lack sophisticated means. Gestures and vocabulary (e.g., "uh" [ʌ] are employed in the absence of speaking. In such cases motivation is present, and very modest developments over a long period of time may be possible (112). Such developments may occur when stages of pre-verbal, vocal development have been mastered, for example, babbling and the preceding stages of putting phonemes together. This last stage has been described by Goda and may be examined in order to appreciate the discriminations that can be made among pre-verbal but vocal retardates. Goda found five levels of utterance: (1) isolated sounds, (2) vowels plus consonants, (3) consonants composed of vowels and consonants repeated self-consciously for pleasure, (4) the pleasurable syllables of others plus the personal repertoire, and (5) acquisition of single words (27).

Articulation

Having previously considered descriptive statements about severity which give depth to consideration of language in retarded persons, we may now consider the sounds produced by the retarded in actual speaking situations. In doing so we attend to the clinical mode of description which takes speech and breaks its communicative integrity into non-communicating (i.e., meaningless) sounds and blends of sounds. Since the majority of retarded children are in the mild (educable) range, we will give attention to them, primarily. In 1945 Wilson reported the status of articulation in 225 children in Des Moines, Iowa (109). The Bryngelson and Glaspey Test Cards were administered and the responses were recorded. Ten per cent (10%) of the children had articulation problems and 2.2 per cent and 2.7 per cent had additional disorders of voice and rhythm. Voiceless-*th* (θ) was the most common error followed by *r, v, z, l, j, sh, s,* voiced-*th* (ð), *ch, k, g, ng, y, f, h,* and *wh.* The most common substitutions (5 out of 14) were (1) for voiceless-*th; f, s, t,* and *z* (2) for *z;-th, j, t,* and *d* (3) for *r;*[1] *w* (4) for *v; b,* and *w* (5) for voiced-*th;*[2] *d,* and *f.* The description given by Wilson is essentially similar to that given by Bangs three years earlier (4). He found the general articulation pattern of the retarded similar to that of speech defective persons of normal intelligence, with the possible exception of a higher incidence of omitted sounds. Corroboration may also be found in Batza's account of speech patterns in educable retarded children (5). Batza found that substitutions were usual, and that voiced and voiceless-*th* were most common errors. Riello's dissertation treated the same problem (80). The articulation of eighty-two sounds and blends by fifty-five males and forty-five females with a mean IQ of 68, a mean MA of seven years and nine months, and mean life age of eleven and a half was rated by three trained observers.

---

[1] initial position
[2] medial position

Forty-one per cent of the children had defective speech, and most of their problems were substitutions (50 per cent). The second most common error was omission of sounds (28 per cent); while distortions were less common (19 per cent), a few children inserted additional sounds (3 per cent).

A sub-population of educable children has been considered on occasion—those who live in residential settings. Daum analyzed the articulation of such children and found a pattern essentially similar to that described by Wilson, and Batza, and Riello. Omissions were more common in children between seven and twelve years of age, while substitutions were more common in the older portion of her sample of fifty children, those between fourteen and nineteen years of age (16). Speech defects were more common in boys than girls.

A University of Maryland thesis by Masket advances this discussion in two ways (58). First it considers children below IQ 50, and it raises the issue of community versus institutional living, a matter studied discretely in the investigations by Daum and Wilson. The children described by Masket were matched groups of twenty-six children with mean IQ's of 46; one group attended a day school in Baltimore, while the second lived at the Rosewood State School. The usual phonemes were defective; however, there was a statistically greater incidence of consonant omissions and substitutions in the Rosewood sample; vowel errors and blend errors were also statistically more common in the Rosewood children. Consonants were mostly substituted in the initial position, they were most frequently omitted in the final position, and distortions were most common in the medial position. Rigrodsky's investigation, to be considered in Chapter 9, found medial v, medial θ, final θ, medial z, and initial v the five most common errors in retarded persons at the Fort Wayne State School (81).

Vocabulary

Having considered how retardates speak, we may consider the words which they employ in the course of their conversations. Vocabulary grows with the passage of time in gifted, normal, and retarded children. Each year adds to the number of words children use; the increment is generally proportional to the growth in mental age and chronological age with mental age being nearly five times more significant, according to Bangs (4). In the case of mental age the nature of the increment is quantitative, that is, more words are added, but more important is a qualitative change in the ways in which words can be used. In the earliest years children use words as representations of reality (tacts) and as ways to manipulate the behavior of others in order to obtain things, etc. (*mands*). Eventually words are used to express and perceive ineffable matters such as abstractions and states of mind, items which no gesture can convey. According to Papania, growth in the dimension of word usage by retarded children follows the progression found in normal children (75). However, he observed a reduction in the number of abstract definitions given by retarded children at a given mental age when compared to non-retarded children at the same mental age. Level of responses was measured using the method developed by Feifel in his study of disturbed people (23). Quality, according to Papania, did not relate to mental age, although the grosser formulation of his data, correctness of response to the Binet vocabulary list, did.

Obviously, the mental age concept is not as watertight as is sometimes believed, despite its value in comparison to IQ. The problem is not clear-cut because mental age tends to be decided by abilities very close to the verbal material of vocabulary sub-tests. Work by Ohlsen tends to support the possibility that language performance can, in theory, discriminate more precisely between levels of maturity (71). Ohlsen equated bright, average, and retarded children by developing groups with similar mean Binet mental ages of eight years. Twenty-five concrete and twenty-five abstract words from the Ammons Full Range Picture Vocabulary Scale were administered to them; no differences were found between girls, but retarded males in regular and special classes differed in abstract scores from bright males. The studies of Papania and Ohlsen together suggest that the vocabularies of retarded children can yield a great deal of information, certainly more than a simple count of words known. Vocabulary can yield information about the way children manipulate realities, and describe the realities words convey to them. Going beyond that point, it is probable that vocabulary is capable of yielding even more information by providing more precise statements of mental maturity. That is, perhaps vocabulary can be treated to yield two rather than one mental age; the forms may be traced in Badt's work. Badt conducted a study of abstraction in sixty mild institutional cases ranging in age from seven to fifteen (3). Her data consisted of correct responses to the Binet treated to yield a quantified statement of level of abstraction. The scoring allocated one point to a correct response which used description, and three and five points, respectively, to words correctly defined by use and abstraction.

Brain injured, retarded children use words in a manner different from that employed by retarded children free from brain injury. According to Bijou and Werner, definitions are qualitatively superior in brain-injured, retarded children (9). Asked to define fifty-seven words from Thorndike's word list, a group of brain injured, retarded children used more than one mode of definition more frequently than familial retarded children (p<.01), who consistently used only one—definition by function. The brain injured children frequently employed definition by independent properties, e.g., *ocean:* "a big deep hole full of water." The brain injured retardates had wider vocabularies according to Bijou and Werner; their mean score on forty-four words was 15.68, which was significantly larger than the familials' score of 12.79. Both groups were matched by IQ and MA; the means for brain injured were MA 9-5, IQ 68, the means for familials were MA 9-4, IQ 69.

Finally, we may consider the size of vocabularies in retarded persons, defining words as single, unequivocal elements in an individual's lexicon. The restriction just invoked is important because it is common in studies of vocabulary size and because, methodologically, it sidesteps two problems: (1) multiple meanings of a word, and (2) very different words being conveyed by the same sounds and letters (e.g., *light* a match; a feather is *light;* birds *light* on a branch). A little earlier the size of normal children's vocabularies was presented. They are quite large, usually larger than we think. They grow by virtue of the varied experiences and stimuli which everyday living presents. Indeed, normality in a linguistic sense is possible only by experience in the ambience of everyday life. Retarded children are linguistically impoverished—in the relevant sense of vocabulary size—partly because of intellectual limits to full perception of reality. They are also restricted because they tend to be denied the opportunity for normal experiences by over-solicitous parents, and by similar restrictions on their mobility.

Still another source of restriction is institutional living, a topic covered in more detail in Chapter 4. For our purposes here, it is sufficient to recall the effects of total institutions on language output, as described by Schlanger (86). Advancing the discussion, we may consider vocabulary size in institutionalized retarded persons. Mein and O'Connor analyzed the oral vocabularies of eighty persons between ten and thirty years of age with Binet mental ages between three and seven years (63). From written records of conversations in which 28,732 words were produced, they calculated that 2,419 different words were employed. Individual vocabularies ranged in size from 106 to 677 words. Even the largest of these repertoires is small and well below what would be expected from normal children. In all probability, the reason for this small vocabulary involves more than intellectual problems. In institutions patients receive a great deal of their stimulation from each other. This can be no great stimulus in a low-grade population. Also, as Wolfensberger, Mein, and O'Connor have shown, the lexical repertoire available in institutions is quite small (*111*). The lexical repertoire consists of a *core* vocabulary which is a list of words used by at least 50 per cent of a given population, and a *fringe* vocabulary which is individual. The core vocabulary of an institutional population undoubtedly has a qualitative value which sets the conceptual level for group members. It undoubtedly develops in each institution, and it would be interesting to see what flavors the lexicon of new institutions acquire from the acceptance of their first patient over the next several years. Fringe vocabulary and its size may well have interesting correlates in institutional populations. It may be that the size of *fringe* vocabulary is an empirical measure of integration into communal life. Conceivably, run-aways might be distinguishable in this regard, as might persons who do—and do not—experience successful rehabilitation. Implicit in these observations is the belief that language can be a vital medium for describing mental retardation. As a matter of opinion, the author believes that language can be a data language, *mutatis mutandis,* as accurate and more relevant than the biological terms now so unwisely emphasized in the study of retardation. Language, properly appreciated, is the medium in which future research on retardation can be profitably conducted.

Syndromes

A description of language in retarded children requires one more element, that is an account of the special qualities of language in retarded children who have specific syndromes. In this section we shall consider several of the more relevant syndromes: (1) the deaf retarded and (2) mongoloid children, with a few observations on some of the others.

1. *The deaf retarded.* There are children whose care is complicated by the limited formulations of disability which the helping professions have developed and which structure the services they render both by programming and by the legal precedents they support. Not the least of these is the concept of single disability; it is the idea that one problem in a child—usually one sensory modality—is the responsibility of a discipline. It is, of course, contrary to the reality that children experience regularly, and which the professions encounter regularly. The problem becomes acute when a child has a disability such as retardation and a second disability to an equal degree, for example, a hearing loss. The state of such children is indeed serious because the resultant disturbances of normal development often produce parataxic distortions—disturbances of feeling and perception which can be serious enough to amount to an additional problem, complicating things even

more. For the moment we need consider only the disabilities of retardation and deafness.

In many respects, the issue of deaf, retarded children is without complete structure, even at the point of such simple matters as the scope of the problem. Comparing speech defective retardates with non-speech-defective retardates, Wilson found a twofold incidence of hearing loss in the former (*109*). Eight of 50 special class defectives had hearing losses, an incidence of 16 per cent. Only 14 of 175 comparable children had hearing losses (8 per cent). Kodman and his assistants measured the hearing of 189 persons at the Kentucky State Home (*44*). Incidence of loss, defined as pure-tone threshold of thirty decibels of one or more frequencies between 250-8,000 c. p. s., was about 19 per cent in the younger patients and 24 per cent in the older patients. The incidence for all patients was 21.43 per cent. The evidence shows that hearing loss can have immediate significance for the linguistic development of retarded children. Keeping in mind the corpus of evidence previously introduced in this chapter on the linguistic consequences of retardation, the addition of the loss of hearing becomes even more significant. In general, hearing loss in the retarded becomes worse as the severity of the condition increases. The reason is not necessarily an increment in the damage to the cochlea and its nerve endings but the persistent problem of interpreting the impulses which reach the mind. According to Abernathy, who attempted measurement of hearing, mildly retarded persons responded to pure tones better than moderate and severely retarded persons. Only one person in three at the intellectual level IQ 20-29 responded to pure tones (*1*). A part of this finding might be attributed to the alien quality of the stimulus, but the unresponsiveness is an observed fact: the severely retarded are not usually as responsive to auditory stimuli as brighter persons.

Other studies tend to describe the incidence of hearing loss in the retarded as higher than usual. The author has examined a number of studies including McPherson's questionnaire investigation which gives about the highest figure on incidence of hearing loss in the retarded, around 50 per cent (*57*). Other estimates are all quite high; Birch and Mathews gave an incidence of 50 per cent, and contributed an additional finding in their account of two hundred and forty-seven persons from ten to thirty-nine years of age; they reported disabling loss in 32.7 per cent of their cases (*10*).

In addition to studies in retarded populations, there have been studies in deaf populations. Perhaps the best description of the status of retarded deaf children has come from Frisina (*24*). He described the abilities of 82 children in a population of 891 residents of several schools for the deaf, an incidence of 9.2 per cent in a population classed primarily as auditorily handicapped. He found that this group of children, with an average mental age of eight and a life age of thirteen to fourteen, had several distinctive attributes. From a battery of tests, he concluded that the children used vision in a manner that he considered evidence of compensation for their auditory limitations. Concrete situations enabled them to perform best, he felt, and the double restriction of hearing and intellectual problems did not restrict their functioning to a homogenous style. The audiometric profiles of the children were typically symmetric, going from a 60 decibel loss at 125 c. p. s. to 95 db at 1,000 c. p. s. The mean reading level of the children was two and a half years; it is higher than might be expected; academic retardation averaged almost six years. This finding may be interpreted by recalling that schools for the deaf usually stress reading more than other educational enterprises, which feel that reading should develop only after language attainment is fairly good. Schools for the deaf frequently stress early reading by the analytic method in order to build a basis for broader language developments. There is a curious contradiction here since for reasons of linguistic immaturity reading is sometimes delayed in programs for retarded children. Given the case of deaf and retarded children in a program centered around intellectual deficit, it is not likely that a program stressing language in the form of reading achievement would help as much as a program built around auditory deficit. Presumably, optimal programming for children will one day broadly recognize the insularity of single, disability planning which now seems to afflict us. When that time comes it will be because the broad issues of diagnosis discussed in Chapter 6 have been translated into realistic programming and because personnel will be equipped to work on more than one disease and within more than one modality.

2. *Mongoloid children.* Mongolism remains one of the great perplexities of mental retardation in the sense that its origins are now open to inspection through the innovations of chromosomal count. In many ways the progress is less than commonly supposed; more information can lead to more unanswered questions. Generally speaking, we have not been given a microscope through which to view mongolism in recent years; rather, we have been given a kaleidoscope, a device in which objects may be viewed, but only at the price of appreciating their complexity.

Mongolism remains an ambiguity because of something else. Its existence in the domain of clinical medicine is beyond dispute, but once one leaves that currently productive line of inquiry the syndrome becomes less substantial. A syndrome exists because it is a meaningful configuration in the data language of a discipline. Medicine has a data language, an amalgam of etiological and biochemical facts synthesized through the language of clinical practice into the form of consistent description. It does not follow that a syndrome in one data language has reality in another, e.g., the descriptive and analytic terminology of linguistics, or the emerging data language of descriptive behaviorism. On a day by day basis, this detached observation is clouded by the fact that mongoloid children *look* mongoloid. More fundamentally, the breadth of the clinical syndrome, mongolism, depends on more than appearance; i.e., the term has broad relevance only if the children have a consistent syndrome in a data language when we do not look at their faces, and the almost irrelevant configuration of their features. For the term to be broadly rather than narrowly significant, mongoloid children should function linguistically, academically, and socially in a consistent way. In this discussion we shall consider the linguistic aspects of mongolism. The intent is to provide descriptive statements, but in doing this we may shed light on the larger conceptual issue just raised.

Incidence is an obvious starting point, and both experience and research lead to the conclusion that there is a close relationship between Down's disease and the probability of language disorders. Schlanger and Gottsleben found mongoloids most likely to have language disorders, while familial cases of mental retardation were least likely to be linguistically handicapped (88). According to Blanchard, the incidence of deviant language patterns in mongoloid children at Pacific State Hospital is 100 per cent (11). Fifty of sixty-three mongoloid patients had defective articulation while the remaining thirteen had other language disorders. The nature of non-articulatory disorders in children with mongolism or Down's syndrome is interesting. Stuttering seems to be more commonly encountered in the syndrome than in cases of other syndromes and familial defectives. Gottsleben found twelve stutterers among thirty-six cases of mongolism (12/36) which is more than twice the incidence he found in a comparable group of non-mongoloid children (5/36) (30). Figures on a larger population given by Schlanger and Gottsleben show an equally disproportionate number of mongoloid stutterers (45 per cent), with the next largest proportion within the cases of organicity (18 per cent), and the least proportion (10 per cent) within the cases of familial deficiency (88). Just why there should be this interesting relationship is hard to grasp. The probability of the deviant physical structure being a direct cause is not easy to accept. The search for physical correlates of stuttering has long since proved fruitless. It may be that the appearance of mongoloid children—that otherwise irrelevant trait—leads to differential treatment, and that the problem arises in children *secondarily* to their biological deviations and *primarily* to the interpersonal problems their appearances may precipitate. This is only a suspicion, but the reality of deviant patterns of verbal interaction could be assessed using the dyadic model of retardation as a small-group phenomenon alluded to earlier in Chapter 2 and in the work of Siegel (*90*), and Siegel and Harkins (*91*).

Voice is generally included in considerations of language in mongolism (*33, 76, 101*). Quality is often described as poor, though not universally so. Pitch is also commonly referred to, and in specific instances it is found to be lower than we might expect (*101*). On the other hand, no generalization of lower pitch is defensible in light of Michel and Carney's analysis at the Parsons State Hospital and Training Center (*65*). They found the mean pitch of eight mongoloid males to be, in their phrase, "essentially normal," despite other tendencies to be more like younger boys in development. In this regard pitch in the mongoloid is like pitch in other retarded persons, that is, normal (*20*).

Other aspects of language may be mentioned. It follows that mongoloid children are slow to begin the skills which mark the normal process of growth towards maturity. First words come late in mongoloid children according to Strazzulla; they appeared at 33.4 months in mongoloid children between IQ 40 and 70 (*101*). Phrases appeared at forty-eight months and sentences at sixty months. The content of the sentences, namely the lexical structure of mongoloid language, has been reported by Mein (*62*). Mongoloid members of a group of forty institutionalized persons were matched by sex, CA, and MA with nonmongoloids. There was no difference in the number of different words in samples of language, but the percentage of nouns used while giving descriptions of pictures was higher.

A general comment may now be offered. An incidence of language defects exists in mongoloid persons to a degree higher than that found in non-retarded and in retarded non-mongoloid persons. This incidence incorporates many kinds of linguistic errors, but they are errors found to some extent in other persons who are also retarded. This means that while linguistic problems and mongolism are highly related, the relationship is not unique and does not consist of a configuration peculiar to mongolism and not to other retarded persons. It seems unlikely that we need retain phrases such as *dyslalia mongolia* (*107*) in the terminology of linguistics or retardation; on the other hand we can support the generalization of linguistic defect, varied in phenotypic expression, closely associated with mongolism. In passing, we may note that the same conclusion applies to deviant articulation in cretinism (89) and PKU (18).

3. *Other syndromes.* One of the few possibilities for combatting mental retardation lies in the reduction of damage due to premature birth. The essence of the problem is delivery at a time when survival and normal development can only be assured in symbiosis with the mother. Survival before the optimal time for independent living is possible, but in the case of rather small babies, those below three and a half pounds, it rarely occurs without incurring damage to the nervous system. As recently as thirty years ago about a third of all preemies died (32), and while the figure has dropped, survival has probably been at the expense of the nervous system. Prime symptoms have been mental retardation and language. A form of language disability has been low level of achievement at given developmental ages (21). Sixty-six preemies were evaluated by Kastein and Fowler and only sixteen of them were considered entirely normal (41). The linguistic symptoms presented generally involved clear evidence of organicity, which is commonly related to linguistic disturbance (25), and in some cases there were sensory disorders. In small preemies, studies generally show that academic and social maladjustment are present when the children are older. Other material on prematurity may be found in Chapters 7 and 8 where the findings of Drillien (21), Davis (17), and others are discussed.

Blanchard has related articulation maturity to early accidents of development (11). Within a list of ten etiological factors associated with mental retardation in 297 children at Pacific State Hospital, the three most likely to be followed by deviant language were (1) mongolism, (2) mechanical birth injury, and (3) prenatal infections. Least likely to contribute to language disorders were (1) postnatal infections, (2) postnatal brain injury, and (3) functional retardation. Essentially congruent findings are found in the numerous studies by Schlanger, whose investigations are a prime source of information about language in the mentally retarded (83-88). He classified the residents of the Training School by level of linguistic development (87). His first group consisted of persons using single words and gestures. One out of every four was a case of mongolism, and this same disease category accounted for half of the persons in his second category of incomplete sentences of two or three words. The group with the least linguistic immaturity were familials.

Speech Therapy

Current thought about speech therapy is marked by several distinctive elements. There is, to begin with, a recognition that much of the

previous antipathy to linguistic therapy based on intellectual limitations was unfair to retarded children; it contributed to the severity of
the problem which is, in part, immaturity in the linguistic sphere of
intellectual activity. At the moment, there seems to be more willingness
to begin linguistic stimulation with children. The reasons for the previous antipathy generally given are the limitations of service due to
scarcity of personnel and a general antipathy to retardation as another
discipline's problem. Apart from these, there has probably been another reason, and it is advanced as speculation, not as fact. It is possible that previous antipathy to offering language therapy to retarded
children was based on the meaning retardation has to people in the
helping professions. It is possible that retardation has a meaning to
speech pathology and medicine which is unique, and based on the concept of personal service and amelioration. Both speech pathologists and
physicians base their professional *raison d'etre* on remission of symptoms. Both tend to be frustrated more than persons in other helping
professions when stringent limits to full remission are facts of life. Both
professions tended to withdraw from interest in retardation at one
time, but that trend seems to be reversed, particularly in the case of
speech pathologists.

This is a fine development, and one more seems in order, though less
attainable. It is the development of new roles to develop programming on more imaginative lines. The author has presented information
on this subject elsewhere (*The Exceptional Child*, p. 36) and it is sufficient to point out that language instruction is not currently unified; it
is divided among the helping professions as "teachers" deal with the
written language and "therapists" work with oral language; while there
are exceptions, this split is generally to the detriment of unified programming and the welfare of the children to be served. (For further
discussion of speech therapy in a technical sense, see Chapter 9 where
several therapies applicable to the retarded are presented.)

Research

From time to time scholars have attempted to formulate language on
a basis comparable to its complexity. That is, recognizing that linguistic behavior is more than the picture of a single concept such as TTR
(type/token ratio) or articulation might seem to imply they have attempted to develop comprehensive concepts. Maintaining the tradition
of careful description, people have developed broad empirical procedures to define language. Allusion to measurement is no accident at this
point in the discussion. There is no alternative in serious studies of language to descriptions based on aggregates of measures—procedures we
sometimes describe as scales. Rather than thinking of scales as devices

which yield scores, it is much wiser to think of them as explicit models of linguistic behavior. If one explains the language of children by referring to TTR, phonemic maturity, and rhythm, one says, implicitly, that language consists of those concepts. What one leaves out is, implicitly, not important, unless the discussion is intended to be only a limited consideration.

There have been several scales of language developed in the last decade or so. These and a summary of other measures applied to the language of retarded persons are presented in Table 5·1.

Kolstoe developed an instrument which he used to evaluate the level of development of retarded children (45). His *Observational Rating Scale for Language Ability* consisted of twenty items at five levels of competence, respectively. The lowest level is "crying communicatively," and the highest is using complex sentences. The scale is intended to be applied to oral language—as well as to written materials. Its elements are based on items routinely encountered when dealing with retarded children.

A related scale was developed by Lyle, and called, reasonably, an *Ad Hoc Scale of Verbal Ability* (50). The components were (1) comprehension of words, (2) word naming, (3) definitions of words, (4) speech sounds, (5) complexity of language, (6) verbal intelligence, (7) clarity, and (8) frequency of speech. These were evaluated by a rating procedure. Factor analysis revealed, predictably, a common factor of verbal ability.

Another different scale with many provocative aspects is the *Illinois Test of Psycholinguistic Ability* (43). Essentially, language is formulated as a process with specific empirical aspects which may be described through nine tests labelled (1) auditory decoding, (2) visual decoding, (3) auditory-vocal association, (4) visual-motor association, (5) vocal encoding, (6) motor encoding, (7) auditory-vocal automatic, (8) auditory-vocal sequential, and (9) visual-motor sequential. Persons not familiar with the instrument should examine the papers by McCarthy and Kirk (56), Kirk and McCarthy (43), McCarthy (55), which describe the instrument and give illustrations; Chapter 6, *Psychodiagnostics*, may help also. For the purposes of this chapter, the ITPA is a model of language behavior, and it has the following interesting aspects.

Origins. The scale is deductive; that is, it is the operational form of processes, the locus of which is the central nervous system. The processes themselves were first described by Osgood (73), in his inspired idea of "what goes on in the head." He believes that thought, using verbal symbols, operates in directions and at levels using different representatives of reality. Language for Osgood, Kirk, and McCarthy is the manipulation of symbols within the nervous system, a process which becomes measureable when a person is asked to enter into the execution of tasks in the test situation.

Validity. A question of practical but greater theoretical interest is the matter of validity. Recall that the ITPA is an empirical representation of a deductive model. Normally, tests are inductive in their origin, and may be validated empirically by correlation with a criterion series. The ITPA is provocative because its deductive basis precludes empirical validation. Validity consists of congruence with the theoretical model, the validity of which in the conventional sense of correlations is not really amenable to analysis. The fundamental step is probably validating the Osgood-Kirk-McCarthy model. In all probability, that step will be accomplished by the procedure appropriate for theoretical-deductive models—comprehensiveness. That is, one asks if there are data—linguistic events—which the model does not handle. Validation is replaced by comprehensiveness, and the limitations of the model are remedied by extending it. Operationally, new tests are devised and added to the battery. The reason for discussing the matter in detail is a wish to show that empirical formulations of language are not simple-minded concepts based on enumeration, but concepts whose manipulation requires rather serious study if they are to be fully appreciated.

By an interesting coincidence, we may have empirical validity by analogy, if you please, for the Osgood model, in an inductive, client-centered model of language. Wepman has extensive clinical experience with persons handicapped by aphasia, the symbolic limitation of language due to brain injury, and the absence of damage to the organs of speech. Wepman has proposed a model of language in aphasic persons which is extremely close to the Osgood model (73). Based as it is on clinical experience, Wepman's model of language processes has inductive validity of a compelling order. Being a representation of observable processes, its constructural value is immense.

For this discussion, it is relevant to indicate that the Osgood model (deductive) is surprisingly close to the Wepman model (inductive). At the risk of being misunderstood, it seems appropriate to observe that validity by analogy may give the Osgood model the respectability the Wepman model commands by induction. Both representations of language are intellectual contributions of the first order. We may expect to see study of language in the retarded advanced considerably in the future as the Wepman and Osgood ideas are disseminated through the Kirk-McCarthy test and through Wepman's writings.

Lassers and Low developed an instrument to evaluate the effectiveness of speech training with retarded children (46). *The San Francisco Inventory of Communicative Effectiveness* (*SFICE*) has two parts. The *Communicative Attributes Rating Scale* is applied to evaluate speech in a situation which stresses communication. The following qualities are examined: (1) immediacy, (2) frequency, (3) enthusiasm, (4) involvement, (5) ease of social relationships. These measures of *communicative relationships* are followed by evaluation of quality of communicative behavior; the following properties are employed: (1) understandability, (2) articulation, (3) length of response, (4) appropriateness, (5) complexity of ideation. An additional overall rating not based on the two sub-measures is obtained. *Verbal Output Scale* is the second major part of the SFICE. It consists of measures of (1) response length (words per response), (2) sentence complexity, (3) grammatical complexity. Because of the obvious psychometric problems, the SFICE is applied to a corpus of language preserved on a tape recording.

The *Parsons Language Sample* (*PLS*) is a rather different scale (98). There are two major parts to the instrument; the first is the (I) *vocal* section. It is composed of a (1) *tact* subtest of picture and object naming, (2) an *echoic* subtest of ability to repeat sentences, and (3) *an intraverbal gesture,* consisting of responses to questions exemplified by "where is your ear?" The reader will recognize some of the terms as those introduced earlier in the chapter when Skinner's work, *Verbal Behavior,* was mentioned. The PLS was developed by Spradlin at the Parsons State School in Kansas using Skinner's wholly descriptive work as a model. The PLS is valid because it analytically and discriminately describes retarded persons whose linguistic behavior can be discriminated by institutional workers (98), (114).

Of lesser scope but of no less interest have been the discrete measures which are listed in Table 5·1. Grouped by category they represent formulations of language as it appears to empiricists. Perhaps the most attention has been paid to oral language, with vocabulary receiving the next higher amount of consideration. Structure of language in the retarded has probably been studied least. A paradigm for such work can be found in Strickland's study of language in elementary school children (102). As a program of studies, Strickland's work illustrates the breadth of goals one must maintain if accounts of language are to be comprehensive.

In addition to seeing description and research advanced by the development of new information and new tools of measurement, we may expect to see old stumbling blocks re-erected. If (as we shall see in the

Functional Therapy section of Chapter 9), levels of psycholinguistic functioning in retarded persons can be advanced, then we may have to endure one more acrimonious debate about "incurability" and making retarded children "normal." When that nexus of problems was debated between 1945 and 1950, a great deal of oversimplification and premature generalization about retardation was indulged in. Presentation of detached studies on increments of psycholinguistic growth may be expected to increase. At that time we may hope that more general sophistication concerning language will eliminate the more unprofitable lines of debate.

Leads. Some aspects of language in retarded children have received little or no attention, and our knowledge of them is correspondingly restricted to either guarded statements or generalizations based on clinical judgment, with all the attendant contingencies. We know very little about the way retarded children, and indeed normal children, learn the rules by which word endings and verb forms are changed. In addition to acquiring the rules of morphology, children also learn when to break them. For example, a typical three-year-old who believes that the opposite of *nowhere* is *yeswhere* has learned a logical but functionally incorrect way of handling parts of words. That *somewhere* is the correct answer is remarkable, and that children learn to cope with this oddity is even more so. Clearly, retarded children learn to follow the rules; sometimes they do it by reason, sometimes by stereotype. It would be helpful if we could analyze this process with a view to facilitating its acquisition by retarded children. The simple step of applying Berko's procedures would be informative (7).

Another group of ideas we could profitably apply to the study of language in the retarded is that which comes from study of communication processes. *Mazes* are assemblies of words that have no meaning; *communication value* describes the portion of a corpus of language which conveys meaning. Ideas from communication theory have been connected with sociometry by Rosenthal (82); he has shown that isolate status depresses verbal functioning. Undoubtedly, the permutations of this notion which relates to the social position of retarded persons vis-à-vis normals and other retarded individuals are endless. It may be that the sociometric studies mentioned in Chapter 4 are open to fuller explanation by adding communication concepts to sociometric descriptions. Recalling the dyadic studies of Siegel (90), Siegel and Harkins (91) may point the way to further explanations of how intelligence, group membership, language, and sociometric positions are related.

TABLE 5·1

REPRESENTATIVE STUDIES OF LANGUAGE IN THE RETARDED

Factor	Subjects	Investigation
(oral language)		
etiology	350 institutional SS, IQ 27-68	Blanchard (11)
articulation—general	50 institutional SS, IQ 50-70	Daum (16)
articulation—general	52 community & institutional SS	Masket (58)
articulation—consonants	297 institutional SS, IQ 27-60	Blanchard (11)
clarity of speech	32 institutional SS, IQ 20-50	Lyle (52)
voice	249 institutional SS, IQ 21-69	Kennedy (42)
verbal behavior—contingent	42 retarded males	Siegel & Harkins (91)
comprehension of speech	66 premature children	Kastein & Fowler (41)
first-word	40 mongoloid children	Strazzulla (101)
intelligibility of speech	102 educable cerebral palsied SS	Vaughn (106)
phonemes	10 seriously retarded SS	Irwin (34)
semantic conditioning	30 institutional SS, IQ 30-50	O'Connor & Hermelin (70)
stuttering	36 mongoloid children, IQ 20-52	Gottsleben (30)
vocal development	8 mute retarded SS	Goda (27)
number of words	108 educable SS, IQ 45-85	Batza (5)
(organic elements)		
hypha	15 institutional SS	Meader (60)
diadochokinesis	74 institutional SS	Schlanger (83)
diadochokinesis-varied	102 educable cerebral palsied SS	Vaughn (106)
pitch	8 mongoloid SS	Michel & Carney (65)
auditory memory	21 retarded SS, IQ 41-75	Mecham (61)
karotype	sibship of 7	Moorhead, Mellman & Wenar (66)
(scales)		
San Francisco Inventory of Communicative Effectiveness	90 retarded SS, IQ 40-79	Lassers & Low (46)
Differential Language Facility	148 retarded SS	Sievers & Essa (93)

Measure	Sample	Reference
Speech-Age Scale	25 severely retarded SS	Bell (6)
ad hoc Scale of Development	32 institutional SS	Lyle (50)
Observational Rating Scale for Language Ability	30 mongoloid SS, IQ 16-36	Kolstoe (45)
Illinois T. of Psycho-Linguistic Ability	32 educable SS	Smith (96)
(structure)		
Structural variety	106 adolescent SS	Goda & Griffith (28)
sentence length	21 retarded SS, IQ 41-75	Mecham (61)
verbosity	80 institutional SS, IQ 18-49	Wolfensberger, Mein & O'Connor (111)
grammatical errors	133 retarded SS	Carlton & Carlton (13, 14)
divergent responses	71 educable SS	Tisdall (105)
story length	89 special & non-special class SS	Jordan & deCharms (38)
mean length of response	40 retarded girls	Siegel (90)
verbal items of Minnesota Preschool Scale	194 retarded SS, IQ 20-50	Lyle (49)
mean sentence length	74 institutional SS, < IQ 40	Schlanger (84)
lexical variety	108 retarded SS, IQ 45-85	Batza (5)
(vocabulary)		
level of abstraction	60 institutional SS, IQ 50-75	Badt (3)
mode of definition	38 brain injured & non-brain injured	Bijou & Werner (9)
mode of definition	50 institutional SS, IQ 60-75	Papania (75)
abstraction	26 retarded male SS, IQ 48-66	Griffith & Spitz (31)
vocabulary size	80 severely retarded SS	Mein & O'Connor (63)
lexical change	40 severely retarded SS	Mein (62)
concreteness	49 educable SS	Ohlsen (71)
type/token ratio	80 institutional SS, IQ 18-49	Wolfensberger, Mein, & O'Connor (111)
core & fringe vocabulary	80 institutional SS, IQ 18-49	Wolfensberger, Mein, & O'Connor (111)
word naming	16 institutional SS, IQ 25-50	Lyle (52)

One more possible line of inquiry is the syntax of language in the retarded, with a view to identifying discrete patterns. Currently, we have descriptions of retardation by physical characteristics, such as the accounts of mongolism, PKU, and so forth. It is possible that there may be discrete patterns of syntax, configurations of language that are exclusive and constitute the linguistic equivalent of descriptions now being developed by biochemical studies of retardation. It may be that proportions of classes of words constitute syntactic patterns. For example, as a function of mental age, etiology, locus of malfunction (e.g., brain-injury), and degree of severity, retarded children may use more or fewer adverbs as they attempt to convey action through the abstract process of language. They may employ more non-communicative elements in their syntax, words which have no meaning in the act of conveying thought. Examples of this are "um's" and "oh's" and words which are false starts to sentences. Entire phrases are sometimes used by people and then abandoned as thought goes off in a different direction. This is the nonsense portion of syntax and it may have a unique lexicon in various behavior patterns.

In closing, it is well to recall the number of issues that language presents even when not applied to a given category of human beings. Directed to the analysis of the mentally retarded, language becomes more complex because the retarded use it in ways that are distinctive, if not unique. As a final point it is appropriate to reiterate the value that language can have as a medium for exploring the problems of mental retardation.

Several aspects of this chapter may be indicated in order to summarize the main points. First of all, it will be recalled that an interest in language is expression of a point of view intimately associated with the earliest scientific study of retardation by Binet and Simon. Language is both a sub-problem of retardation and a matrix within which retardation may be formulated as a topic for serious study. Retarded children acquire language in ways we do not yet fully understand, although we know some of the external factors whose presence advances and retards its acquisition. Over the years we have gathered descriptions of language in retarded children, and over the past two decades we have done even more. In particular, the last decade has produced a great deal of work, and a number of innovations have appeared. These have been studies of syntax, studies of institutional living, and studies of psycholinguistic behavior. We may hope that the energies now at a new peak of application will continue. Ideally, they should be applied to the propositions about the dynamic forms and processes of language.

Perhaps the biggest threat to future development is the chance of misapplication of novel scales of measurement. In particular, psycholinguistic scales in many ways put us at the cross roads we misread fifty years ago. The work of Kirk and McCarthy seems to the author similar in its dilemmas to the work of Binet and Simon. That is, both contributions are innovations of high intellectual merit, both are provocative spurs to creative research, and both are easy to misperceive as mere technological contributions to measurement.

The onus of responsibility for fruitful application of psycholinguistic measurement will change in the future. If psycholinguistic measurement is used in an enlightened way, that is as a tool to which thought gives significance and purpose, we may expect to see striking developments in the study of language in retarded persons. Such positive development will be favored if current training in mental retardation is rigorous and enlightened, that is, if it is conducted by persons who are themselves active in the study of language, people who see the act of raising fruitful questions more exciting than conveying answers. Conversely, study of language will become sterile if psycholinguistic measurement loses identity as dynamic creative scholarship. Such a hazard exists, in the author's opinion, because people may manipulate psycholinguistic tools as though they were thermometers, to repeat an idiom, and confuse the patients' temperature with his illness. Future study of language can be exciting if we maintain the standard of excellence that has been established by the innovators of psycholinguistic research.

SUMMARY

The study of retardation is aided, and also complicated, by language. This functional aspect of human behavior develops under normal circumstances at a fairly predictable rate. When an exception arises, as in the case of the retarded child, the explanations for the deviation are usually inadequate. This is because explanations for linguistic growth are usually incomplete under the best of circumstances. There are many negative influences on language. Some of them emerge from the behavioral aspects of retardation, while others arise from the pattern of values and attitudes demonstrated by parents. In Chapter 5 we have looked at a number of specific issues and have seen that the incidence of language disorders varies. We have looked at the nature of articulation problems and considered the quantity and quality of vocabulary in specific syndromes. Speech problems tend to be responsive to attempts at therapy, and there is currently more optimism about speech therapy than we have known in the past. Over the last several years, there has been more growth in the language aspects of retardation than in any other comparable period.

BIBLIOGRAPHY

1. Abernathy, E. A., "The Auditory Acuity of Feebleminded Children," unpublished dissertation, Ohio State University, 1938.

2. Abt, I. A., Adler, H. M., and Bartelme, P., "The Relationship Between the Onset of Speech and Intelligence," *J. Amer. Med. Assoc.*, 1929, *93*, 1351-1355.

3. Badt, M. I., "Levels of Abstraction in Vocabulary Definitions of Mentally Retarded School Children," *Amer. J. Ment. Def.*, 1958, *63*, 241-246.

4. Bangs, J. L., "A Clinical Analysis of the Articulatory Defects of the Feebleminded," *J. Speech Dis.*, 1942, *7*, 343-356.

5. Batza, E. M., "Investigation of the Speech and Oral Language Behavior of Educable Mentally Retarded Children," unpublished dissertation, Northwestern University, 1956.

6. Bell, D. M., "Method of Teaching Speech and Language to the Severely Mentally Retarded Child," unpublished dissertation, University of Denver, 1958.

7. Berko, J., "The Child's Learning of English Morphology," *Word*, 1958, *14*, 150-177.

8. Binet, A., and Simon, Th., *Mentally Defective Children*, Longmans, Green, 1914.

9. Bijou, S. W., and Werner, H., "Language Analysis in Brain-Injured and Non-Brain Injured Mentally Deficient Children," *J. Genet. Psychol.*, 1945, *66*, 239-254.

10. Birch, J. W., and Mathews, J., "The Hearing of Mental Defectives; Its Measurement and Characteristics," *Amer. J. Ment. Def.*, 1951, *55*, 384-393.

11. Blanchard, I., "Speech Pattern and Etiology in Mental Retardation," *Amer. J. Ment. Def.*, 1964, *68*, 612-617.

12. Boder, D. P., "The Adjective-Verb Quotient: A Contribution to the Psychology of Language," *Psych. Rec.* 1940, *3*, 310-343.

13. Carlton, T., and Carlton, L. E., "Oral English Errors of Normal Children and of Mental Defectives," *Elem. Schl. J.*, 1945, *45*, 340-348.

14. ———, "Errors in the Oral Language of Mentally Defective Adolescents and Normal Elementary Children," *J. Genet. Psych.*, 1945, *56*, 183-220.

15. Carroll, J. B., "Language Development," *Encyclopedia of Educational Research*, 3rd ed., 1960.

16. Daum, M. P., "A Study of the Articulation of a Group of Fifty Institutionalized Children with Intelligent Quotients Between Fifty and Seventy," unpublished thesis, Kent State University, 1953.

17. Davis, D. C., "Comparative Study of the Growth and Development of Premature and Full Term Children with Special Reference to Oral Communication," unpublished dissertation, Northwestern University, 1951.

18. Diedrich, W. M., and Poser, C. M., "Language and Mentation of Two Phenylketonuric Children," *J. Sp. Hear. Dis.*, 1960, 25, 124-135.

19. Donovan, H., "Organization and Development of a Speech Program for the Mentally Retarded Children in the New York City Public Schools," *Amer. J. Ment. Defic.*, 1957, 62, 455-459.

20. Drexler, A. B., "An Investigation of Pitch, Sound Pressure Level, and Rate in Institutionalized Mentally Retarded Adults," unpublished Ph.D. dissertation, Purdue University, 1958, Cited by Rigrodsky, S. (81).

21. Drillien, C. M., "A Longitudinal Study of the Growth and Development of Prematurely and Maturely Born Children: Part III, Mental Development," *Arch. Dis. Childhd.*, 1959, 34, 37-45.

22. Fairbanks, H., "The Quantitative Differentiation of Samples of Spoken Language," *Psych. Mon.*, 1944, 56, 19-38.

23. Feifel, H., "Qualitative Differences in the Vocabulary Responses of Normals and Abnormals," *Genet. Psych. Mon.*, 1949, 39, 151-204.

24. Frisina, D. R., "Psychological Study of the Mentally Retarded Deaf Child," unpublished dissertation, Northwestern University, 1955.

25. Gens, G. W., "Correlation of Neurological Findings, Psychological Analyses and Speech Disorders among Institutionalized Epileptics," *Train Schl. Bull.*, 1950, 47, 3-18.

26. _____, "The Speech Pathologist Looks at the Mentally Deficient Child," *Train Schl. Bull.*, 1951, 48, 19-27.

27. Goda, S., "Vocal Utterances of Young Moderately and Severely Retarded Non-Speaking Children," *Amer. J. Ment. Def.*, 1960, 65, 269-273.

28. _____, and Griffith, B. C., "The Spoken Language of Adolescent Retardates and Its Relation to Intelligence, Age, and Anxiety," *Child Devpm.*, 1962, 33, 489-498.

29. Goodwin, F. G., "A Consideration of Etiologies in 454 Cases of Speech Retardation," *J. Sp. Hear. Res.*, 1955, 3, 300-303.

30. Gottsleben, R. H., "The Incidence of Stuttering in a Group of Mongoloids," *Train. Schl. Bull.*, 1955, 51, 209-217.

31. Griffith, B. C., and Spitz, H., "Some Relationships Between Abstraction and Word Meaning in Retarded Adolescents," *Amer. J. Ment. Def.*, 1958, *63*, 247-251.

32. Hess, J. H., Mohr, G. J., and Bartelme, P. F., *The Physical and Mental Growth of Prematurely Born Children*, U. of Chicago Press, 1934.

33. Hotchkiss, F. C., "A Suggested Therapy Program to Improve the Communicative Ability of the Mongoloid Child Based on a Review of the Literature," unpublished thesis, Southern Connecticut State College, 1960.

34. Irwin, O. C., "The Developmental Status of Speech Sounds of Ten Feeble Minded Children," *Child Devpm.*, 1942, *13*, 29-39.

35. Irwin, O. C., "Speech Development in the Young Child: 2. Some Factors Related to the Speech Development of the Infant and Young Child," *J. Sp. Hear. Dis.*, 1952, *17*, 269-279.

36. Jones, L. V., Goodman, M. F., and Wepman, J. M., "The Classification of Parts of Speech for the Characterization of Aphasia," *Lang. Speech*, 1963, *6*, 94-107.

37. Jordan, T. E., "Early Developmental Adversity and Classroom Learning: A Prospective Inquiry," *Amer. J. Ment. Def.*, 1964, *69*, 360-371.

38. ———, and deCharms, R., "The Achievement Motive in Normal and Retarded Children," *Amer. J. Ment. Def.*, 1959, *64*, 457-466.

39. Karlin, I. W., and Kennedy, L., "Delay in the Development of Speech," *Amer. J. Dis. Child.*, 1936, *51*, 1138-1149.

40. ———, and Strazzulla, M., "Speech and Language Problems of Mentally Deficient Children," *J. Speech Hear. Dis.*, 1952, *17*, 286-294.

41. Kastein, S., and Fowler, E., "Language Development Among Survivors of Premature Birth," *A. M. A. Arch. Otolaryng.*, 1959, *69*, 131-135.

42. Kennedy, L., "Studies in the Speech of the Feebleminded," unpublished dissertation, University of Wisconsin, 1930.

43. Kirk, S. A., and McCarthy, J. J., "The Illinois Test of Psycholinguistic Abilities—An Approach to Differential Diagnosis," *Amer. J. Ment. Def.*, 1961, *66*, 399-412.

44. Kodman, F., et al., "The Incidence of Hearing Loss in Mentally Retarded Children," *Amer. J. Ment. Def.*, 1958, *63*, 460-463.

45. Kolstoe, O. P., "Language Training of Low-Grade Mongoloid Children," *Amer. J. Ment. Def.*, 1958, *63*, 17-30.

46. Lassers L., and Low, G., "A Study of the Relative Effectiveness of Different Approaches of Speech Therapy for Mentally Retarded Children," Final Report, U. S. Office of Education, Cooperative Research Program, 1960.

47. Lewald, J., "Speech Defects as Found in a Group of Five Hundred Mental Defectives," *Proc. Amer. Assoc. Study Feebleminded,* 1932, 56.

48. Lubman, C., "Speech Program for Severely Retarded Children," *Amer. J. Ment. Def.,* 1955, *60,* 297-300.

49. Lyle, J. G., "The Effect of an Institution Environment Upon the Verbal Development of Imbecile Children: I. Verbal Intelligence," *J. Ment. Def. Res.,* 1959, *3,* 122-128.

50. _____, "The Effect of an Institution Environment Upon the Verbal Development of Imbecile Children: II. Speech & Language," *J. Ment. Def. Res.,* 1959, *4,* 1-13.

51. _____, "The Effect of an Institution Environment Upon the Verbal Development of Imbecile Children: III. The Brooklands Residential Family Unit," *J. Ment. Def. Res.,* 1960, *4,* 14-23.

52. _____, "Some Factors Affecting the Speech Development of Imbecile Children in an Institution," *J. Child. Psychol. Psychiat.,* 1960, *2,* 121-129.

53. McCarthy, D., *Language Development of the Preschool Child,* University of Minnesota Press, 1930.

54. _____, "Language Development in Children," in Carmichael, L. (ed.), *A Manual of Child Psychology,* Wiley, 1954.

55. McCarthy, J. J. (ed.), *Selected Studies on the Illinois Test of Psycholinguistic Abilities,* University of Wisconsin, 1963.

56. _____, and Kirk, S. A., *The Construction, Standardization, and Statistical Characteristics of the Illinois Test of Psycholinguistic Abilities,* University of Wisconsin, 1963.

57. McPherson, J. R., "The Status of the Deaf and/or Hard of Hearing Mentally Deficient in the United States," *Amer. Ann. Deaf.,* 1952, *97,* 375-386, passim, 448-449.

58. Masket, L. J., "A Comparative Study of Articulation Problems of Non-Institutionalized and Institutionalized Mentally Retarded Children," unpublished thesis, University of Maryland, 1958.

59. Mathews, J., "Speech Problems of the Mentally Retarded," in Travis, R. (ed.), *Handbook of Speech Pathology,* Appleton-Century-Crofts, 1957.

60. Meader, M. H., "The Effect of Disturbances in the Developmental Processes Upon Emergent Specificity of Function," *J. Sp. Dis.,* 1940, *5,* 211-220.

61. Mecham, M. J., "The Development and Application of Procedures for Measuring Speech Improvement in Mentally Defective Children," *Amer. J. Ment. Def.,* 1955, *60,* 301-306.

62. Mein, R., "A Study of the Oral Vocabularies of Severely Subnormal Patients: II. Grammatical Analysis of Speech Samples," *J. Ment. Def. Res.*, 1961, *5*, 52-62.

63. _____, and O'Connor, N., "A Study of the Oral Vocabularies of Severely Subnormal Patients," *J. Ment. Def. Res.*, 1960, *4*, 130-143.

64. Metraux, R., "Speech Profiles of the Pre-School Child 18-54 Months," *J. Sp. Hear. Dis.*, 1950, *15*, 37-53.

65. Michel, J., and Carney, R., "Pitch Characteristics of Mongoloid Boys," *J. Sp. and Hear. Dis.*, 1964, *29*, 121-125.

66. Moorhead, P. S., Mellman, W. J., and Wenar, C., "A Familial Chromosome Translocation Associated with Speech and Mental Retardation," *Amer. J. Hum. Genet.*, 1961, *13*, 32-46.

67. Mowrer, O. H., "Hearing and Speaking: An Analysis of Language Learning," *J. Speech Hear. Dis.*, 1958, *23*, 143-152.

68. Myklebust, H. R., "Babbling and Echolalia in Language Theory," *J. Sp. Hear. Dis.*, 1957, *22*, 256-360.

69. Nice, M. M., "Length of Sentences as a Criterion of a Child's Progress in Speech," *J. Educ. Psych.*, 1925, *16*, 370-379.

70. O'Connor, N., and Hermelin, B., "Some Effects of Word Learning in Imbeciles," *Lang. Speech*, 1959, *2*, 63-71.

71. Ohlsen, R. H., "The Effects of Concretion and Abstraction on Vocabulary Performance of Mentally Retarded, Average, and Bright Children," unpublished dissertation, University of Kansas, 1963.

72. Osgood, C. E., "A Behavioristic Analysis of Perception and Language as Cognitive Phenomena," in *Contemporary Approaches to Cognition: The Colorado Symposium*, Harvard University Press, 1957.

73. _____, and Miron, M. S. (eds.), *Approaches to the Study of Aphasia*, University of Illinois Press, 1963.

74. _____, Suci, G. J., and Tannenbaum, P. H., *The Measurement of Meaning*, University of Illinois Press, 1957.

75. Papania, N. A., "Qualitative Analysis of Vocabulary Responses of Institutionalized Mentally Retarded Children," *J. Clin. Psychol.*, 1954, *10*, 361-365.

76. Penwill, M., "Speech Disorders and Therapy in Mental Deficiency," in Clarke, A., and Clarke, A. D. B. (eds.), *Mental Deficiency: The Changing Outlook*, London, Methuen, 1958.

77. Piaget, J., *Language and Thought in the Child*, Meridian Books, 1950.

78. Poole, I., "Genetic Development of Articulation of Consonant Sounds in Speech," *Elem. Engl. Rev.*, 1934, II, 159-161.

79. Rapaport, D., *Organization and Pathology of Thought*, Columbia University Press, 1951.

80. Riello, A., "Articulatory Proficiency of the Mentally Retarded Child.," unpublished Ph.D. dissertation, New York University, 1958.

81. Rigrodsky, S., "Application of Mowrer's Autistic Theory to the Speech Habilitation of Mentally Retarded Pupils," unpublished dissertation, Purdue University, 1959.

82. Rosenthal, F., "Sociometric Position and Language Structure," *J. Educ. Psych.*, 1957, *48*, 483-497.

83. Schlanger, B. B., "Speech Examination of a Group of Institutionalized Mentally Handicapped Children," *J. Sp. Hear. Dis.*, 1953, *18*, 339-349.

84. ———, "Speech Measurements of Institutionalized Mentally Handicapped Children," *Amer. J. Ment. Def.*, 1953, *58*, 114-122.

85. ——— "Speech Therapy Results with Mentally Retarded Children in Special Classes," *Train. Sch. Bull.*, 1953, *50*, 179-186.

86. ———, "Environmental Influences on the Verbal Output of Mentally Retarded Children," *J. Speech Hear. Dis.*, 1954, *19*, 339-343.

87. ———, "Oral Language Classification of the Training School Residents," *Train. Sch. Bull.*, 1957, *53*, 243-247.

88. ———, and Gottsleben, R. H., "Analysis of Speech Defects among the Institutionalized Mentally Retarded," *J. Sp. Hear. Dis.*, 1957, *54*, 5-8.

89. Schreiber, S. L., Bronstein, I. P., and Brown, A. W., "Speech Studies in Cretins: Speech Sounds," *J. Nerv. Ment. Dis.*, 1940, *92*, 169-192.

90. Siegel, G. M., "Verbal Behavior of Retarded Children Assembled with Pre-Instructed Adults," in Schiefelbusch, R. (ed.), "Language Studies of Mentally Retarded Children," *J. Sp. Hear. Dis. Mon. Suppl.*, No. 10, 1963.

91. Siegel, G. M., and Harkins, J. P., "Verbal Behavior of Adults in Two Conditions with Institutionalized Retarded Children," in Schiefelbusch, R. (ed.), "Language Studies of Mentally Retarded Children," *J. Sp. Hear. Dis. Mon. Suppl.*, No. 10, 1963.

92. Siertsema, B., "Language Learning and Language Analysis," *Lingua*, 1961, *10*, 128-147.

93. Sievers, D., and Essa, S. H., "Language Development in Institutionalized and Community Mentally Retarded Children," *Amer. J. Ment. Def.*, 1961, *66*, 413-420.

94. Sirkin, J., and Lyons, W. F., "A Study of Speech Defects in Mental Deficiency," *Amer. J. Ment. Def.*, 1941, *46*, 74-80.

95. Skinner, B. F., *Verbal Behavior*, Appleton-Century-Crofts, 1957.

96. Smith, J. O., "Group Language Development for Educable Mental Retardates," *Excep. Child.*, 1962, *29*, 95-101.

97. Smith, M. E., "A Study of Some Factors Influencing the Development of the Sentence in Preschool Children," *J. Genet. Psych.*, 1935, *46*, 182-212.

98. Spradlin, J. E., "Language and Communication of Mental Defectives," in Ellis, N. (ed.), *Handbook of Mental Deficiency*, McGraw-Hill, 1963.

99. Spriestersbach, D. C., Darley, F. L., and Morris, H. L., "Language Skills in Children with Cleft Palates," *J. Sp. Hear. Res.*, 1958, *1*, 279-285.

100. Steinman, J., Grossman, C., and Reece, R. E., "An Analysis of the Articulation of the Educable Mentally Retarded Child," *ASHA*, 1963, *5*, 791.

101. Strazzulla, M., "Speech Problems of the Mongoloid Child," *Quart. Rev. Pediat.*, 1953, *8*, 268-273.

102. Strickland, R. G., "The Language of Elementary School Children: Its Relationship to the Language of Reading Textbooks and the Quality of Reading of Selected Children," *Bull. Schl. Educ.*, Indiana University, 1962, *38*, No. 4.

103. Tarjan, G., *et al*, "Natural History of Mental Deficiency in a State Hospital: III. Selected Characteristics of First Admissions and Their Environments," *Amer. J. Dis. Child.*, 1961, *101*, 195-205.

104. Templin, M. C., *Certain Language Skills in Children: Their Development and Interrelationships*, University of Minnesota Press, 1957.

105. Tisdall, W. J., "The Efficacy of a Special Class Program on the Productive Thinking Abilities of Educable Mentally Retarded Children," unpublished dissertation, University of Illinois, 1962.

106. Vaughn, A. O., "A Study of the Speech Understandability of 102 Educable Cerebral Palsied Adults and the Relationship Between Speech Understandability and Type of Cerebral Palsy, Sex, Articulation Ability, and Certain Motor Abilities," unpublished thesis, Florida State University, 1958.

107. Voelker, C. H., "Amelioriation of Dyslogia Mongolia," *J. Abnorm. Soc. Psych.*, 1936, *31*, 266-277.

108. Watts, A. F., *The Language and Mental Development of Children*, George Harrap & Co., Ltd., London, 1944.

109. Wilson, L., "A Survey of Speech Defects Among Mentally Retarded Pupils in the Public Schools of Des Moines, Iowa," unpublished thesis, State University of Iowa, 1945.

110. Winitz, H., "Language Skills of Male and Female Kindergarten Children," *J. Sp. Hear. Res.*, 1959, *2*, 377-386.

111. Wolfensberger, W., Mein, R., and O'Connor, N., "A Study of the Oral Vocabularies of Severely Subnormal Patients, III. Core Vocabulary, Verbosity, and Repetitiousness," *J. Ment. Def. Res.*, 1963, *7*, 38-45.

112. Wood, B., "The Effects of Specialized Speech Training on Selected Feebleminded Subjects at the Florida Farm Colony," unpublished thesis, University of Florida, 1952.

113. Young, F. M., "An Analysis of Certain Variables in a Developmental Study of Language," *Genet. Psych. Mon.*, 1941, *23*, 3-141.

114. Schiefelbush, R., and Copeland, R. (eds.), *Language and Mental Retardation: Empirical and Conceptual Considerations*, Holt, Rinehart, and Winston, 1966.

This bibliography consists of works referred to in this chapter. Other references to language and mental retardation may be found in the bibliography for Chapter 9, "Therapeutic Considerations," and in Jordan, T. E. (ed.), *Perspectives in Mental Retardation*, Southern Illinois University Press, 1966.

Chapter 6

PSYCHODIAGNOSTICS

In any consideration of mental deficiency there comes a time when it seems appropriate to arrange the information into a meaningful pattern. When it is so arranged, it is possible to communicate the meaning to another person. Another outcome of presenting information in an orderly arrangement is that it is possible to identify areas in which more information may be needed.

In considering significant amounts of information there is the choice of arranging it in such a fashion that it illuminates one variable. In that instance the data usually take the form of several cases and the variable in question. In this chapter an alternative arrangement will be pursued: namely, several variables will be considered, and the consideration will stress gathering and ordering the data around one subject. This is sometimes called the case-study technique.

There still remains a problem in methodology, however. *How* one gathers information partially determines *what* one gathers. Obviously, the data one gathers determines how one views the subject of the case study. The next steps, analysis and eventual disposition, develop from the original data. Clearly, the initial choice of what to gather and how to gather is quite crucial.

The issues of content and technique, the what and how just discussed, may be schematized as (1) anecdotal or analytic evidence, and (2) objective or subjective methods.

Anecdotal evidence is generally an observation of striking behavior. It is usually more negative than positive, but, more crucially, it is rarely typical of an individual's behavior patterns. This is not an intrinsic failing of anecdotal evidence, but it is a common failing when people use this technique.

Analytic evidence is evidence of a more deliberate sort. It consists of statements in such a form—data language—that they can be verified by another person without ambiguities concerning the behavior involved.

Objective methods are those which allow one to contrive a situation in which a finding may be replicated. They tend to be relatively standardized but, more important, to consist of a technique which is largely independent of the investigator's disposition and which is communicable to another person. Perhaps the objective methods are best defined as those which permit separate but related investigations to meet the scientific standard of *non-random agreement* between investigators. This phrase means that a finding stands as scientifically defensible when two entirely independent observers, investigators, can agree nonrandomly on its existence. This same standard is met when two investigators agree that a phenomenon does *not* exist and have used the same technique in independent settings.

Subjective methods of investigation are those whose credibility lies more in the skill of the user than in the inherent and empirical nature of the technique. While such methods have many drawbacks, it is freely admitted that subjectivity has its place in a scientific study of human beings; the subjectivity is unfortunate, but what is loosely described as "clinical judgment" in an experienced investigator may be piercingly valid in its estimations and therefore invaluable.

LEVELS OF ANALYSIS

The lowest level of analysis in the study of mental retardation is simply looking at a human being and deciding whether or not he is intellectually normal. This technique is adequate for gross cases of mental retardation, but it fails to discriminate when applied to the majority of defectives. This is the technique which neighbors and relatives often apply in gauging the degree of retardation in a child. Its simplicity is proportional to its lack of validity.

A slightly higher level of analysis is exemplified in many school settings. A manifest failure on some task is often used to judge a child's ability. The task may be a paper-and-pencil measure of intelligence, the act of learning to read, or, in a few instances, performance on an individual test of ability. The use of an individual intelligence scale is the best of these methods, but by itself it may be quite inadequate. Far too often serious questions about children are settled by giving the Stanford-Binet; contrary to popular belief, this process does not provide an adequate solution to such serious problems. In far too many cases people are sent forth to measure the world with a Binet-box. The problem of mental retardation, and the problem of diagnosis are too complex for this approach (37).

Some school systems have personnel called "school psychologists." These may be testing technicians at the M.A. level who have had some guidance and testing courses and some experience in teaching children. An equally inept person is the individual with a doctorate who is armed with many techniques but who lacks instructional experience. There are very few school personnel who meet the requirements of competence in the school setting—training in the scientific techniques supplemented by experience in teaching.

Perhaps the best level of analysis is the rarest; this is the level achieved by the inter-disciplinary team working in a clinic setting who jointly possess several sorts of techniques from the several disciplines, with appropriate experience. The few clinics of this sort are usually attached to hospitals and universities. They supply conclusions about children to various agencies in fairly wide areas. The findings are generally based on many man-hours of investigation and many techniques, some subjective, some objective.

A most interesting discovery on this level of analysis of behavior is the number of unanswered questions which remain after several specialists have seen a child. This stands in sharp contrast to the disposition of children's problems by appeal to IQ's, often largely irrelevant, and to the use of the more informal ways of studying children. Such methods leave their users with a high degree of satisfaction and confidence but may be largely inadquate when the problems are complex.

THE PURPOSES OF EVALUATION

Purposes I

All diagnostic procedures are fundamentally measurement procedures. All methods of measurement, anecdotal or analytic, objective or subjective, have the same purpose, and this purpose obtains whether the results are applied to one person or to several. *The purpose of diagnostic procedures is to make some sort of predictive statement about a person's status at some time in the future.*

In the case of the retardate, the goal of the evaluation may be to determine whether or not he will be a dependent person at maturity. A common goal of evaluations is to decide how much a child may be expected to learn in the classroom; a corollary to this is the attempt to specify the ultimate level of learning when school-leaving age is reached. Vocational plans are based on predictive statements about appropriate occupations and abilities.

A general word of caution is in order. The precision of predictive statements about human beings is low. In effect, the attempt to predict any person's future status is hazardous except for the severely retarded. (In such cases psychological evaluations are usually intended merely to substantiate non-psychometric judgments.) Three British writers, Kirman, and Illingworth and Birch, have called attention to the hazards of predicting intellectual growth in children, but they seem to suggest that the problems are not insurmountable (65) (51). Generally speaking, the attempt to predict human behavior is like trying to predict the fall of a leaf. One makes quite cautious predictions in such cases.

Much confusion arises when people think that the goals of evaluation are an attempt to reach the perfection of the legendary crystal ball. Actually, the goal is to increase the accuracy of statements above the level which guessing or chance would reach.

Purposes II

Children are referred for diagnostic examinations for many reasons. Schools typically want to know why a child is performing poorly. Frequently, nothing arouses suspicion in a teacher's mind as quickly as poor reading progress. The consideration of any learning problem may well be schematized as some interaction of (1) learner variables, (2) task variables, and (3) method variables (63). Poor reading progress usually raises much concern about one of these, the child's ability. In this instance an interesting problem arises. Intelligence, or intelligences, depending on how one formulates the factorial basis of ability, is construed as a general thing, i.e., capacity to learn; but the purpose of the analysis may require a competence beyond the clinician, namely, the ability to relate psychometric capacity and the complex of affective elements to an instructional issue—specific methods of teaching reading and the strategies of instruction.

The purpose, then, is a very important consideration in the school-initiated examination; it dictates the approach to the issue and may raise many problems for the agency without a broadly-trained staff.

Growth

Another purpose arises when, rather than seeking basic information, the clinical method is called on to supply supplementary information. For example, a pediatrician may need more information to study a child whose physical and motor growth is slow. In this instance a clinical facility may be called on to conduct a partial case study and to answer a specific group of questions posed by the physician.

A similar request may come from a court wanting background information on a young offender. It is not unreasonable to make such a request since most juvenile courts adopt a rather open-minded position. In the case of a first offender, the court may look for symptoms of recidivism, of latent hostilities, and of problems that may or may not be amenable to treatment. In this instance a mosaic of factors is required, and the emphasis may well be on the empathic and analytic skills of the examiner, since he cannot look into his file drawer for a test of probation-value or of respect for property. He may, on the other hand, be able to indicate aspects of the total life-space of the child that the court may wish to investigate in other ways.

Adoption

Children frequently come up for adoption, and agencies may wish to match the child's background with that of prospective parents. Placing a child of normal intelligence and interests with intellectual parents or with parents with high ambitions may be as catastrophic for the child as the initial loss of parents. In this instance the clinical method may identify potentially unplaceable children; on the other hand, it may well identify adults who verbalize concern for children but who may be unsuited for non-intellectual reasons. Such people may be too rigid to really accept children or too demanding to provide the non-material necessities of life. In the context of mental retardation there is the obvious need to identify intellectually inadequate children who present severe placement problems.

Purposes III

The purposes of the clinical evaluation can be approached in another way. The purpose can be expressed as the attempt to gather information in all, or several, of the following areas.

The Presented Problem. It is no exaggeration to say that the utility of an evaluation depends on a precise formulation of the problem precipitating the request for services. A complete work-up on a child is a goal-directed activity taking its individual direction from the nature of the problem presented. A word of warning is necessary, however, because the presented problem may not be the real problem. Mental retardation as a phenomenal description of a child's ability may be secondary to an emotional problem; the emotional problem may be the real issue meriting attention. There is also the possibility that the origins of disability may be in another area of functioning. For example, low academic achievement may be attributable to a hearing loss, while the person making the referral may be convinced that a lack of academic aptitude is the locus of both the symptoms and the cause.

Identifying Information. On occasion a child may have been seen by several agencies. His full name and his guardians' names are essential in a set of records. Other information which may or may not be immediately useful is the ethnic background of the child, his religion, the names and ages of siblings, school name and specific grade, and other agencies that have seen or are seeing the child. The name of the person making the referral, his address, etc., are quite vital.

Background Information. There seems to be reason for believing that a child's present difficulties are best understood in light of his past history—educational, social, and familial. There is emerging evidence of an empirical sort from the studies of Rogers and his associates that problems in school-age children may be really comprehensible only when a full developmental history is available (89). This situation, of course, raises the questions of where and how such information can be obtained. Parents are obviously the best source of data, but there is reason to view them as not necessarily clear in their memories of past events (15). School records and other sources are of great value, too. Perhaps the best single source of information is the report of a social worker. Usually such information is derived from the basic content of the informant's report, supplemented by an analysis of the interviews and the informants.

Another source of information is an alert "secretary" who observes the behavior of child and parents in a waiting room prior to their meeting professional personnel formally.

The Client. An agency worker usually meets a child and parents at the same time. This initial contact can be vital. The manner in which the child relates to the parents, and to the clinician, can be most informative. A crucial point is when separation from the parent is precipitated by the clinician; this is also very informative.

Of comparable significance is the appearance of the child. Shapiro has pointed out that it is possible for an alert observer to respond to gross neurological signs, giving direction to the medical section of the evaluation (98). Obviously, a confident child's manner gives a meaning to psychometric data quite unlike that to be ascertained when a child is shy and apprehensive.

Psychometric Data. A vital part of an evaluation of a child suspected of mental retardation is the psychometric examination. It should be noted that testing is a *part* of, and not the entire, evaluation process. Usually, the psychometric examination consists of the administration of several scales. Some measure of intellectual maturity is necessary, and one of the several good individual scales of intelligence is appropriate. Personality considerations may be approached either by formal projective techniques or by fantasy questions and story telling. Usually an individual intelligence test supplemented by one or two shorter tests is all that can profitably be given at one session. Several sessions may be necessary with young children. Very often the data from the case history suggest hypotheses to be tested psychometrically, while the psychometric data may in turn suggest hypotheses for further testing or to be explored by other workers. Certain kinds of test performance may suggest lines of inquiry for the neurologist.

From Australia, Kraus has reported some useful guidelines in differentially diagnosing retardation, based on some of Fernald's procedures and using Doll's definition of retardation (67). Kraus advocates the use of weighted criteria when dealing with borderline cases. He believes it is practical to develop a "quantitative summarizing index" (67, p. 189) which would also permit qualitative judgments. A statement of empirical probability of accurate classification can be developed from clinical data, according to Kraus. The approach has the value of strengthening the conclusions developed by clinical means.

Educational Data. The role of educational data depends on the purposes of diagnostic procedures. In agencies dealing with the range of children's disorders, educational material is usually interesting and informative. There are clinics which are particularly oriented to school problems, and in these agencies educational problems may be the reason for referral and may be the context within which all data are synthesized.

If the central theme of a clinic service or a particular child's problems is a set of classroom considerations, the educational data acquire more significance. Other data may be used as they contribute to the consideration of the classroom issues. Failure to make adequate progress in reading is a common cause for referral, and it may have its origins in everything from intellectual immaturity to school phobia. The relevant data are the usual material from interviews and psychometrics, while the educational data on achievement and skills may commonly supply vital information.

In those cases where the presented problem is behavorial, the classroom may be merely the locus of concern. In such cases the direction given to the evaluation arises from considerations more fundamental than the situation where the problems were observed. This may be an increasing tendency as diagnostic services expand and as teachers continue to serve as a screen for mental health problems.

A vital consideration is the skill of clinicians in knowing and employing educational tests. Omission from the interdisciplinary team of an educational diagnostician is quite serious since so many cases are educational in symptom. Were educational data merely relevant, the case for educational analysis would be no less great. Like all other information it is important per se; but it also has the value of providing opportunities for fresh insights by the clinician during evaluation. One might go so far as to suggest that the case studies of many children are probably educational referrals to begin with, but *all* evaluations have an educational component in terms of either disposition or recommendations.

In some states, evaluations of mentally retarded children must include at least an achievement test. This stipulation is made because retardation in a school-age child may specify that concrete attainment be two or three grades below expectation, depending on the child's age.

Medical Data. The subtleties of the evaluation process become obvious when unsuspected damage is reported by a neurologist. When such findings are confirmed by the independent judgments of two examiners, many half-formed, ill-supported notions about a child are rendered more tenable. For example, minimal psychometric indicants of expressive aphasia may be supported by relevant evidence of a mild neurological disorder.

Occasionally, neurological data may restructure a problem. From Israel, Daryn reported on 170 children referred to a clinic in Tel Aviv for psychiatric disorders (27). Referring physicians considered the problems psychogenic, but Daryn found 84 cases of diffuse brain damage among them. EEG readings can be helpful too. Goldman and Rosenberg analyzed data on 132 children (40). Only 16 EEG tracings (12 per cent) could be considered normal, and those of seven retarded children were not among them.

A comparable source of information is a general physical examination in the case of an adolescent or an older person, or a pediatric examination in the case of a child. Here again, there may be vital information only obtainable by a physician. Mental retardation may be but one of many symptoms of developmental disorder in a child. The pediatric examination may put all the stigmata and functional data into perspective. Menninger, for example, has pointed out the relationship between psychiatric data and other data in comprehending the status of an individual (77). The relationships are rarely self-evident, and it is a considerable task to create a meaningful picture from separate sorts of evidence.

A CASE STUDY

Having considered some of the elements of the total study, let us look at the sort of picture of a retardate that emerges when a deliberate attempt is made to study a child, using psychological techniques. The following study will illustrate some of the data that emerge from the application of such techniques, and the composite picture of abilities and functioning that emerges. A valuable study which may be consulted for illustrative data is the report of Ravenette and Hersov (87). Their study goes from clinical to experimental study of behavior. The study which follows reports the case of a boy seen in a clinic's outpatient population. The original purpose for which the boy was referred was to determine his level of ability.

The material reported in this paper comes from observations of the subject, psychometric techniques, and a physician's report.

W. M., a white male, the youngest of three boys, was born September 30, 1943, and was twelve years and three months old when he came to the attention of the writer. At this time he was 68 inches tall and weighed 220 lbs. Because of his unusual appearance, a medical opinion was requested with the following findings:

"On physical examination his appearance was that of a dull, obese, husky male. A definite speech impediment was noted, characterized by a deliberate manner indicating some speech therapy. His height and weight were far out of normal percentile range. Fundoscopic exam revealed a decrease in number of retinal vessels and a pallor of the optic nerve discs. His blood pressure was 130/90 and his skin revealed multiple pigmented nevi. His genitalia were extremely mature showing adult characteristics.

"To summarize my clinical findings: there was mental and motor retardation, precocious development, both sexually and physically, gigantism, elevated blood pressure, and multiple pigmented nevi . . . hyperpituitarism and Von Recklinghausen's Disease."

The physical appearance of the siblings is also noteworthy. There is a fourteen-year-old boy who stands 6'2" and weighs 160 lbs. The oldest boy is 6'2" and weighs 215 lbs. Unlike the subject, the siblings apparently are of normal intelligence. Both do satisfactory school work which, while no guarantee of high intellect, is at least indicative of a degree of intelligence adequate for most purposes. The parents are normal in appearance, slight overweight being the only observable physical anomaly. The father works as an "operator" at a chemical plant, and the mother does part-time work at a laundry.

Psychometric Report. The following psychological techniques were employed: The Wechsler Intelligence Scale for Children, The Coloured Progressive Matrices (1947), the Rorschach Test, The Michigan Picture Test, and observations made during the working sessions. An articulation test and a pure-tone audiometric test were also administered.

The results of the Wechsler Intelligence Scale for Children were as follows:

Verbal Scale IQ, 72	Information	7	Picture Completion	6
Performance Scale IQ, 61	Comprehension	8	Picture Arrangement	5
Full Scale IQ, 64	Arithmetic	3	Block Design	4
	Similarities	4	Object Assembly	3
	Vocabulary	6	Coding	4

The test scores indicate widely differing levels of ability. In general he operates at the level described by Wechsler as "mentally retarded." The performance items indicated consistently low ability with the general level of performance items clearly in the range usually allotted to the mentally retarded.

The verbal scale, as a whole, presents a slightly better picture. An IQ of 72 puts the subject in the borderline category. Comprehension, a subtest which places emphasis on items of day-by-day living, was below average, but not to a gross degree. It may be interpreted to mean, when taken by itself, at least an acceptable degree of skill in the social side of life, an awareness of the conventions of society. The Information score, while not high, suggests an impairment rather than a complete failure to grasp everyday items of information. Vocabulary is lower, while Arithmetic and Similarities suggest a definite lack of ability for situations requiring those skills.

Some rather interesting observations were made during this testing period. The client was most co-operative, entering into all the tasks with enthusiasm. However, he tended to withdraw very quickly from frustrating situations or situations where his failure was unmistakable. His tolerance for frustration was not high. His answers to questions, complicated by articulation difficulties, were simple and direct. No further questioning was profitable at any time after the client had answered a question to his own satisfaction. The results of the WISC suggest that the client is a fairly well socialized boy whose lack of ability comes more sharply into focus when the life-situation changes from one which emphasizes the veneer of sociability and affability to one requiring specific skills and abilities of the kind usually considered indicative of certain intellectual ability.

The Coloured Progressive Matrices (1947), a non-verbal "test of fairly complex reasoning abilities," consists of three series of incomplete designs, A, Ab, and B. The client's performance on these culture-free, performance items was as follows: set A, 8 correct choices, Ab, 5 correct responses, and 5 on set B, for a total score of 18. This is a score at the minus 2σ level for children of the client's age. As a qualitative note, his errors were gross, being a failure to grasp the nature of the problems rather than near misses. The Matrices indicated clearly defective ability in a situation where reasoning was essential.

The Rorschach plates were administered to gather some information about the subject's perceptual and apperceptual processes. The responses were quite atypical and, in summary, were as follows:

R = 8	Init. R.T. (Average)	11.6 sec.
Total time 125 sec.	" " (8 9 10)	10 sec.
T/R 15.6 sec.	" " (2 3 8 9 10)	10 sec.
$\dfrac{\text{No. R. 8.9.10}}{\text{R}} = 25\%$	" " (1 4 6 7)	8.8 sec.
	W/m	5:0
$\dfrac{\text{No. R. 8. 9. 10}}{\text{R}} = 50\%$	M/FM	0:0
	M/C	0:0
W = 60 (%)	F%	100
D = 40 "	F + %	25
d = 0 "	A%	75
p = 12 "	H%	25
Cards rejected, No. 7 and No. 10		

The subject's responses were quite brief, and attempts to produce elaborations during the inquiry were quite unsuccessful. The rejections were not accompanied by any display of emotion; the subject simply replied to the question, "What might this be?" with "I don't know," after studying the card for a few moments.

The significant characteristics of this record were (1) the small number of R, (2) the brevity and superficiality of responses, (3) absence of color as a determinant, (4) stereotypy in response, (5) rejection of plates VII and X, (6) F per cent, (7) High A per cent, and (8) general poverty of content. The poverty of the client's inner life is apparent. He operates at an immature level, having comparatively little ability for problem solving, and, in the absence of other indications, his card rejection is felt to be an escape mechanism from a frustrating situation. (This tendency was also apparent in his WISC responses.)

The Michigan Picture Test is a set of drawings analogous to the TAT. There are differences in rationale, but the test materials are essentially the same, being human figures in situations open to numerous explanations. In view of the client's demonstrated economy of expression and low tolerance for frustrating situations, the pictures were selected on the basis of obvious relevance to a boy's life. The following cards were selected: No. 7, No. 1, No. 2, No. 4B, No. 3, No. 8B, No. 11G, and No. 12. The responses were what might have been expected in view of the other results. The responses were brief, superficial, and not of sufficient caliber to justify any judgments about the client's interpersonal relations. The only potentially useful information which was obtained was in the reaction times to the cards. The mean r.t. to all cards was 5.1″, and the range was from 3″ to 8″. Since it is not clear whether the 8″ r.t. was the consequence of the difficulty level of the card or the dynamic significance of the picture, no conclusions can be drawn about the longest r.t.

Diagnostic Summary. The over-all picture of the boy presented by the psychometric results and supplemented by interviews is that he is a quiet, passive, affable boy of limited intelligence. He seemed to cooperate well, and there were no indications of overt conflicts. He has a low threshold for frustration which will probably interfere with any attempt at education. He is educable, in a minimal sense, and, while capable of solving simple problems, he probably will not be capable of working without fairly close supervision.

Summary

The psychological characteristics of a boy diagnosed as having Von Recklinghausen's disease and hyperpituitarism were presented. The relative value of psychometric techniques as they contributed to an understanding of the boy is interesting. The WISC provided an opportunity to assess global intellectual capacity and the differing levels of abilities for different tasks. Clues relating to the subject's reaction to frustrating situations appeared. The Matrices gave an opportunity to see how the client responded in a problem-solving situation in which verbal abilities played no part. Performance there was low, and the errors were gross. The Michigan Picture Test failed to provide any useful data, and, while not intended to be used as the writer used it, it did not appear to be a useful instrument in cases of known or suspected mental retardation. Rorschach's Test, with its emphasis on perceptual and apperceptual processes, was most helpful. The dearth of intellectual content and the absence of affective cues were readily apparent (57).

This study is somewhat condensed, but it is a fairly typical example of how psychodiagnostic instruments are used: Several comments may be made about this study:

1. It attempts to understand the retardate in terms of more than intellectual endowment.

2. The study relates the individual to his life situation.

3. The variety of instruments is broad.

4. Very little attention is paid to the IQ, per se.

5. An attempt is made to depict the boy's current level of intellectual functioning and patterns of behavior.

6. An attempt is made to extrapolate from the data by making a prediction about future capabilities and limitations.

It is unwise, however, to conclude that psychometric data can be self-structuring in all cases. There are such instances, for example simple case studies designed to validate placement in special classes; however, in other cases psychometric data may not be available or the problem may require a different focus. An example of these last two considerations is the following anecdote in which test data are subordinate to social data in studying a child.[1]

Billy was born two years ago to Mr. and Mrs. F. The F. family rents a six-hoom house for eighty dollars a month, and the income is derived from the father's job as a construction worker and from the mother's job as a waitress. Total income is probably about $400 a month. Both parents are Catholic, and the children are being raised in that faith, although the parents practice their religion indifferently.

Mrs. F. has no contact with her mother, step-father, and five siblings. She experienced great emotional upset when she was placed in the first of a series of foster-homes at the age of fifteen. She expresses bitterness towards her family about this situation. Mrs. F. married her husband after knowing him for several years and shortly after she left high school. She reports continuous marital difficulty and has ruled out divorce because of the financial burden. She has a financial obligation to the social agency now assisting her and Billy which goes back several years. Mrs. F. believes her husband to be "tied to his mother's apron strings," as she puts it, and she actively dislikes the rest of his family. There is evidence of mental retardation in her family; she reported the condition in a nephew and in an uncle.

Aged twenty-two, Mrs. F. is an attractive young woman who dresses neatly. She and her husband rarely go out together, and she is respon-

---

[1] The materials in this section were originally developed by Miss Audrey M. Thaman and Dr. Allan Barclay, with the permission of Dr. A. Roger Sharp, Director, Child Development Clinic, St. Louis University Medical School. The formulation presented here is the responsibility of the author.

sible for running the household. She spends the check which her husband gives her each week. Recently, she has taken a night job as a waitress from 9 p.m. to 5 a.m. which increases the family income at the expense of her sleep and the care of the children. Mrs. F. says she does not care for her husband, and she sees him as an inadequate person. She rejects Billy, reports she ignores him, and says he makes her sick and nervous. She reported feeding him milk and baby cereal, although he previously took junior food. During interviews she manifested inappropriate affect, being giddy and flippant while discussing her problems. Her behavior promoted a clinician to observe that Mrs. F. would probably have serious problems without the complications due to Billy's problems. Discussing care of her other children, Mrs. F. seemed interested in her daughters but less concerned with her second boy. She reported that Mr. F. shows more affection for Billy's brother, Jimmy, than for her; she also commented that she does not like little boys. She conveyed to an agency worker eagerness to see Billy placed outside the home.

Mr. F., one of four children, is twenty-five years of age and is considered a nice-looking young man. He gives an impression of his family quite different from that given by his wife. He felt Billy "is really no trouble, hardly ever cries," an opinion which was subsequently replaced in an interview with expressions of helplessness and inadequacy. He spoke well of his wife and felt they get along well. He spends a good deal of his leisure time motorcycle racing and in the company of his brother. Contact with his parents is limited because they and his wife do not get along. He is perceived by his parents as immature; he does not handle money well, shirks responsibility, and pouts when he does not get his way. His emotional involvement in the complex of problems centered around Billy seems much less than that of his wife.

The F.'s have three other children, apart from Billy. Two girls, Mary, aged three, and Jane, aged four months, are in good health and seem adequately cared for. Jimmy, aged fourteen months, is adequately cared for, although he is probably less nurtured than the girls, if Mrs. F.'s expressed attitudes towards boys are considered.

No information is available concerning Billy's maternal grandparents. The paternal grandparents are pleasant people in their late fifties. They see Billy only infrequently because of the strained relations with the daughter-in-law. However, it was their report to the hospital where Billy was delivered which led to the developments in this account. They reported that Billy's mother was making funeral arrangements for his anticipated death. They believe Mrs. F. has serious personality problems and is an inadequate wife and mother.

Billy has a medical history with entries from his birth, two years ago, to the present. At six months gestation his mother began pre-natal care, and she reported continuous anemia and loss of weight rather than the considerable gain she experienced in other pregnancies. Vaginal bleeding was reported from the fifth month; other adverse experiences were edema and uterine infection. Pregnancy was terminated ten weeks prematurely, after labor lasting almost three hours. Billy weighed three pounds and six ounces, a situation complicated by the development of jaundice due to rh incompatibility. His weight dropped to two pounds six ounces, and he stayed in the hospital where he received blood-exchange therapy. He weighed five and a half pounds at age two and a half months and was discharged.

Shortly after he was admitted to the hospital again and underwent surgery for hernia repair. Medical records reveal that an x-ray at three months indicated a healed rib fracture. Battering was suspected. Billy was also hospitalized for pneumonia when he was six months old and again at thirteen months.

A complete physical work-up and psychological evaluation were developed at age eighteen months. Billy appeared frail and emaciated, weighing ten pounds and three ounces. Motor development up to that time had been slow. Billy held his head up at age eight months, and rolled over at one year. At the time of examination, however, he could not sit, even with support. On examination, he was promptly hospitalized, and staff reported he ate well, contrary to the mother's reports. An EEG gave essentially normal results and skull films showed retarded bone growth, but no other disorders. Malnutrition and mental retardation due to kernicterus and anoxia was the diagnosis. During hospitalization at eighteen months he put on weight and became more alert. Psychological study reported profound retardation (AAMD Level V) with trainability the potential level after further care. His mental and social ages at eighteen months were two months, and re-evaluation after twelve months was advised.

After medical care Billy was discharged to a foster home and subsequently seen by agency personnel at age twenty-two months. At that time he weighed nineteen pounds, had started to crawl, and demonstrated increased interest in his environment. Concomitant work with the parents indicated they would probably relinquish their rights and that permanent placement would be effected by a social agency.

Comment. This last piece of information is current at the moment of writing, and only time will tell what Billy's future holds. It seems clear that he will have a future due to the hospitalization at eighteen months. But for that he probably would have died, and his mother's funeral plans would have been realized.

We can see from the material just presented that descriptive psychological statements make a good deal of sense when diagnosticians can put them in a reality context. The psychologist severely annotated his psychometric statements about Billy and declined either to stress or to render in terms of finality the picture of psychological and social functioning. When the entire situation is viewed in terms of the contributions of several disciplines, a reasonably comprehensive picture emerges. It is hard to see what body of material, what disciplinary formulation, can possibly be omitted if responsible conclusions are to be reached. If rational disposition of human problems is to be undertaken, we need every scrap of evidence we can gather in order to describe the picture a child presents at examination in accurate terms. Social material can go a long way toward explaining the past and present. In some instances it can help predict the future. Certainly the last observation holds since therapeutic intervention by the attending physician certainly saved the child's life.

DIAGNOSTIC INSTRUMENTS

There are many tests which can be used to assess the psychological characteristics of a human being. New tests are continually being developed (88), and some continue to be used as they have been for the last twenty-five years, with only minor changes (109). Whatever the age of an instrument, or its area of sensitivity, it still conforms to some standards of acceptance. Most people summarize the standards of acceptance under the following headings:

1. Validity
2. Reliability
3. Usability

Validity refers to the extent to which the test measures what it says it measures. *Reliability* is a little more complicated but refers to the internal and sequential consistency of the instrument. *Usability* covers such considerations as cost (some tests are prohibitively expensive in terms of man-hours to use), ease of interpretation and scoring, and other matters related to practical use. The issues of validity and reliability are important. A standard text on educational and psychological measurement may be consulted for more information (92).

MEASURES OF INTELLIGENCE

The most obvious way of schematizing intelligence tests is to describe them as *group* tests or *individual* tests.

Group Intelligence Tests

Schools commonly employ group tests, instruments that can be given to many children at once and, if necessary, at several separate sittings, to screen out the bright and the dull. Most group tests can be described as paper-and-pencil tests, since they require no manipulation by the tester. The subject works on problems printed in a booklet and marks his answer on the same page or on an answer sheet that accompanies the booklet.

Group measures are not intended to place children but merely to screen them to identify the significantly high and low performers. These children are then supposed to be given individual examinations. Some of the group tests of intelligence are:

1. *The California Tests of Mental Maturity.*
2. *The SRA Primary Mental Abilities Test.*
3. *The Davis-Eells Games.*
4. *The Progressive Matrices.*

The last two of these scales, the *Davis-Eells Games* and the *Progressive Matrices*, are interesting in that they seem to avoid some of the cultural biases which lower the test scores of children who belong to minority or deprived groups. A discussion of the many group tests may be more appropriately found in such books as Anastasi (*2*), Freeman (*31*), and Buros (*17*).

Individual Intelligence Tests

The most widely used test of intelligence is probably the 1937 revision of the Binet by Terman and Merrill. Called the Stanford-Binet and available in two forms, L and M, the scale offers problems of various sorts at age levels from age two to the superior adult. Administered to school-age children, it requires a child to pass all tests at what is considered a basal year and to take tests of increasing difficulty grouped in years. The child continues until he fails a complete "year" or group of tests.

In a previous chapter the author has pointed out that what is defined as intelligence depends on an individual's level of maturity. The Stanford-Binet, with its remarkable range, shifts significantly in its content as the child's age rises. The "intelligence" measured by the scale shifts from motor activities to increasingly verbal tasks as one progresses through the age levels.

Performance on the items is recorded as months of credit. Passing all tests at a year which has six sub-tests gives credit of twelve months of age. The cumulative months of credit are added together to obtain what is termed a *mental age*. This scale is the best single predictor of school success in children, and the scale is strikingly effective in the range of the school years. This is not to say that the Stanford-Binet is perfect; the standard of perfection is irrelevant in assessing behavior. It can be said, however, that this scale exceeds chance levels strikingly when it orders subjects by increasing or decreasing mental maturity.

The Stanford-Binet has some sensitivities. Mention has been made earlier of the Bond and Fay study on the performance of good and poor readers (*14*). A few years prior to that study, in 1947, Thompson and Magaret reported the differential response of normals and a group of 441 retardates (*110*). These investigators reported twelve items on which retardates did significantly better than normals and nineteen items on which normals significantly surpassed retardates. The total pool of items was drawn from the years between II-6 and XIV. A similar study by Sloan and Cutts identified "hard" and "easy" items for mental retardates. They found that the "Verbal Absurdities," "Sentence Memory," and "Opposite Analogies" items were most frequently hard for their subjects. "Definitions," "Vocabulary," "Picture Absurdities," "Counting," and "Bead Stringing" were comparatively easy (*104*). Saltzman reported the sensitivity of the Binet to socio-economic factors. Using children in New York matched by non-verbal intelligence and divided by neighborhood, the study demonstrated that the differences typically encountered in an urban setting can have a profound effect on Stanford-Binet scores. The children of adequate intelligence—nonverbal—but from poor homes achieved significantly lower scores (*94*).

If one deals with children who are for the most part English-speaking, or Spanish-speaking, there is a natural tendency to think that cultural problems in mental deficiency are peculiar to one's own society. This is not the case; most societies have some class, caste, and ethnic divisions which confound the problems of intelligence. An example of this is the problem of the Maori in New Zealand. By and large the Maori seem to have received better treatment than most autochthonous groups, but Walters has indicated that levels of ability among the Maori are not easily categorized; they seem subject to all the problems implicit in the studies of Negro and Spanish minorities, as well as in the studies of the hill folk and the sub-cultural defectives (*113*).

Generally speaking, the Stanford-Binet takes up to one hour to administer. The result is that subjects who are immature get tired or may fail items as a way of demonstrating resistance. Performance fluctuates as children react to persons administering tests. Pettigrew recalled this event in his discussion of intelligence (*86*). He recorded a 1936 finding by Canady that Negro children produced better results (6 points) when tested by Negro examiners. A shorter scale is always a help in evaluating mentally retarded subjects, but the price is usually a drop in the validity of the instrument. Several years ago Birch devised a short form of the Binet and tried it out on a sample of 255 retardates; he reported that the short forms he derived from the 1937 Binet were satisfactory (*13*).

Altogether, the Stanford-Binet is our best single measure of ability. If care is taken to make sure that the subjects tested have no sensory or motor disabilities and that they come from fairly typical backgrounds, the results can be very useful. An indication of the scale's over-all value is that it is often used as the criterion measure of intelligence when new tests are being developed. The most recent revision of the Binet was in 1959. Sternlicht has found it applicable to the study of mentally retarded persons (*107*).

A test which has now been in use for some years is the *Wechsler Intelligence Scale for Children* (*WISC*). This scale consists of a verbal section which yields a verbal IQ (there is no MA, because of Wechsler's reservations about the concept) from the aggregate score on sub-tests. The sub-tests are called "Vocabulary," "Comprehension," "Information," "Arithmetic," and "Similarities." The other half of the scale is a group of performance items which also yield an IQ. The sub-tests are named "Picture Completion," "Picture Arrangement," "Block Design," "Object Assembly," and "Coding." By combining the scaled scores from the verbal and performance tests it is possible to obtain a full-scale IQ which is indicative of global ability.

The *WISC* differs from the Binet in several ways. It tests in one area until failure is reached; the Binet incorporates kinds of items at different levels, so that a child may be evaluated by differing standards on an item at different levels. The *WISC* yields no mental age, and it breaks down its results into three IQ's. The *WISC* may not be given to children below CA 5. Currently, downward extension of the *WISC* is underway, and we may expect to see considerable enthusiasm for a new instrument applicable to young children.

In a move parallel to that reported in an earlier paragraph from Birch's work, some people have abbreviated the *WISC*. Finley and Thompson (*30*) have found a small scale of five sub-tests—(a) "Information" (b) "Picture Arrangement" (c) "Picture Completion" (d) "Coding" and (e) "Block Design"—accurate in evaluating intelligence. A validity coefficient of .876 with *WISC* full-scale IQ was reported in 1958 and was independently validated on 173 children in 1962.

The revised adult intelligence scale by Wechsler, the *WAIS*, has been used profitably. Silverstein extended the norms to include younger subjects (*100*), and its employment by Warren and Kraus revealed comparable verbal and non-verbal abilities in moderately retarded persons (*116*). They found disproof for the contention that more seriously retarded persons would demonstrate marked discrepancies in verbal and non-verbal skills as a function of probable neurological involvement.

Comparing the two families of scales, Stacey and Levin found a high and positive correlation between the Binet and the Wechsler-Bellevue (105). Orr, in research for a thesis written in 1950, found the Binet and WISC highly comparable (84). This similarity is interesting, since it suggests that the two instruments may be used in a complementary fashion with children of school age. The author commented previously that the Binet is our best predictor of school performance, and it is interesting to note that the WISC is useful in this regard for retardates (95).

A problem akin to that pursued by Thompson and Magaret is that of determining the extent to which test results may form patterns for diagnostic groups. Beck and Lam found that they were able to identify some organic cases of mental deficiency with the WISC from a sample of 104 retarded children (6). Organics tended to do a poorer job on the performance items. No over-all pattern of sub-test results emerged which could be used to distinguish the organic cases from the non-organics.

Working with the WISC, Baroff tested fifty-three cases of endogenous mental deficiency; the mean WISC full scale IQ of the S's was 62.6, and the range was from IQ 42 to IQ 80. It was Baroff's conclusion that no intrinsic pattern of test scores emerged. There were indications of differential performance on test items: "Rank-order analysis revealed relatively superior performance on Object Assembly, Block Design, Picture Completion, and Coding with relatively poor performance on Vocabulary and Similarities. The Performance Scale IQ was higher than the Verbal Scale IQ in 80 per cent of the group" (5, p. 485). Baroff supplements these conclusions by pointing out that pattern analysis is self-limiting. The number of tests involved in the schema increased the probability that uncontrolled determinants influence test performance.

The use of psychometric profiles for diagnostic purposes has been urged by Jastak (52). It is his judgment that psychometric data can yield a measure of potential intelligence: ". . . there is in every psychometric record an ability through which a person's latent intellectual power may be adequately approximated. It is the ability that yields the highest score."

Other intelligence tests may be mentioned briefly. The *Leiter International Scale* is an instrument sometimes used to measure ability. It is not commonly used or routinely used, but it can be very useful.

The *Columbia Mental Maturity Scale*, the *Nebraska Test of Learn-*

ing *Aptitude,* and the *Coloured Progressive Matrices* are instruments often used to measure intelligence. Since these instruments are not routinely used, their attributes will be discussed in detail under a separate heading later in this chapter.

MEASURES OF SOCIAL DEVELOPMENT

The most commonly used test of social development is probably the *Vineland Social Maturity Scale.* This instrument consists of a series of behaviors arranged in approximate age groups. A variety of social behaviors is involved, and the data usually consist of information supplied by an informant, usually the parent. The results are expressed as a *social age,* a concept of maturity analogous to the mental age of the Stanford-Binet. Like the Binet mental age, a social age can be used to develop an index of relative growth. This is called a social quotient and is obtained in a fashion similar to the way in which the intelligence quotient of the Binet is obtained. The social quotient (SQ) is derived by the formula $SQ = \left(\dfrac{SA}{CA}\right) \times 100$, where CA = age in years and months of life.

Generally speaking, a familial defective may have an SQ higher than the IQ. This is a way of saying that the degree of social effectiveness may be less affected than the ability to do abstract tasks. Clearly, an instrument that depends on retrospective reporting is more vulnerable than one which assesses performance directly. Nevertheless, the Vineland is a useful item in the test battery and can give a good deal of information. Mecham has extended the communication portion, and use of his *Verbal Language Development Scale* can be informative.

MEASURES OF PERSONALITY

Like other psychological scales, personality measures may be divided into (a) those administered to only one person at a time or to several persons at the same time and (b) those which are objective in form or those which are essentially subjective. The scales in which subjectivity plays the greatest part are called *projective techniques.*

The paper-and-pencil measures of personality usually take the form of a series of questions or statements; the client responds with some kind of manual activity, either by writing something or, more commonly, by making a check mark. These techniques are not really applicable to the assessment of mental retardates, since they implicitly measure reading skill, apart from personality considerations. The hazards in this area are exemplified in a study published just after

World War II, in which personality data were reported from young mentally retarded children. The Bernreuter scale was employed, but the findings were somewhat attenuated in the minds of some people because of the high level of reading comprehension which this scale requires. It is possible that the personality tests which are written can be given to adult high-grade defectives who have a high degree of reading skill. There is, however, enough reservation to make one think twice about giving such excellent scales as the *Minnesota Multiphasic Personality Inventory* or the *California Test of Personality* to subjects of suspected mental retardation. These are adequate and, in some cases, highly ingenious tools to be used more profitably with normals.

Projective Techniques

The most interesting group of tests to use in evaluating retardates is unfortunately the most complex. Rejecting specific questions and a high degree of structure in their format, the projective techniques are most interesting and flexible devices. They require a great deal of training to administer; and they do not always meet the standards of validity, reliability, and utility.

Briefly defined, a projective test of personality is one in which the client is exposed to material that may be interpreted in several ways. The material presented may be *unstructured*—that is, it may have widely differing meanings, much as clouds can appear to be many things—or it may be semi-structured—for example, it may use pictures of people who may be doing any one of a number of things. A test which was wholly structured would have only one possible meaning; such a device would not allow an individual to *project* his inner dispositions, emotions, and strivings into the situation.

A more detailed rationale of projective testing may be had by reading a text on testing such as Anastasi or Freeman, mentioned previously. In this discussion we shall concern ourselves with the application of projective techniques to the evaluation of suspected or known cases of mental reardation.

The Relevance of Projective Data. It would be naive to assert that all clinicians believe that projective techniques have a place in the evaluation of the mentally retarded. Some have doubts based on the low validity of projective techniques in any circumstances, and some object to the gross subjectivity of interpretations, while others feel that the retarded simply are not sufficiently verbal to express themselves during the communicated part of projection. Jordan and deCharms have presented evidence on the comparative verbal productivity of retardates and normals. The evidence is presented in Table 6·1. These data suggest that, at least in this instance, mental retardation was no barrier to productivity (59).

TABLE 6·1

MEAN NUMBER OF WORDS PRODUCED BY MENTALLY
RETARDED AND NORMAL ADOLESCENT BOYS

Mentally Retarded Special Classes	Mentally Retarded Regular Classes	Controls
173.04	143.79	162.05

The Thematic Apperception Test

Nearly twenty-five years ago, Murray reported his studies on personality (80). His approach may be summarized by saying that he relied on one of the older skills of mankind, story-telling. Murray devised a series of pictures which a subject is invited to respond to by telling a story. Generally, the clinician wants a story with a beginning prior to the scene in the picture; he wants an account of the feelings of the people, and he wants to know how the story turns out. The scenes in the cards are varied. Some examiners choose cards that seem to relate rather immediately to a suspected problem in a client; for example, pictures of two or more people may be useful in exploring interpersonal relationships. In other cases, different sorts of pictures may be chosen. One of the more interesting items is card No. 16, which is quite blank; after a client has seen several pictures, he usually responds to card No. 16 with a story. The themes of all the client's stories are analyzed, and consistent themes are held to be indicative of the inner dispositions of the subject.

There are some drawbacks to this instrument in view of the general requirements of validity and reliability. Utility may be low because of the training required to use the instrument. Also, content in *TAT's* may reflect merely transient rather than fundamental problems.

Sarason has paid a great deal of attention to projective techniques and mental retardation (96, 97). In one study he discussed the application of the *Thematic Apperception Test* to high-grade retarded boys. He found that basic problems emerged in the themes and contents of the stories and that there were indications of response to the specific institution in which the boys resided.

Somewhat similar results are to be found in Beier's, Gorlow's, and Stacy's study of the inner life, the phantasy life, of retarded individuals (7).

The *TAT* has been subjected to modifications and derivations. Revisions for Negroes have been reported, while the application of thematic materials to the study of motivation has been extended by McClelland (71). Jordan and deCharms reported the application of the McClelland constructs and ideas to the achievement motivation of retarded adolescent males (59). In this instance the goal was not to schematize the total inter- and intrapersonal life of the subjects; rather, the use of the thematic materials was a way to look at a narrowly defined form of motivation. It is worthy of note that the pictures used in this study were scenes which generate verbal-achievement imagery. They were not selected from Murray's series but were comparable to them. In each case human figures were presented in a setting open to various descriptions and interpretations. In this case the responses were analyzed for specific kinds of imagery and for certain kinds of outcomes.

Rorschach's Test

The projective instrument par excellence is probably Herman Rorschach's set of ten cards which bear images resembling those one would obtain by dropping ink on a sheet of paper and then folding the sheet vertically. First described in 1921 (90), the scale has been viewed controversially ever since. Objections to the test probably epitomize all the worst that can be said about tests which are not objective, reliable, well standardized, and usable.

A way of indicating the strong passions which this scale arouses in theorists is to point to the crucial problems of scoring and interpretation. Skills are passed from master to apprentice, and analysts tend to form coteries which are distinguished by some mystique or other. One is either a Klopfer-like scorer, a Piotrowski-like analyst, or an adherent to some other point of view. Nevertheless, clinicians can and do use the Rorschach profitably in the study of mental retardation. The onus is on the skill of the clinician, and some are extremely skilled.

Two studies by Jolles illustrate the value of the Rorschach technique in the study of mentally retarded subjects (53, 54). The first of these studies was an examination of a group of thirty-four children, all of whom were below IQ 80 and who were candidates for special class placement. Jolles was able to demonstrate the presence of multiple disorders in mental retardates. He reported the following disorders in his subjects:

1. Twenty-one cases of anxiety neurosis.
2. Eight schizoid subjects.
3. One depressive child.
4. One character neurosis.

By and large, Jolles felt that he could identify in these S's potential ability which was not otherwise apparent. Functionally, the children were not at an average level; they were phenomenally inadequate children.

In another interesting study, Jolles used the Rorschach technique to identify subjects who were probably of normal intelligence but whose effectiveness was reduced by neuroses. The value of such findings in a differential diagnosis is quite obvious. To reiterate an earlier consideration, the Stanford-Binet would probably not give a comprehensive picture of such individuals. Sloan's study mentioned in Chapter 3 is another study which may be consulted.

An interesting Rorschach study was reported by Werner in 1945 (119). He applied the Rorschach to two groups of defectives, to a group with a known pathology (brain injury) and to another which he identified as familials. The following differences were reported between S's who were brain-injured and those who were not:

1. No very-small-detail responses by the brain-injured group.
2. More use of the white space for responses by the brain-injured.
3. Fewer human- and animal-movement responses in the brain-injured.
4. More response to color by the brain-injured.
5. Familials saw more human figures, organics more animal figures.

When individual scales of intelligence are used, there may be some ambiguities in interpretation. For example, it is not easy to decide what disposition is appropriate for borderline cases of mental retardation, those individuals who are clearly below average but not clearly in the retarded group. An intelligence test simply supplies information, and the clinician must then somehow make up his own mind. Personality data from projective techniques can be helpful. For example, in Font's paper the Rorschach was applied to a group of borderline cases. Font asserted that the Rorschach protocol could help in distinguishing (1) cases where there was a functional basis for the low performance; (2) stable from unstable subjects; and (3) those cases where a disturbed personality led to unacceptable behavior, as opposed to behavior situationally determined (34).

The House-Tree-Person Test

The best test is obviously one which produces an abundance of data otherwise unobtainable. A test which is useful in some people's hands is the task of drawing (1) a house, (2) a tree, (3) a person. An interview, in which the subject is questioned about his drawings, follows this task. According to Buck (16), the tree may indicate the client's felt relationship with his environment and his ability to derive satisfaction from that relationship. The person is held to indicate what the subject would like to be or to represent some valued figure in the subject's life. The house equals home and family. In the hands of a skilled interviewer this technique can be most valuable, but everything hinges on the skill of the interpreter. Cutts has found the H-T-P useful in testing mental retardates for (1) home adjustment, (2) school adjustment, (3)social adjustment, (4) ego structure, and (5) ego defenses (26).

The Children's Apperception Test

This is a scale much like the *TAT*, except that the subject interprets scenes with animals in them rather than human beings. The evidence suggests that one gets little from the *CAT* that cannot be obtained from the *TAT* (4).

The Blacky Pictures

A far more sophisticated instrument is the series of pictures by Blum depicting the experiences of Blacky, a little dog. The Blacky scale is far more ambitious than the *CAT*. For one thing it has a highly sophisticated rationale which determines not merely content but the specific scenes in which Blacky appears.

The test is based on an approach to personality which is dynamic. Blacky's adventures are actually depicting stages or incidents in the dynamic formulation of psycho-sexual development. The clinician's interpretation of the child's response is therefore governed by the over-all rationale which led to the development of the pictures. Only those clinicians who are skilled in the idiom and thought of the dynamic approach to personality can profit from the child's responses to Blacky. It follows that the skill needed to interpret is greater and that the utility of the findings may be restricted to those clinicians who also subscribe to Freudian conceptions of personality development.

Other Tests

There are many other tests in addition to those just mentioned. It remains to be seen if they have utility in evaluative work with retardates. Some of the less commonly used projective techniques are The *Mosaic Test*, The *Make a Picture-Story Test*, The Machover *Human Figure Drawing Test*, and the *Szondi Test*. In all probability the crucial element in the use of any of these techniques is the clinician's sensitivity to people. If the examiner's antennae are sensitive to human nature, the projective techniques may be useful. Failing this, the projectives may be a rather useless and elaborate procedure.

SPECIAL TESTS OF INTELLIGENCE

A very serious limitation to the utility of the Binet and the *WISC* is their positive requirement that the subject be free from sensory, motor, and communicative disorders. The reality of working with a population of retardates is that this stipulation is not always met. At the risk of underestimating two good instruments, one might suggest that the Binet and *WISC* are excellent, *in toto*, for those children who have nothing wrong with them. This is clearly an exaggeration, but there are many times when these two instruments simply cannot be used with children when some evaluation is necessary. It should produce some evidence beyond a social and educational history and a *Vineland Social Maturity Scale*.

The Progressive Matrices Test

This is an interesting test developed over a period of years in England. Beginning with a 1937 version, it developed into a children's scale more than ten years ago.

The rationale of the scale is derived from Spearman's work, and it seems quite interesting. The format of the *Coloured Progressive Matrices* (1947), the scale for use with children, is three series each of twelve incomplete visual designs. The child selects one of a series of given alternatives to complete the design. The test is available as a booklet, and the client's essential task is to indicate his choice of the alternatives. The utility lies in the flexible way the child may express his choice. The alternatives are printed beneath the incomplete design, and the examiner can use any of several methods to establish the child's selection.

The validity of the scale seems high (75) (106), and the norms have been established for an American sample in the last few years (46). The range of otherwise almost untestable children who can take this test is wide; it can be used with cases of (1) poor articulation, (2) non-reading, (3) cerebral palsy, (4) auditory handicap, (5) cultural deprivation, (6) multiple handicap, and (7) non-English-speaking background. An additional virtue is that it seems to be intrinsically appealing to children.

There are some serious technical reservations which should be noted: the item placement may not be sound; difficulty may be too great at the top end; item discrimination may not be acceptable. Several studies have examined the instrument in detail (56) (58) (75) and reported its value. The instrument does seem to merit attention, since it has great potential for use with children. Orme found it useful with a population of retarded persons (*83*).

The Children's Picture Information Test

Kogan and Crager have reported standardization of an instrument for evaluating the abilities of children with multiple handicaps. The scale consists of forty items, multiple-choice in form, which consists of pictures of objects found in the confined environment of the physically handicapped child. The child is asked to indicate which of the response items goes with the presented problem item. The standardization seems to have been done with great care, and the authors have supplied a model amount of data on their standardizing procedures. Validity is reported against the Stanford-Binet and seems adequate (*66*).

The Goodenough Draw-a-Man Test

It is the rare instrument that stands the test of time. Goodenough's simple test of mental maturity seems to be one of the more durable items in the clinician's battery. The instructions to draw a man are comprehended by retarded subjects, and, if no motor disorders are present, a skilled scorer can produce a valid estimate of mental level. Birch reported high validity against the Stanford-Binet in sixty-eight retarded subjects between ten and sixteen years of age (*12*). Had the S's been of normal intelligence, the relationship might not have obtained. The validity is attributable to their advanced chronological age but reduced mental age.

Another study of the Draw-a-Man has directed attention to its value as a predictor of school readiness. Coleman, Iscoe, and Brodsky have reported data which indicate that this little test, quickly administered easily scored, can be most helpful in deciding whether children are mature enough for school (*23*). In view of the almost complete lack of rigorous, empirical data in this problem area, it is to be hoped that the results may be widely disseminated. If nothing else, this study suggests some ways of finding out when and if children are mature enough to begin formal schooling. In the case of retarded youngsters this is clearly a crucial issue.

The Columbia Mental Maturity Scale

Several years ago a non-verbal scale of ability was produced that essentially tested the perception of similarities and differences. The problems are presented on long strips of cardboard-like material, and the child is asked to perform a discrimination task and to report his re-

·onses. He continues with the test until he has failed several problems in a row. The utility of this scale is established by work such as at of Canter (*18*). Unlike many psychometric studies which merely port results, Canter's work offers a series of basic criticisms of the instrument and suggests revisions, such as (1) re-evaluating the order of difficulty, (2) assembling the concepts in unitary groups, and 3) expressing the results as a measure of learning aptitude.

Other Scales

Two scales which can be very helpful in the evaluation of retarded id multiple-handicap cases are the Ammons *Full Range Picture Vocabulary Test* and the *Nebraska Test of Learning Aptitude*. The Ammons is a picture-vocabulary scale with a great deal of utility in evaluating intelligence in retardates. It can be used in many settings. Conell, for example, reports the use of this scale with retarded Chippewa idian children (*24*). The *Nebraska Test of Learning Aptitude* is a ale that is often routinely used when children are deaf or when they ive a significant hearing loss in the speech range. The instructions for is scale can be given by pantomime; unfortunately, the scale has awbacks, not the least of which is the problem of communicating dictions to the subject. The results are expressed not as absolute measures of ability but as indicants of aptitude for learning. Another instrument for appraising abilities of deaf children is the *Advanced Performance Scale*, from the Central Institute for the Deaf. It used four aditional items in the school years from five to thirteen, the Seguin, ohs, Healy, and Knox tests (*11*).

The Peabody Picture Vocabulary Test

In recent years the *Peabody Picture Vocabulary Scale* (*PPVT*) developed by Dunn has become a valuable tool in the assessment of intellectual maturity of persons between two and a half and eighteen ears. As with similar scales, of which the *Full Range Picture Vocabulary Test* by Ammons is a good example, children are asked to point to ie picture among several when given a cue such as *man*. Quickly administered and scored, the *PPVT* is analogous to the devices used to st articulation. Perhaps one day we will have a series of pictures hich can be used for intellectual, linguistic, and personality appraisal. owever, the *PPVT* is uniquely a mental test, and it places minimal ›mands on the sensory and motor equipment of children. Vision is, of ·urse, the vital modality, but even so the scale has proved valuable ?9). Children with serious visual problems can use the scale in selecd instances if enlarged materials are presented. Other special popu-

lations to which the *PPVT* has application are deaf children (*48*), cri
pled children (*78*), retarded children (*79*) (*62*), and Spanish-spea
ing children (*25*). Bright children have presented problems due
ceiling effects (*38*), but extrapolated norms are available. Tempor
stability is good according to Goldstein, Moss, and Jordan (*41*). V
lidity is high when measured against the Binet scale (*62*) and is
course higher when other picture scales are used as criterion measure
Minimal demands are placed on the examiner, who records the sele
tion of choices from a basal series of eight correct responses to a ce
ing of six errors. The results are interpreted as mental age, percentile
and IQ's. The widest application of the scale has been its inclusion
the research program of Operation Headstart, the preschool progra
for culturally deprived children which started in 1965.

Three good discussions of special problems in evaluating intelligen
in the handicapped may be found in Newland (*81*) and more recent
in the excellent summaries by French (*32*) and by Allen and Colli
(*1*). Gallagher *et al.* have presented data on the comparability of thr
tests used with the handicapped. Their data were derived from a sar
ple of children who had suffered damage to the central nervous syster
The data indicated that the tests were all useful but that they were n
precisely comparable to each other (*36*).

EDUCATIONAL TESTS

In many evaluations of children the educational skills and the pe
terns of achievement and capacity are quite important. In some ca
studies, educational data are no more relevant than pertinent data fro
any other area of behavior, but in those cases where the referral com
from a school, educational data may be invaluable.

Perhaps the most relevant area of instruction is reading. Readir
and its complex, the language arts, is the most crucial area of instru
tion in the elementary school. Its critical significance for seconda
schools is that reading skill is necessary in all the subject-matter fielc
Whenever a child is suspected of low intelligence, there may well I
confusion about whether he is incapable of learning to read; wheth
he is ready to learn to read; or whether his low performance in readir
may be due to specific, identifiable skill deficiencies. There are te:
which parallel these alternatives and which can be used in a test be
tery.

Reading Readiness

Most tests of reading readiness are an amalgam of items that me
sure intellectual maturity and visual discrimination. Their validity

usually of an empirical sort, consisting of a relationship with actual growth in reading in the primary grades. An example of a readiness measure is the *Harrison-Stroud Reading Readiness Profiles*. This scale consists of five group tests, (1) "Using Symbols," (2) "Making Visual Discriminations," (3) "Using the Context (oral)," (4) "Making Auditory Discriminations," and (5) "Using Context and Auditory Clues." There is an optional scale which can be used individually to see whether a child knows the names of the letters. About one hour and a quarter, divided into three sessions, is required to give these scales.

Reading Diagnosis

Much as a scale like the *Wechsler Intelligence Scale for Children* gives an analytic picture of discrete abilities, a reading diagnostic scale measures specific strengths and weaknesses in the reading skills. An excellent diagnostic scale is the *Durrell Analysis of Reading Difficulty*. This scale is administered individually and is really a well-structured observational scale. The scale can be given to children whose reading achievement and skills are as high as sixth grade. The materials test reading performance in oral and silent reading, comprehension, listening, work recognition, word analysis, spelling, and handwriting. This is an excellent scale, which can yield highly informative, and occasionally surprising, results.

Language Tests

At rare intervals a scale appears that is quite unique. The *Illinois Test of Psycholinguistic Ability* (*ITPA*) is exceptional because it is derived from prior formulation of cognitive processes. This is unusual because cognition tends to be defined in terms of test functions rather than as a conceptual proposition which subsequently yields an operational form. Also, the *ITPA* has been standardized carefully, and it has a narrow range of applicability—unlike most scales which purport to study all levels of maturity. Another virtue of the scale is its continuity with educational diagnosis: most scales help classify children but do not develop data of direct instructional value.

The *ITPA* has nine sub-tests which cover three dimensions of linguistic process (a) communication output and input (b) levels of organization (c) psycholinguistic processes. At the operational level the *ITPA* is close to Wepman's model of language developed from his studies of aphasic behavior (55). Developmentally it represents Kirk and McCarthy's (64) extension of ideas formulated by Osgood and structured by Sievers (99). A good deal of work has been done on the *ITPA* (70); and its value will grow in much the same way as that of Taylor's scale, which reified study of anxiety in the 1950's. Chapter 9, "Therapeutic Considerations," touches on the use of the *ITPA;* Chapter 5 discusses a number of linguistic measures applicable to studies of children.

DECISIONS IN DIFFERENTIAL DIAGNOSIS

Data are not self-interpreting, nor do tests supply all the necessary evidence. There comes a time in the psychodiagnosis of mental retardation when some judgments have to be made. At this point the clinician may be on his own, since his data may help him reject some of the more obvious hypotheses but not help him accept some others.

This section will consider three problem areas of diagnosis, three issues which arise as serious alternatives in children who are held to be mentally retarded but who seem to suffer from some other, less obvious defect. The three issues to be considered separately are (1) brain injury, (2) aphasia, and (3) emotional disturbance. While aphasia can be schematically subsumed under brain injury, its significance as a diagnostic entity justifies attention to it as a separate issue.

Brain Injury

Earlier in this chapter attention was called to the manner in which purposes influence the treatment of data gathered in an evaluation. There has also been some discussion of how data can aid in rejecting and accepting hypotheses concerning the significance of behavior. An issue which has come increasingly into focus has been the effect of injury to the nervous system, specifically to the brain. It is not that the cerebrum of the brain-injured individual is an object of attention in psychodiagnostic evaluations, but rather that attention is directed to the correlate of brain injury, disturbances of behavior. Such behavior may take the specific forms of hyperactivity, perceptual disorders, convulsive attacks, perseveration, distractability, and an inability to learn. A client with such symptoms, a child for example, appears to be quite a problem. To the untrained, his activities or failures are not really any different from those of other non-learners or trouble-makers. To the teacher faced with the responsibility of instructing, it is vital to know how and where such behavior differs from other patterns of behavior. It is vital to know whether inattention is functional, and thus the responsibility of the child and teacher, or attributable to an inability to shut out extraneous stimuli, and thus beyond the child's conscious efforts. If the inattention is involuntary, it follows that the teacher should try to reduce the number of stimuli impinging on a child and overwhelming his discriminatory defenses.

Much of the work on brain injury has been done by Strauss and his associates. Strauss identified the behavorial attributes of brain-injured children as: (a) disturbances in perception, (b) disturbances in concept formation, (c) disturbances in language, and (d) disturbances in emotional behavior (*108*, p. 714).

More information on the difficulties which the brain-injured child experiences will be found in Chapters 5 and 10. Having sketched the nature of the brain-injured child's behavioral deviations, it is now appropriate to describe how his behavorial difficulties appear in diagnostic settings.

It is important to reiterate a point. The concern in this discussion will not be for the *pathology* of the problem but for the *dysfunction* which is its operational counterpart.

There are children who have disturbances of function that call attention to themselves. It is this manifest, phenomenal problem that is the issue here, since in retardates it is the manifold dysfunctions which are the difficulty. The neurology of the conditions can be set aside, since it reflects a fundamental problem in its own right, as the next chapter will show.

The following examples illustrate the way in which perceptual, motor, and conceptual dysfunction may appear. It is assumed in this instance that no gross neurological signs make attention to behavior superfluous.

In those instances where children are poor at drawing, and the goal of their drawing is some representation of an object, perceptually disturbed children may have difficulty producing a coherent series of lines, despite nominally adequate motor control.

A high degree of distractibility which is traceable to a central lack of inhibition may be manifested in children by an unduly short attention span, lack of resistance to distractions, and a serious degree of excitability.

Persistence of previously appropriate behavior in a context where it is no longer wholly appropriate is indicative of a dysfunction of normal behavior.

When there are no difficulties beyond an unexpected degree of stereotypy of behavior, the cause may lie in an organically determined inflexibility. Usually the locus of such injury is important to neurologists and neurosurgeons. Reitan's studies suggest that fairly conventional perceptual-motor tasks can reveal a good deal of information on the site of a lesion. Of course there are many types of brain injury, and they present different symptoms. Excellent discussions may be found in the papers by Graham and Berman (*44*) and by Haynes and Sells (*47*). The empirical findings of Friedman and Barclay that neurologically defined brain-injured subjects may perform quite similarly to the non-brain-injured should be kept in mind (33). The investigators found no difference in performance on the scales of Graham and Kendall and of Benton and on three sub-scales of the *Wechsler Adult Intelligence Scale (WAIS)*. Perceptual motor tasks reveal significant information, but not in all circumstances.

Under standardized conditions the following situations have been identified as empirically significant indicants of brain injury. Graham and Kendall reported the results of asking seventy brain-injured and seventy controls to reproduce fifteen designs. They found the organics did consistently poorer than the controls (45). The application of the Graham-Kendall test is helpful in diagnostic settings with retarded children, as long as one keeps in mind some of the reservations suggested by Gallagher (35).

A fairly recent English measure of brain damage seems to be useful. Walton and Black have reported data on a scale which requires the subject to learn a series of words. The standardization and cross-validation seem to indicate that the scale may be profitably incorporated into standard psychometric batteries (114, 115).

Krout has advocated that the disabilities of brain-injured subjects must be evaluated by a two-stage process. In the first stage a global measure of ability would be obtained; in the second, the Graham-Kendall, the Hunt-Minnesota, and the Goldstein-Scheerer scales would be applied (68).

Several writers have advocated the use of the marble-board as an indicant of organically based perceptual dysfunction (10) (118). The child is asked to reproduce a standardized group of designs created by placing marbles on a board with appropriate recesses. Gallagher's findings (35) are less indicative of the value of this technique than are the findings of Bensberg (10).

Werner's studies of the performance of organic mental retardates deserve attention. Of his many studies, two will illustrate his findings. In 1946, Werner published a thorough experimental account of "Abnormal and Subnormal Rigidity" (117). In this study he identified rigidity as a problem in retardates and then extended his findings by identifying specific forms of rigidity peculiar to brain-injured retardates. Working with Strauss several years earlier, Werner had established the interesting failure of brain-injured children to resolve ambiguities of figure and ground relations. Their drawings of material presented tachistoscopically failed to preserve the approximation of the original figures. Familial defectives were able to produce only crude drawings, but these productions contained the organization of the original stimuli.

Holland and Beech have demonstrated a significant difference between brain-injured and non-brain-injured subjects in the perception of the spiral aftereffect at a highly significant level (50).

A similar finding using a similar perceptual modality was reported recently by Schacter and Apgar (102). They found a significant difference in the perception of brain-injured children on visual tests employing a critical flicker-frequency.

McMurray's findings on sorting, using three figures and three colors on twenty-seven cards, demonstrated the conceptual rigidity of the brain-injured. "It was demonstrated that the brain-injured were significantly more rigid in conceptual thinking as shown by their greater tendency to perseverate on a card-sorting task. The exogenous child is indeed less able to shift his mental set from a sorting principle such as color to another such as form or number" (72, p. 369).

McMurray has also demonstrated the differential performance of exogenous retardates when perceiving Lissajou's figures, which use perspective. The exogenous group perceived a significantly smaller number of reversals than a group of endogenous retardates. McMurray rejected inadequate memory as a cause of the exogenous child's poor performance and maintained that the perception of stimuli was faulty (73).

Perhaps the most comprehensive study in recent years of the performance of brain-injured children is Gallagher's monograph about the performance of familial and organic children on several psychological tasks and tests (35). The findings are based on forty-eight paired subjects. The procedures are deliberate, while the design is inclusive. Gallagher's discussion is excellent, and among the points he raises are two particularly important questions:

> It makes sense to ask the question: Are the differences that can be seen between these two groups substantial enough to create recognizable differences in the total patterns of development of the children in these groups? The writer believes that this study and previous research direct an affirmative answer to this question. A second crucial question might be: Do these differences imply the need for drastically modified educational and training programs or merely slight modifications in existing programs? . . . The range of different problems and lack of problems within the brain-injured group is large enough to cast considerable doubt on the notion that plans can or should be made for brain-injured children as though they were a homogenous group (35, p. 65).

Gallagher is suggesting that, in addition to discriminating between brain-injured and non-brain-injured retardates, more delineation within the brain-injured group is necessary.

Aphasia

One of the specific entities which can be subsumed under brain injury is aphasia. This is a loss of language due to damage to the temporal lobe of the brain, particularly Wernicke's and Broca's areas.

There are not many aphasic children. Yet the diagnosis is fashionable, much as cerebral palsy was fashionable around 1950. At that time, in many discussions, problem children were held to be cases of cerebral palsy; at the slightest provocation inadequately trained personnel would mutter "spastic" and feel that a day's work was done. Currently there seems to be a minor epidemic of aphasia, with children who are simply non-verbal, or cases of severe hearing loss, being given this diagnosis. In some cases uncomplicated mental retardation of a genetic sort, i.e., non-brain-injured, who are born into upper-middle-class or professional families probably receive more consideration in this regard than do others.

Di Carlo has discussed aphasia as an overworked construct (28). The value of his observations is the evidence he uses to support his opinion. He analyzed the skills of sixty-seven children and found that the posited entity "congenital aphasia" was replaced by numerous entities. Di Carlo found more adequacy by representing the problems of sixty children through several aggregates of multiple deficiencies. The disabilities were configurations of auditory memory span, auditory discrimination, and auditory synthesis.

The purpose of these aspersions is not to deny the validity of diagnoses of aphasia but rather to suggest that this is a somewhat overworked category at the moment. It may well be that differential diagnoses ten years from now will hinge on suppressed left-handedness or forms of toilet training, much as aphasia seems to be a current concern. There is little doubt that there are fashions in diagnostic evaluations of children as there are in other human endeavors.

Having urged a degree of caution in diagnosing aphasia, we may consider the cases where the entity does exist and see how it may be manifested in children's performances.

The condition of aphasia is a language dysfunction originating in damage to the areas of the cerebral cortex where speech is initiated motorically and formulated symbolically. The form of aphasia which is seen by most people is the state of an elderly person following a stroke. In such people there may be partial or total paralysis, accompanied by total or partial disruption of the language process. The language dysfunction may be an inability to develop symbols, or to comprehend them, or both. The presented symptoms are those of mutism and emotional ability or sometimes depression.

The condition in children may be slight or severe. There may or may not be symptoms of mutism, hearing loss, the various -plegias, perseveration, and rigidity. A superficial examination of such children results in judgments of mental retardation, disobedience, character disorders, deafness, and the like. Since there are many children who are multiple-handicap cases, it is not impossible for aphasia to exist along with the conditions it seems to simulate. Since most examinations involve communication between clinician and child, it can be seen that the differential diagnosis is most difficult. In some cases behavioral evidence is equivocal and neurological findings are more definitive.

Some of the ways in which sub-normal performance may be traced to aphasia are as follows. First, there is the evidence, just discussed, of brain injury. Second, since the specific symptom is language, or the lack of it, some cues may appear in verbal materials. An example of this is a marked difference in the ability to use words and concepts expressively and receptively. A child may respond to a series of common objects when told, "Show me the one we———with," depending on the object, by indicating it correctly. He may then fail when asked, "What is this called?" Such differences are usually not clear-cut and consist of comparatively better or worse performance.

The eventual judgment will lie with the clinician. In some cases there may be enough of a difference to develop an hypothesis of aphasia, but the ultimate decision may be made in light of neurological evidence of organicity.

A comparable problem in differentiation is deciding whether severe language retardation constitutes a problem because of low capacity to develop language—mental retardation—or because of a serious hearing disorder. That deafness does not present intrinsic limitations to concept formation is not always accepted. Rosenstein, however, supplied evidence on the adequacy of concept formation in the deaf in 1959 (91).

The best compendium on the use of background data to differentially diagnose hearing and aphasic disorders is probably that of Goldstein, Landau, and Kleffner (43).

Using 183 children, they derived data by investigating (1) puretone audiograms, (2) case histories, (3) caloric tests of vestibular function, (4) neurologic examinations, (5) electroencephalograms, and (6) skull X-rays. The resulting analysis showed a pattern of data which is presented in Table 6·2. In some ways the use of background information in this manner is analogous to the technique advocated by Riggs and Rain at the Vineland Training School. This analysis of the material illustrates the problems of differential diagnosis. In cases of aphasia the frequent presence of other disorders makes judgments cautious;

TABLE 6·2
DIFFERENTIATING CHARACTERISTICS OF DEAF AND APHASIC CHILDREN

| | Most Useful | | | Least Useful | | |
	Etiology	Auditory	Motor System	Vestibular	EEG	Skull X-rays
DEAF	Meningitis Severe infantile infection Family history of hearing loss	Sloping audiogram	No major abnormality	Normal, except for children with meningitis, etc.	—	—
DEAF or APHASIC	Maternal rubella Complication during pregnancy Rh Complication of labor and birth Convulsive disorder	Sloping audiogram Moderately severe hearing loss Normal hearing or flat audiogram with moderate hearing loss	Minor abnormality Major abnormality	Normal, depressed or no response (with sloping audiogram and moderately severe hearing loss) Depressed (with normal hearing or moderate hearing)	Normal or dysrhythmic Focal abnormality	Normal Anomaly of cranial vault
APHASIC	Congenital brain abnormality Family history of speech or neurologic disorder					

TABLE 6·3
SCHUELL'S CLASSIFICATION OF APHASIA

Classification	Findings	Prognosis
Group I Severe impairment.	1. Impairment of auditory recognition. 2. No functional speech, reading, or writing.	Poor. Can learn to repeat and copy, but language does not become functional.
Group II Impairment of reauditorization (auditory retention span, auditory recall).	1. Impairment of auditory retention span. 2. Inconsistent articulation errors resulting from imperfect auditory imagery. 3. Word-finding errors. 4. Reading and writing reflect errors found in speech.	Excellent. Approximate former performance level. Speech, reading, and writing improve simultaneously as a result of auditory stimulation.
Group III Impairment of reauditorization with co-existing visual involvement.	1. All findings reported for Group II. 2. Confusion of letters and words which look alike. 3. Reversals, distortions, and substitutions of letters which look alike found in writing.	Recovery of speech good. Reading and writing slower. Good results not obtained if marked spatial disorientation is present.
Group IV Impairment of reauditorization with co-existing sensori-motor involvement.	1. Auditory recognition is intact, but impairment of auditory retention span and of auditory recall is frequently severe. 2. Repetition is impaired. Articulation errors are consistent.	Limited recovery. Speech is defective and hesitant and vocabulary frequently limited, but language is functional as acquired. Reading and writing lag behind speech.
Group V Scattered auditory, visual, and motor findings compatible with generalized brain damage. Some language functions retained.	1. Patients usually make errors in trying to follow directions and understand paragraphs. 2. Reading comprehension reduced. 3. Cranial nerve findings usually present. 4. Slurred speech. 5. Distortions in drawing and writing.	Guarded. Patients often get more speech, but are incapable of sustained effort and do not make consistent progress.

225

by no stretch of the imagination can a differential diagnosis of aphasia be reached easily or quickly.

Of the several standardized approaches to diagnosis, the one by Schuell may be considered (103). Schuell's examination has four parts: (1) auditory disturbances, (2) visual disturbances, (3) speech and language disturbances, and (4) visual and writing disturbances. Subjects are classified on the basis of findings into five groups which have differing symptoms and degrees of intensity. Table 6·3 shows Schuell's classification.

As a way of summarizing this abbreviated discussion of aphasia, a few points may be noted. Aphasia is not a tidy, discrete entity; it overlaps and simulates other conditions. The diagnosis of aphasia is a very difficult task and cannot be done by everyone, at least not competently. The functional significance of a diagnosis of aphasia does not preclude the presence of other entities. As a last point, the differential diagnosis stands as a way of making predictive statements about disposition and treatment.

Emotional Disturbance

Examiners are sometimes called on to consider the presented pattern of behavior in a child who is a suspected case of mental retardation mainly because he acts abnormally. His behavior is unusual, but the people who identified him at a screening level are unable to make a more precise judgment.

In cases of aphasia or generalized brain injury the diagnostic entities are fairly clear. Unfortunately, the same degree of clarity is not present for the severe behavioral disorders. The result is that a differential diagnosis can eliminate some reasonably clear conditions but cannot deal as equitably with the emotional states which are less uniform and well defined.

To make this point a little clearer: entities such as compulsion, neuroses, fears, obsessions, hostility, and the like are not the issue. What *is* the issue can be described by considering a case reported by Lazure:

> Pierre est devenu "très sérieux" depuis la naissance du bébé: il passe des heures à jouer seul de façon stéréotypée, e.g., à pousser son camion préfére, et il ne montre plus d'intérêt envers les autres enfants. Ou encore, il se réfugie dans la salle de toilette et y demeure trés longtemps, occupé à déchirer du papier: si l'on interrompt l'un ou l'autre de ses rituels, il entre dans une grande colère et pleure sans toutefois verser des larmes (69, p. 19).

Here is a child who is acting in an abnormal fashion apparently precipitated by the birth of another child. Not only were there the symptoms

of solitary play with his favorite truck, his solitary occupation of tear-
ing up paper in the bathroom, and his emotional outbursts, but we are
told that the previously established sphincter control disappeared and
that language was also lost.

Such a child is obviously behaving in an alarming way. A clinician
might see here a child who would not communicate. What are the
ways of gathering information about this child? To reiterate a point,
the Stanford-Binet simply would not do; a hearing test would also accomplish nothing, while the reflexes would probably appear entirely
adequate to a neurologist.

Consider another case; this is an account of twin girls, three years
old, whose behavior has always been abnormal, reported by Chapman:

> During the latter half of the first year of life the parents began to
> notice abnormalities in the behavior of both girls. They were listless,
> apathetic, and not as active physically as normal children. They did not
> respond to speech, and the parents wondered if they were deaf. Neither
> twin made an attempt to talk . . . they did not play with each other, or
> with other children. If one of them accidentally infringed on the ac-
> tivity of the other, they became agitated and moaned and walked
> away (20, p. 622).

One more example from the literature—Kanner presents this case:

> Donald T. at seven years of age was asked the Binet question: "If I were
> to buy four cents worth of candy and give the storekeeper ten cents,
> how much money would I get back?" He obviously knew the answer.
> His reply, however, was not "six cents," but, "I'll draw a hexagon." Two
> years previously, at five years of age, Donald had been scribbling with
> crayons; all the while he kept saying with conviction "Annette and
> Cecile make purple." It was learned that at home Donald had five bot-
> tles of paint. He named each one after one of the Dionne Quintuplets.
> Blue became "Annette," the red became "Cecile." After that *Annette*
> became the word for blue and *Cecile* for red. Purple not being one of
> the five colors remained *purple* (61, p. 717).

This child would again give the Binet examiner some difficulty. It
would violate the canons of testing to accept his answer; but the essence of "hexagon" is the right concept. Here is a disturbance of the
language process which is an embarrassment of riches, rather than an
omission. A glance at Figure 6·1 will illustrate the commonality of the
language dysfunction in the three cases, though this is manifested in
vastly different ways.

The Entities

At this point the three cases seem to be quite different. This is probably because the accounts are set in a time perspective. Were the in-

formation simply presented as data, the behavior of the child vis-à-vis the diagnostician, the problem would be no less difficult, but not primarily because of the lack of extra information.

The chief reason would be the lack of a theoretical schema based on prior data, and inductively built, to relate one case to the other, one symptom to the other. There are psychoanalytic formulations, but they represent a mystique and rarely meet the criteria of empirical science.

The few models that are extant to handle the data in emotionally disturbed children are largely the personal formulations of a few very clever people. Understanding more about the affective disorders at this point is largely a matter of seeing children through their eyes. Unfortunately, Bender, and Kanner cannot communicate with large numbers of people didactically; thus their excellent formulations are not generalized to any great extent.

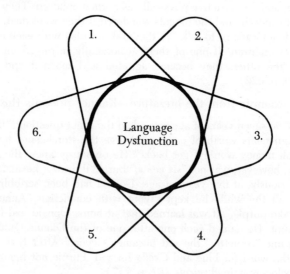

Language is a factor in many abnormal patterns of behavior.
1. mental retardation, exogenous & endogenous. 2. cerebral palsy.
3. aphasia. 4. schizophrenic-autistic states. 5. hearing & deafness.
6. isolation amentia.

Figure 6·1

Language and the Behavorial Syndromes

Some of the theoretical problems in the area of affective disturbances have been discussed thoroughly. Kanner's papers are very informative (60, 61); and so are Goldstein's, particularly the one in which he expands on some of Kanner's ideas (42).

Cassel has pointed out that a very serious problem is the failure to describe the entities involved (19). In the first case, the one presented by Lazure, the investigator pinned his differential diagnosis on several key points: the loss of affective contact with reality; the autism—the isolation of the child; the obvious regressive components, sphincters, and language; the narcissism of the behavior, its stereotypy and bizarre quality. Lazure presents his judgment in the form of a diagnosis of psychotic reaction (69).

The second study concerned the little girls. In this instance there is no history of a crucial incident; there is no identifiable precipitating factor. The unique thing is that the children's condition at three is an extension in time and growth of their earlier condition. Their indifference was noted between the age of six months and their first birthday. By age three their isolation was established, and they were presented for examination. In this case the aloneness, the concern for the self (αὐτος), is an obvious thing. Kanner's entity, an autistic state, is the conclusion of the author (20).

The third case is one presented by Kanner and Lesser (61), (60, 123). They discuss the schizophrenic-like thought process of the boy and the literalness of his language in other ways. These authors also mention the extent to which autistic children are mistakenly thought to be deaf or hard of hearing.

The role of language in childhood schizophrenia has also been of interest to research workers. Goldfarb, Braunstein, and Scholl have reported on their investigations of this entity (39). They report no systematic language pattern.

Bender has used the phrase "Childhood Schizophrenia" to describe some of her disturbed children. She finds that the disturbances affect every aspect of the child's functioning and points out the uniqueness of individual patterns (9). Colbert and Koegler's comments on toe-walking exemplify the bizarre things that occur in children and the uniqueness of their behavior (22).

A relevant clinical entity is Heller's disease. This is a condition, fortunately rare, in which growth is normal in early childhood but regression begins between eighteen months and four years. Unlike the "true" schizophrenic state and autistic state, there are some conclusions about etiology. Two papers, Benda and Melchior (8), and Roy (93), have entertained seriously a somatic basis for this disease. Others formulate the problem as functional, pointing to the continued growth of the child's metabolic and motor systems (121).

The opposing points of view are not easy to reconcile; but more fundamentally, they are not even easy to relate. The reasons are the lack of a data language to describe the evidence and the uniqueness of the behavior patterns from child to child. The relative infrequency of these conditions precludes wholesale gathering of data.

Since the term *autism* has become more widely known in recent years, it is appropriate to point out that understanding has not kept pace with use of the term. The Japanese psychiatrist Makita has specified three entities (74). He has reiterated Kanner's use of (a) *infantile autism* in connection with schizophrenic processes; he has examined (b) *autismus infantus,* the organically based consideration; and he has used (c) *pseudoautism* for conditions of uncertain neurotic and organic origin.

Rimland's formulation of autism appeared in 1964 (88). His approach is primarily cognitive; and he views autism as a condition in which brain mechanisms, conceivably activated by the reticular formation, are malfunctioning. The psychological state is one of narrowed memory associations with emotional disturbance (affect) produced by a discrepancy between internalized expectations of reality and actual experience. Rimland has since developed a diagnostic checklist beyond the form in which it appears in his 1964 monograph. Eighty items constitute *Form 2,* and they are designed primarily for children between ages three and five.

Relevance to Mental Retardation

Having discussed the entities which may be considered in evaluating deviant patterns of behavior, we can now relate the issues to mental retardation. In addition to children who are schizoid or mentally retarded, there are the children who are schizoid and manifest it essentially by appearing retarded; a further consideration is the child who is both psychotic and retarded. Still one other consideration is that the individual may present an extremely atypical pattern which leads the diagnostician to include several entities to be sure the diagnosis is not considered inadequate.

All of these conditions would appear to most people to be quite similar, and even a skilled diagnostician would find more commonalities than distinctive elements among such patterns. It is only in the textbooks and the classic cases in the literature that behavior patterns are really lucid.

To summarize, one possible consideration that diagnosticians may keep in mind is that a child functioning at a retarded level is really psychotic. This has been uncovered on several occasions (3, 82, 112). The reverse of this situation has also been studied. This is the situation where a diagnosis of psychosis is made with an additional diagnosis of mental retardation. The little empirical evidence on this aspect of the problem of differential diagnosis is both revealing and enlightening.

Evidence presented by Chapman and Pathman is revealing because it demonstrates that the joint diagnosis was made because the behavior was psychotic but not distinctive; probably because of this last attribute the examiners appended the diagnosis of mental retardation (21). This data is enlightening because it demonstrates the inherent difficulty in making differential diagnoses even when the clinician is well trained. Obviously, when the client is a child, the difficulty is increased. Children who are disturbed have not reached the maturity of development which can be capitalized on in treatment. Also, in terms of presented symptoms, a little regression can take them back so far. When this occurs, they give up speech, and the whole basis of communication with the child is lost. The differential diagnosis may not then be possible from direct verbal interaction with the child but may have to be made by an indirect, inferential process.

DIAGNOSTIC POSSIBILITIES

Looking to the future we may hope to see more effective procedures for studying children. New scales will appear and clinicians will become more sophisticated. One way to increase the validity of procedures is to develop more comprehensive systems of thought within which clinicians may manipulate findings. One approach would be extension of the studies of syntax mentioned in Chapter 5, "Language." It may be that discrete patterns of syntax can be found in entities such as familial retardation, given specification of ecological factors such as social class and the size of the sibship. More interestingly, there might be more discrete patterns of syntax than known types of retardation. In that case language would yield precise patterns of retardation parallel to, but much more valuable than, current innovations in, for example, chromosomal descriptions. If this were to occur if would be similar to the differentiation of distractability which Zuk has proposed as an alternative to the global concept previously in use (122). Returning to language, however, we have a paradigm in the aphasia studies of Wepman and his associates (55). They have articulated computer operations with a corpus of 343,011 words. The result is that most of a specific sample of language can be analyzed automatically for grammatical functions. This yields linguistic descriptions based on syntax.

SUMMARY

This chapter has attempted to consider some of the conceptual problems in the process of evaluating children presented as possibly retarded. The inherent difficulty of differential diagnoses and the psychometric considerations have been examined. The chapter has considered some of the nosological entities encountered in atypical children and pointed out the ambiguity of many behavior patterns. The over-all conclusion may be reached that diagnostic judgments about children are difficult to make and require a great deal of skill and sensitivity.

BIBLIOGRAPHY

1. Allen, R. M., and Collins, M. G., "Suggestions for the Adaptive Administration of Intelligence Tests for Those with Cerebral Palsy," *Cerebral Palsy Rev.*, 1955, *16*, 11-14.

2. Anastasi, A., *Psychological Testing*, Macmillan, 1954.

3. Angus, L., "Schizophrenia and Schizoid Conditions in Students in a Special School," *Am. J. Ment. Def.*, 1948, *50*, 227-238.

4. Armstrong, M. A., "Children's Response to Animal and Human Figures in Thematic Pictures," *J. Consult. Psych.*, 1954, *18*, 67-70.

5. Baroff, J. S., "WISC Patterning in Endogenous Mental Deficiency," *Am. J. Ment. Def.*, 1959, *64*, 482-485.

6. Beck, H. S., and Lam, R. L., "Use of the WISC in Predicting Organicity," *J. Clin. Psych.*, 1955, *11*, 154-158.

7. Beier, E. G., Gorlow, L., and Stacey, C. L., "The Fantasy Life of the Mental Defective," *Am. J. Ment. Def.*, 1951, *55*, 582-589.

8. Benda, C. E., and Melchior, J. C., "Childhood Schizophrenia, Childhood Autism, and Heller's Disease," *Internat. Rec. Med.*, 1959, *172*, 137-154.

9. Bender, L., "Childhood Schizophrenia," *Nerv. Ch.*, 1942, *1*, 138-140.

10. Bensberg, G. J., "A Test for Differentiating Endogenous and Exogenous Mental Defectives," *Am. J. Ment. Def.*, 1950, *54*, 502-506.

11. Bilger, R. C., "Limitations on the Use of Intelligence Scales to Estimate the Mental Age of Children," *Volta Rev.*, 1958, *60*, 321-325.

12. Birch, J. W., "The Goodenough Drawing Test and Older Mentally Retarded Children," *Am. J. Ment. Def.*, 1949, *54*, 218-224.

13. _____, "The Utility of Short Forms of the Stanford-Binet Tests of Intelligence with Mentally Retarded Children," *Am. J. Ment. Def.*, 1955, *59*, 462-484.

14. Bond, G. L., and Fay, L. F., "A Comparison of the Performance of Good and Poor Readers on the Individual Items of the Stanford-Binet Scale, Forms L and M," *J. Ed. Res.*, 1950, *43*, 475-479.

15. Bryan, J. H., London, P., and Lauterbach, C., "Parent Attitudes and Child Guidance Practices," *U. S. Armed F. Med. J.*, 1959, *10*, 848-851.

16. Buck, J., "The H-T-P, A Projective Device," *Am. J. Ment. Def.*, 1947, *51*, 606-610.

17. Buros, O. K., *The Fourth Mental Measurements Yearbook*, Gryphon Press, 1953.

18. Canter, A., "The Use of the Columbia Mental Maturity Scale with Cerebral Palsied Children," *Am. J. Ment. Def.*, 1956, *60*, 843-851.

19. Cassel, R. H., "Differentiation Between the Mental Defective with Psychosis and the Childhood Schizophrenic Functioning as a Mental Defective," *Am. J. Ment. Def.*, 1957, *62*, 103-107.

20. Chapman, A. H., "Early Infantile Autism in Identical Twins," *Arch. Neur. Psychiat.*, 1957, *78*, 621-623.

21. Chapman, L. J., and Pathman, J. H., "Errors in the Diagnosis of Mental Deficiency in Schizophrenia," *J. Consult. Psych.*, 1959, *23*, 432-434.

22. Colbert, E. G., and Koegler, R. R., "Toe Walking in Childhood Schizophrenia," *J. Pediat.*, 1958, *53*, 219-222.

23. Coleman, J. M., Iscoe, I., and Brodsky, M., "The 'Draw-a-Man' Test as a Predictor of School Readiness and as an Index of Emotional and Physical Maturity," *Pediat.*, 1959, *24*, 275-281.

24. Condell, J. F., "Note on the Use of the Ammons Full Range Picture Vocabulary Test with Retarded Children," *Psych. Rep.*, 1959, *5*, 150.

25. Corwin, Betty J., "The Influence of Culture and Language on Performance on Individual Ability Tests," unpublished study reported by Dunn, personal communication.

26. Cutts, R. A., "A Projective Interview Technique," *Am. J. Ment. Def.*, 1956, *61*, 191-197.

27. Daryn, E., "Problems of Children with 'Diffuse Brain Damage'," *Arch. Gen. Psychiat.*, 1961, *4*, 299-306.

28. DiCarlo, L. M., "Differential Diagnosis of Congenital Aphasia," *Volta Rev.*, 1960, *62*, 361-364.

29. Dunn, L. M., and Vergason, G. A., "Effects of Illustration Size on PPVT Test Performance," *Peabody Papers Hum. Devpm.*, 1964, Vol. 2, No. 3.

30. Finley, Carmen J., and Thompson, J. M., "An Abbreviated Wechsler Intelligence Scale for Children for Use with the Educable Mentally Retarded," *Amer. J. Ment. Defic.*, 1958, *63*, 473-480.

31. Freeman, F., *Theory and Practice of Psychological Testing*, Holt, Rinehart & Winston, 1955.

32. French, J. L., "Intellectual Appraisal of Physically Handicapped Children," *J. Genet. Psych.*, 1959, *59*, 131-141.

33. Friedman, E. C., and Barclay, A., "The Discriminative Validity of Certain Psychological Tests as Indices of Brain Damage in the Mentally Retarded," *Ment. Retard.*, 1963, *1*, 291-293.

34. Font, M., "Some Clinical Applications of the Rorschach Technique in Cases of Borderline Deficiency," *Am. J. Ment. Def.*, 1950, *54*, 507-511.

35. Gallagher, J. J., "A Comparison of Brain-Injured and Non-Brain-Injured Mentally Retarded Children on Several Psychological Variables," *Mon. Soc. Res. Ch. Dev.*, 1957, No. 65.

36. _____, Benoit, E. P., and Boyd, H. F., "Measures of Intelligence in Brain Damaged Children," *J. Clin. Psych.*, 1956, *12*, 69-72.

37. Garfield, S. L., "Problems in the Psychological Evaluation of the Subnormal Individual," *Am. J. Ment. Def.*, 1959, *64*, 467-471.

38. Garrett, Jane, "Comparison of the Peabody Picture Vocabulary Test and Wechsler Intelligence Scale for Children," master's thesis, George Peabody College for Teachers, Nashville, Tenn., 1959.

39. Goldfarb, W., Braunstein, P., and Scholl, H., "An Approach to the Study of Childhood Schizophrenia: The Speech of Schizophrenic Children," *Am. J. Orthopsychiat.*, 1959, *29*, 481-486.

40. Goldman, D., and Rosenberg, B., "Electro-Encephalographic Observations in Psychotic Children," *Compr. Psychiat.*, 1962, *3*, 93-112.

41. Goldstein, H., Moss, J., and Jordan, Laura, "The Efficacy of Special Class Training on the Development of Mentally Retarded Children," unpublished report, Institute for Research on Exceptional Children, Urbana, Ill., 1964.

42. Goldstein, K., "Abnormal Mental Conditions in Infancy," *J. Nerv. Ment. Dis.*, 1959, *128*, 538-557.

43. Goldstein, R., Landau, W. M., and Kleffner, F. R., "Neurologic Assessment of Some Deaf and Aphasic Children," *Ann. Ot. Rhin. Laryng.*, 1958, *67*, 468-480.

44. Graham, F. K., and Berman, P. W., "Current Status of Behavior Tests for Brain Damage in Infants and Preschool Children," *Amer. J. Orthopsychiat.*, 1961, *31*, 713-727.

45. Graham, F. K., and Kendall, B. S., "Performance of Brain Damaged Cases on a Memory-for-Designs Test," *J. Abn. Soc. Psych.*, 1946, *41*, 303-314.

46. Green, M. W., and Ewert, J. C., "Normative Data on Progressive Matrices," *J. Consult. Psych.*, 1955, *19*, 139-142.

47. Haynes, J. R., and Sells, S. B., "Assessment of Organic Brain Damage by Psychological Tests," *Psych. Bull.*, 1963, *60*, 316-325.

48. Hedges, M. F., "An Analysis of Three Picture Vocabulary Tests for Use with the Deaf," study in press reported by Dunn, personal communication.

49. Heimburger, R. F., and Reitan, R. M., "Easily Administered Written Test for Lateralogy Brain Lesions," *J. Neurosurg.*, 1961, *18*, 301-312.

50. Holland, H. C., and Beech, H. R., "Spiral After-Effect as a Test of Brain Damage," *J. Ment. Sc.*, 1958, *104*, 466-471.

51. Illingworth, R. S., and Birch, C. B., "The Diagnosis of Mental Retardation in Childhood," *Arch. Dis. Chldhd.*, 1959, *34*, 269-273.

52. Jastak, J., "A Rigorous Criterion of Feeblemindedness," *J. Abn. Soc. Psych.*, 1949, *44*, 347-378.

53. Jolles, I., "Diagnostic Implications of Rorschach's Test in Case Studies of Mental Defectives," *Genet. Psych. Mon.*, 1947, *36*, 89-197.

54. _____, "A Study of Mental Deficiency by the Rorschach Technique," *Am. J. Ment. Def.*, 1947, *52*, 37-42.

55. Jones, L. V., Goodman, M. F., and Wepman, J. M., "The Classification of Parts of Speech for the Characterization of Aphasia," *Lang. Speech*, 1963, *6*, 94-108.

56. Jordan, T. E., "Formboard Equivalence in the Colored Progressive Matrices," *J. Clin. Psych.*, 1959, *15*, 422-423.

57. _____, "Psychological Findings in a Case of Von Recklinghausen's Disease and Hyperpituitarism," *J. Clin. Psych.*, 1956, *12*, 389-391.

58. _____, and Bennett, C., "An Item Analysis of the Colored Progressive Matrices," *J. Consult. Psych.*, 1957, *21*, 222.

59. _____, and deCharms, R., "The Achievement Motive in Normal and Mentally Retarded Children," *Am. J. Ment. Def.*, 1959, *64*, 457-466.

60. Kanner, L., "Emotional Interference with Intellectual Functioning," *Am. J. Ment. Def.*, 1952, *56*, 701-707.

61. _____, and Lesser, L., "Early Infantile Autism," *Pediat. Clin. N. Am.*, 1958, *5*, 711-730.

62. Kicklighter, R., *Comparison of PPVT and RSB Test Scores of Educable Mentally Retarded Children*, Atlanta, Ga., 1964.

63. Kingsley, H., and Gary, R., *The Nature and Conditions of Learning*, Prentice-Hall, 1957.

64. Kirk, S. A., and McCarthy, J. J., "The Illinois Test of Psycholinguistic Abilities—An Approach to Differential Diagnosis," *Amer. J. Ment. Def.*, 1961, *66*, 399-412.

65. Kirman, B. H., "Prognostic Difficulties in Mental Retardation," *Internat. Rec. Med.*, 1959, *172*, 197-203.

66. Kogan, K. L., and Crager, R. L., "Standardization of the Children's Picture Information Test," *J. Clin. Psych.*, 1959, *15*, 405-411.

67. Kraus, J., "Differential Diagnosis in Borderline Cases of Mental Deficiency: A Suggestion on Methods," *Austral. J. Psychol.*, 1960, *12*, 189-198.

68. Krout, M. H., "Is the Brain Injured a Mental Defective?" *Am. J. Ment. Def.*, 1949, *54*, 81-86.

69. Lazure, D., "Un Cas de Réaction Psychotique Chez un Enfant D'Age Pre-Scholaire," *Canad. Psychiat. Assoc. J.*, 1959, *4*, 19-22.

70. McCarthy, J. J., and Kirk, S. A., *The Construction, Standardization, and Statistical Characteristics of the Illinois Test of Psycholinguistic Abilities*, University of Illinois, 1963.

71. McClelland, D., *Readings in Motivation*, Appleton-Century-Crofts, 1955.

72. McMurray, J. G., "Rigidity in Conceptual Thinking in Exogenous and Endogenous Mentally Retarded Children," *J. Consult. Psych.*, 1954, *18*, 366-370.

73. _____, "Visual Perception in Exogenous and Endogenous Mentally Retarded Children," *Am. J. Ment. Def.*, 1954, *58*, 659-663.

74. Makita, K., "Early Infantile Autism, Autisms Infantilum, and Pseudo-Autism," *Fol. Psychiat. Neurol. Japan*, 1964, *18*, 97-111.

75. Martin, A., and Wiechers, J., "Raven's Colored Progressive Matrices and the Wechsler Intelligence Scale for Children," *J. Consult. Psych.*, 1954, *18*, 143-144.

76. Mein, R., "Use of the Peabody Picture Vocabulary Test with Severely Subnormal Patients," *Amer. J. Ment. Defic.*, 1962, *67*, 269-273.

77. Menninger, K., "The Psychological Examination in the Psychiatric Case Study," *Bull. Menninger Clin.*, 1959, *23*, 131-143.

78. Moed, G., Wright, B. W., and James, P., "Intertest Correlations of the Wechsler Intelligence Scale for Children and Two Picture Vocabulary Tests," *Educ. Psychol. Meas.*, 1963, *23*, 359-363.

79. Moss, J. W., "An Evaluation of the Peabody Picture Vocabulary Test with the PMA and 1937 Stanford-Binet on Trainable Children," unpublished paper, University of Illinois, Institute for Research on Exceptional Children, 1962.

80. Murray, H., *Explorations in Personality*, Harvard University Press, 1938.

81. Newland, T. E., "Psychological Assessment of Exceptional Children and Youth," in Cruickshank, W., *Psychology of Exceptional Children and Youth*, Prentice-Hall, 1955.

82. O'Gorman, G., "Psychosis as a Cause of Mental Defect," *J. Ment. Sc.*, 1954, *100*, 934-943.

83. Orme, J. E., "The Coloured Progressive Matrices as a Measure of Intellectual Subnormality," *Brit. J. Med. Psych.*, 1961, *34*, 291-292.

84. Orr, K. N., "The Wechsler Intelligence Scale for Children as a Predictor of School Success," master's thesis, Indiana State Teachers College, 1950.

85. Paddle, K. C. L., "Some Observations on the High Grade Unstable Mental Defective," *Am. J. Ment. Def.*, 1947, *51*, 654-659.

86. Pettigrew, T., "Race, Mental Illness, and Intelligence: A Social Psychological View," *Eugen. Quart.*, 1964, *11*, 189-215.

87. Ravenette, A. T., and Hersov, L. A., "Speed of Function and Educational Retardation: The Psychological and Psychiatric Investigation of an Individual Case," *J. Child Psychol. Psychiat.*, 1963, *4*, 17-28.

88. Rimland, B., *Infantile Autism*, Meredith, 1964.

89. Rogers, M. E., Lilienfeld, A. M., and Pasamanick, B., "Prenatal and Paranatal Factors in the Development of Childhood Behavioral Disorders," *Acta. Psychiat. Neurol. Scand. Suppl.*, 1955, No. 102.

90. Rorschach, H., *Psychodiagnostik*, Grune and Stratton, New York, 1949.

91. Rosenstein, J., "Perception and Cognition in Deaf Children," Ph. D. dissertation, Washington University, 1959 (also, *J. Sp. Hear. Res.*, 1960, *3*, 108-119).

92. Ross, C. C., and Stanley, J. C., *Measurement in Today's Schools*, Prentice-Hall, 3rd ed., 1954.

93. Roy, V. I., "Zur Frage der Dementia Infantilis Heller," *Helvet. Paed. Acta*, 1959, *14*, 288-301.

94. Saltzman, S., "The Influence of Social and Economic Background on Stanford-Binet Performance," *J. Soc. Psych.*, 1940, *12*, 71-81.

95. Sandercock, M. G., and Butler, A. J., "An Analysis of the Performance of Mental Defectives on the Wechsler Intelligence Scale for Children," *Am. J. Ment. Def.*, 1952, *57*, 100-105.

96. Sarason, S. B., "The Use of the Thematic Apperception Test with Mentally Deficient Children," *Am. J. Ment. Def.*, 1945, *50*, 272-276.

97. ―――, *Psychological Aspects of Mental Deficiency*, Harper & Brothers, 3rd ed., 1958.

98. Shapiro, M. I., "Psychiatric Examination of the Child," *Ment. Hyg.*, 1959, *43*, 32-39.

99. Sievers, D. J., *et al.*, *Selected Studies on the Illinois Test of Psycholinguistic Abilities*, University of Illinois, 1963.

100. Silverstein, A. B., "WISC and WAIS for the Mentally Retarded," *Amer. J. Ment. Def.*, 1963, *67*, 617-618.

101. Smith, L. M., "The Progressive Matrices and the Stanford-Binet with Exceptional Children," *Excep. Child.*, 1958, *24*, 374-375.

102. Schacter, F. F., and Apgar, V., "Perinatal Asphyxia and Psychological Signs of Brain Damage in Childhood," *Pediat.*, 1959, *24*, 1016-1025.

103. Schuell, H., "A Short Examination for Aphasia, *Neurol.*, 1957, *7*, 625-634.

104. Sloan, W., and Cutts, R. A., "Test Patterns of Mental Defectives on the Revised Stanford-Binet Scale," *Am. J. Ment. Def.*, 1947, *51*, 394-396.

105. Stacey, C. L., and Levin, J., "Performance of Retarded Individuals on Stanford-Binet and Wechsler-Bellevue Intelligence Scales," *Am. J. Ment. Def.*, 1950, *55*, 123-131.

106. Stacey, C. L., and Gill, M. R., "The Relationship between Raven's Colored Progressive Matrices and Two Tests of General Intelligence for 172 Subnormal Adult Subjects," *J. Clin. Psych.*, 1955, *11*, 86-87.

107. Sternlicht, M., "A Downward Application of the 1960 Revised Stanford-Binet with Retardates," *J. Clin. Psych.*, 1965, *21*, 79.

108. Strauss, A., "The Education of the Brain Injured Child," *Am. J. Ment. Def.*, 1952, *56*, 712-718.

109. Terman, L., and Merrill, M., *Measuring Intelligence*, Houghton Mifflin, 1937.

110. Thompson, C. W., and Magaret, A., "Differential Test Responses of Normals and Mental Defectives," *J. Abn. Soc. Psych.*, 1947, *42*, 285-293.

111. Thompson, J. M., and Finley, J., "The Validation of an Abbreviated Wechsler Intelligence Scale for Children for Use with the Educable Mentally Retarded," *Educ. Psychol. Measmt.*, 1962, *22*, 539-542.

112. Toolan, J. M., "The Differential Diagnosis of Mental Deficiency in Adolescents," *Am. J. Ment. Def.*, 1955, *59*, 445-451.

113. Walters, R. H., "The Intelligence Test Performance of Maori Children," *J. Abn. Soc. Psych.*, 1958, *47*, 107-114.

114. Walton, D., and Black, D. A., "The Modified Word Learning Test—Its Diagnostic and Predictive Value as a Test of Brain Damage," *Bull. Brit. Psych. Soc.*, 1959, No. 37.

115. _____, "The Predictive Validity of a Psychological Test of Brain Damage," *J. Ment. Sc.*, 1959, *105*, 807-810.

116. Warren, S. A., and Kraus, M. J., "WAIS Verbal Minus Performance IQ Comparison in Mental Retardates," *J. Clin. Psych.*, 1961, *17*, 57-59.

117. Werner, H., "Abnormal and Sub-Normal Rigidity," *J. Abn. Soc. Psych.*, 1946, *41*, 15-24.

118. _____, "Development of Visuo-Motor Performance on the Marble Board Test in Mentally Retarded Children," *J. Genet. Psych.*, 1944, *64*, 269-279.

119. _____, "Rorschach Method Applied to Two Clinical Groups of Mental Defectives," *Am. J. Ment. Def.*, 1945, *49*, 304-306.

120. _____, and Strauss, A., "Pathology of Figure Background Relations in the Child," *J. Abn. Soc. Psych.*, 1941, *36*, 236-249.

121. Yakovlev, P. I., Weinberger, M., and Chipman, C. E., "Heller's Syndrome on a Pattern of Schizophrenic Behavior Disturbance in Early Childhood," *Am. J. Ment. Def.*, 1948, *53*, 318-337.

122. Zuk, G. H., "Clinical Differentiation of Patterns of Distractability in Young Retarded Children," *J. Clin. Psych.*, 1962, *18*, 780-782.

123. Kanner, L., "Infantile Autism and the Schizophrenias," *Behav. Sci.*, 1965, *10*, 412-420.

Chapter 7

THE SOURCES OF MENTAL
RETARDATION

Sooner or later, most discussions of mental retardation introduce the question of what causes the condition. A conversation between doctor and parent may consider this as a means of understanding why a son or daughter has been afflicted with mental retardation as a matter of seeking purpose or justification. In less catastrophic situations the dialogue may consist of a request for identification of the agent responsible for the child's condition.

Our language shapes our thinking so that we think about *one* element and so that we think of some mechanism intruding into the course of normal development. To phrase this another way, we usually expect to find some single agent involved and to find that its role is contributory. Thus, in polio we have identified a particular biological agent which acts directly on an otherwise normal body.

In the study of disease at a more detached level, in-

239

vestigators take great care to avoid having lines of investigation structured by the language. For example, investigators do not look for *the cause* as if it must be one agent, nor do they always look for direct effects. That approach might ignore the role that the *absence* of elements can play in creating a disorder.

The importance of this consideration is that the problem of why mental retardation occurs in one child and not in another must be approached with a high degree of self-consciousness. The investigator needs to be sure that he is not ignoring lines of investigation because the words in which he thinks structure his approach prematurely. He might spend a lifetime looking for the causative factor in a situation when the successful analysis of the problem later discloses the *absence* of *several* agents. Our language may lead us to look under the streetlight to find the key to our problems, while the proper approach might consist of trying an already open door, The metaphor may be as misleading as the streetlight, in this instance, but the problems of methodology are not always evident.

We may now summarize *ad hoc* and say that the investigation of why mental retardation occurs presents problems that are conceptual in nature. The investigator's first job is to schematize his problems in order to see where and how he should begin.

He may begin by breathing life into an old chestnut. He may decide to ask the question "Which is more important in determining human characteristics, heredity or environment?" In this case he faces a forced choice. He elects to make the locus of his investigation either in the individual or in the circumstances of the individual's growth. It may well be that the consideration of this problem reflects what Kantor has called the *metasystem,* the cultural matrix within which any study takes place. Thus English-speaking investigators typically feel more at ease in discussing environmental elements, while some continental scientists look to the paramount role of the hereditary background of the individual. The problem as posed requires one answer or the other. It should be pointed out that this formulation of the problem cannot be met by electing to consider both "important." The issue evaporates into a mist of superficiality if one adopts this resolution of the problem.

The investigations that have resulted from choosing to study the question, "Which is more important in determining human characteristics, heredity or environment?" have followed one of two different lines of study: we analyze either biological or situational issues. Evidence can be marshalled in both cases. Representative studies to support the environmental argument may be found in the work of Millen and Woollam (89); Ford, Patterson, and Treuting (41); Hicks (53); Coffey and Jessop (*19*); and Dennis (*29*). The genetic argument can be supported by considering contributions by Zellweger (*131*); Klein and Franceschetti (*64*); Higgins (*54*); Reed, Reed, and Palm (*104*); and Richards and Rundle (*107*).

It should be pointed out that these studies are not attempts to settle this issue, nor should they be considered as directly to the point. Rather, they should be considered as indicating that one can find interesting studies to substantiate a preference for environmental or hereditary lines of investigation.

A REFORMULATION

A more productive way to formulate the problem of the various loci of factors that influence development is to investigate the comparative contributions of both environmental and genetic elements. This position assumes that one cannot have environmental factors alone and that genetic factors cannot be studied except as they emerge in some situational context. The utility of this approach has also been pointed out by the British authors Hilliard and Kirman, who give essentially the same reasons in suggesting this conceptual statement of the problem (*55*).

A paper by Runner illustrates the value of this approach and illustrates the techniques involved (*109*). The data reported represent an analysis of the inheritance of susceptibility to congenital deformity. The problem was an attempt to produce developmental disorders in a strain of mice by introducing special agents at the ninth day of gestation. The particular aspect that is relevant at this moment is that the use of an inbred strain results in virtual control of the hereditary background. The manipulation of the particular treatments is the controlled introduction of environmental elements. The results of the study may then be discussed as meaningful since they represent an analysis under conditions of controlled interaction. The situation is realistic because both heredity and environment are considered at the same time under scientific conditions.

DESCRIPTIVE APPROACHES

There are other approaches which are, for the most part, neither right nor wrong, but different. There have always been descriptive studies that give modest answers to modest questions. Munson and May scrutinized the possibility of cleft palate, a developmental disorder, being accompanied by "subnormal intelligence" (*91*). They suggest that among persons afflicted with this disorder there may be more cases of lower intelligence than is usual in a population sample.

Dutton has surveyed the size of mentally retarded British boys (36). Skeletal age was used to calculate a developmental quotient (DQ) which was essentially normal except in cases of a "metabolic" origin. Weight showed that both metabolic and mongoloid boys had low DQ's. Dutton's summary reports the interesting finding of a generally low level of growth efficiency encountered in the "metabolic" group most consistently.

Occasionally, massive descriptive studies are undertaken. Mac-Mahon and McKeown derived a sample from a population of 718,693 babies (83). Their object was to investigate the incidence of hare lip and cleft palate as they relate to maternal age and birth rank. The results are important, since they show that some children who have both of these developmental disorders have other malformations. The 1955 Onondaga County Survey in New York State is another example of what a large descriptive study can unearth. In this case a basic amount of information was amassed which contributed to the demography of mental retardation. The details of this study were reported in a previous chapter.

An interesting survey has related the incidence of congenital malformations to natural background radiation (43). Gentry and his associates have cautiously reported a higher incidence of birth disorders in areas where natural background radioactivity is above average. This is a most careful survey that warns against rash inferences and conclusions about radiation hazards.

The Scandinavians have produced some prodigious surveys that illustrate what can be done on a large scale. Alm followed nearly a thousand premature babies over twenty years (1); Inghe reported a tendency towards lower intelligence scores in his extensive analysis of paupers in Stockholm (56). Hansen reported data on 2,621 cases of cerebral palsy in Denmark (48). Essen-Möller studied the incidence of mental retardation among 2,550 persons in two rural parishes of south Sweden (38).

The studies commented on so far have been finished. Neel reported studies which were not merely unfinished, but also unstarted (92). He suggested three lines of development that would require masses of data. First, he suggested that studies in the comparative incidence and nature of congenital disorders be initiated; his suggestion was to study comparable groups in different circumstances—e.g., Negroes in the United States and in Africa. Secondly, he advocated detailed studies of parents of retarded children. Finally, he encouraged intensive analysis of the siblings of affected children. A comparable proposal has been offered by Pasamanick (98). Hedberg et al. reported outcomes of pregnancy in 3,000 women, and expressed intent to study 15,000 pregnant women by prospective means (51).

INFERENTIAL STUDIES

Differing largely in the subtlety of their design and the modesty of their samples are the inferential studies. Runner's study, already alluded to, used an inbred strain of mice (109). The application of precise controls permitted inferences to be drawn about the physiological mechanisms which developed malformations in the young. As a result, Runner was able to sketch the effects of the treatments, the *teratogenic* agents, as they disturbed body chemistry.

Zellweger has discussed the genetic mechanism of Hurler's Disease (131). His analysis of the mechanism is largely inferred from the study of a number of cases seen in Lebanon, many of whom were related by blood. A similar inferential process may be seen in the studies of the same disease reported from Holland by Van Pelt and Huizinga (119). A sex-linked form of spastic paraplegia was traced back to 1780 in a family studied by Johnston and McKusick (58).

RESEARCH AND THE DISCIPLINES

Another way to formulate the problems of methodology is to consider the contributions of the various disciplines. On this basis the investigator may use methods employed by other investigators but be distinguished from them because he approaches one aspect of the problem and draws his hypotheses from his particular discipline.

Some of the disciplines that offer fruitful lines of investigation are education (33), psychology (29), sociology (39), physiology (115), biology (128), genetics (131), *cytology* (12), teratology (124), medicine (2), and radiology (53). These studies will be discussed a little later. For the moment it is sufficient to consider the modes in which the disciplines contribute. Traditionally, investigation has been a rather solitary activity; scholars pursued their investigations alone or, at most, with their students. Whatever integration occurred happened when individuals incorporated the work of others in order to extend their own horizons, or to provide a literary survey of the work of a number of individuals. A rather different approach is in favor at the moment, not so much because of rational conviction but more because of the power of the purse. The alternative to the traditional form has two main points of departure. One is that integration of disciplines is planned for; the second is that the integration is held to be effective before as well as after actual research; that is, in the planning stages. While this approach is ideal in theory, several human and rather practical problems exist. To begin with, the discipline of medicine is almost invariably the pivot for integration. Such a point of view is contrary to the historical reality of deep commitment lying in disciplines other than medicine. The suspicion persists that the use of medical schools as foci for work in mental retardation is epistemologically naive. This approach pursues the end of ultimate medical findings at the expense of behavioral research with its quicker and intellectually firmer possibilities.

Another aspect of the current integration is that it is generally programmed to the detriment of individualism in favor of intellectual collectivism.

Apart from the author's preference for individuality and the rewards of personal over group endeavor, there exists a factual hazard which collective research cannot avoid. A research team is usually drawn from the ranks of a highly mobile group, university personnel. University-wide organization and planning is unrealistic when it presumes that staffs are permanent, and will remain so. Its research objectives can only presume a degree of faculty stability, often contrary to reality.*

Unfortunately, both government and private agencies encourage group research. To some extent this is because many people influencing research on mental retardation have never done any. More subtle and widespread is the foolish notion that research is an activity whose successive stages can be predicted quite narrowly. More realistically, it is an enterprise within which interests evolve and unsuspected challenges arise. The structure which collective research stresses is unfortunately contrary to the history of human inquiry. It presumes that one can guarantee the future of a line of thought, and it requires inertia in intellectual development and personnel that simply does not happen; indeed, it becomes less probable with each passing day. The only realistic form that group activity can have lies in the aggregate of investigators conducting individual research programs; collectivity, in that case, lies in propinquity rather than ideas.

TOOLS OF RESEARCH

The different tools of research used by the investigator of mental retardation illustrate the extent to which investigations in this area draw from various disciplines.

---

* The author recently examined a building designed for a collective research enterprise. None of the questions it was designed to explore will be answered, because none of the persons for whom it was designed are still connected with the agency which sponsored it.

1. *Microscopy.* An obvious use of the microscope is that it makes visible what is otherwise invisible. The building-blocks of the body, the cells, may thus be examined and their internal elements explored (71). The analysis of body cells taken from mongoloid retardates has been reported from Sweden (12). By examining samples of bone marrow and skin at a magnification up to 3,500 times it has been possible to study some unusual distributions of chromosomes.

2. *Radiation.* A standard diagnostic procedure is the use of X-rays. While not routinely administered to pregnant women nor deliberately employed to investigate the condition of fetuses *in utero,* the X-ray technique has yielded some important information in recent years (41, 53). It suggests some ways of diminishing the number of serious and malignant diseases of childhood.

3. *Chemistry.* The understanding of how prenatal growth can be shifted into abnormal patterns is an important line of research. Such understanding is best reached by laboratory studies which permit the necessary care and control. The introduction of trypan blue, a dye, has produced serious malformations in experimental animals (110). Wilson has pointed out that the mechanisms of such disorders can be generalized as actions specified (1) by agent and (2) by time (126).

The effect of hormones as teratogenic agents, elements which produce malformations, has been commented on by investigators in Prague (115). It appears that between the seventh and tenth week of pregnancy the administration of hormones can produce an important change in the growth of the fetus.

4. *Dietary Controls.* Runner, and Nelson have demonstrated the effects of nutrition on the course of fetal development (109, 93). It appears that introducing or withholding dietary elements has the same general effect on development in mice.

5. *Biological Methods.* Witschi has made a basic contribution to teratology by investigating growth in frogs (128). It appears that the age of the egg, a largely uncontrollable condition except in laboratory animals, plays a role in both twinning and the development of malformations.

6. *Behavioral Techniques.* Apart from investigating how prenatal elements affect growth, there is the possibility of analyzing environmental influences, as Runner's work indicated. In considering the effects of environment, Warkany has pointed out that environment acts on the human fetus even before birth, making preventive measures much more complicated (124).

In the postnatal period, opportunities for analyzing influences are not very controllable. By accident, children may grow under conditions which may be considered experimentally as different treatments. From Iran, Dennis has reported the patterns of growth in children in institutions and has related the developmental status of these groups of children to the circumstances attending their care (29).

7. *Serological Techniques.* In recent years the introduction of techniques to analyze blood samples has been reported. The application of these techniques has unearthed data concerning rare conditions (23, 24, 88, 122) and some which are more frequent (35, 108). In such cases the methodology employed usually seems to add to the accrued knowledge; yet understanding the disorders does not necessarily lead to immediate preventatives and cures. This, of course, is a general problem in any branch of knowledge, since it is easier to comprehend smaller, homogeneous masses of data. On the other hand, while new information reduces the possibility of pat formulations of problems, it does encourage more firmly grounded, if only modest, formulations.

8. *Actuarial Techniques.* An apparently endless and usually profitless task is the accumulation of masses of facts and figures about mental retardation. Surveys cannot create new information and data; they can only catalogue the already existing knowledge. The problem, of course, is that many investigators confuse gathering data with research *in toto,* rather than relegating it to the status of a necessary procedural step. Schlesinger and associates carried data tabulation to the point of utility by investigating "survivorship" in cases of cerebral palsy (111); Erhardt's classification of 11,551 obstetrical reports (37) and the analysis of 5,000 birthdates by Knobloch and Pasamanick (68) are other examples of useful tabulation of data.

9. *Mathematics.* Apart from the arithmetic and algebraic branches of mathematics, there are some conceptual areas that provide useful tools. The late Von Neumann developed a system of techniques which goes by the name, "Theory of Games." This is a system for making decisions which bases its gambits on probability theory. Farber has demonstrated the utility of this tool in his analysis of the ways in which a family responds to the presence of a mentally retarded child (39).

10. *Epidemiological Methods.* These are the unique methods of studying disease—part procedural, part mathematical—which are intended to establish cause-and-effect relationships and to suggest preventive methods. Classic studies have been conducted on the effects of mustard-gas poisoning (14) and, in the nineteenth century, on the origins of cholera (82). Applications to mental retardation have been few, and more use of the approach seems indicated (20). The research program of Pasamanick and his associates is the widest application to date (97). Quite striking is the study by Stoller and Collman on the

origins of Down's disease (*114*). That remarkable work, incorporating data from Watertown, South Dakota (*52*), found a provocative similarity to outbreaks of viral disease such as hepatitis. A final example is a program of studies conducted in Hawaii. The Kauai Pregnancy Study, as it is known, examines the development of all live issue born in the late 1950's (*8, 9*). The percentage of infants below IQ 75 has been reported as 3.2. Further reports will be valuable because the program is concerned with social as well as biological aspects of development.

11. *Longitudinal Child Study.* Related to the preceding example in some ways is the use of long-term studies of groups of children. In Drillien's program of studies, children of low birth weight were examined at intervals of six and twelve months for several years (*31*). This technique is *prospective*, as opposed to *retrospective* technique which goes back to early stages of life. Unpublished work by the author rejects the common supposition that retrospective technique yields results comparable to those developed by prospective means (*60*).

In summary, the range of tools and areas of scholarship that can be brought to bear on the problem of mental retardation is quite large. Perhaps one way in which the present decade differs from preceding decades is the increasing involvement of the tools of the several disciplines in the problems of mental retardation.

SOURCES OF MENTAL RETARDATION

Historically, most accounts of mental retardation have either explicitly or implicitly associated the condition with the total family background. According to this point of view, mental retardation was held to represent lingering malevolent characteristics which might burst forth, like the "madness" of the nineteenth-century Gothic novel. In like manner, other deviations, social as well as biological, have traditionally been ascribed to family background. Thus, if the environment were puritanical, the community might identify drunkenness and sabbath-breaking as equally vicious examples of the lurking family pathology. Marriage with relatives of the handicapped individual was to be shunned, lest "it" come out in subsequent generations.

Some time ago this author analyzed the reasons for commitment to a state mental hospital about 100 years ago. The nosological categories were quite blurred, and the diagnostic categories quite faint. Patients were admitted for conditions ascribed to the following cryptic sources: "gourmandism," "excessive smoking," and "broken heart."

Traditionally, people have been responsive to some characteristics but not to others. Physical disorders which are identified as serious health problems in this generation were not always so considered. Further, when they were, they were confused by ignorance about etiology. Tuberculosis has not always been considered an infection, for example, nor have orthopedic disorders based on nutritional deficiencies been considered avoidable. It is not exaggeration to say that such ambiguities exist today.

There are several ways to schematize the sources of mental retardation. In this section the various mechanisms will be ordered primarily in time. This means that those mechanisms whose time locus is *in utero* will be considered first, then those of the birth process, and lastly the mechanisms whose locus in time is after birth.

HEREDITY AND MENTAL RETARDATION

Clearly the earliest of all processes to affect the growth of a child is the hereditary mechanism. It operates from the time the chromosomes of the parents polarize after the fertilization process.

As positive as this statement is, it can only be followed by less positive statements about the genetic endowment that accrues to a given child. Much of the material in genetics is retrospective, and it is only in relatively selected instances that predictive, prospective statements can be offered. It is entirely possible, for example, to follow a condition quite distinctly through five human generations and still be faced with uncertainty about the *penetrance*, the statistical occurrence, of a condition in the next generation (63).

At the moment the opinions given on the role of heredity in determining mental retardation are conflicting. A 1960 estimate by Kratter puts the number of cases in which a genetic mechanism is involved at about 45 per cent (70). Pasamanick has commented on the interesting nature of genetic disorders but says that they are numerically quite insignificant. He puts the number of organically defective individuals whose disorders are hereditary at approximately 5–10 per cent. Kanner has summarized the varying estimates on the contribution of heredity. In this résumé he has listed estimates ranging from 29 per cent all the way to 90 per cent (61). Such estimates are quite incompatible and demonstrate the uncertainties in this area. About the only generalization that seems to hold is that estimates of the number of cases of hereditary mental retardation seem to have dropped somewhat over the years.

While there is uncertainty about the frequency of hereditary components in the development of mental retardation, there is increasing accuracy in our descriptions of chromosomal mechanisms.

Genes and Chromosomes

In recent years the pace of scholarship has increased in virtually all fields of empirical study. The biological sciences have been no exception, and many of the substantive innovations which are occurring at the moment are at best *ad hoc* summaries. The phenomena on which they are based are themselves subject to continued extension. The remarks in the following paragraphs are made at a time when the author is all too conscious of the tentative state of biochemical observations on mental retardation. The need for closure is likely to persist, since unifying formulations of knowledge can emerge only after sufficient data have accrued. That point will not be reached in genetics for quite some time.

Some things are clear, however. The classical formulation of genetics, which was largely a statistical model of transmission, has been followed by biochemical study of genetic materials. One aspect of this is the investigation of DNA (deoxyribonucleic acid) in molecular genetics. It seems that DNA constitutes a genetic code for living materials and that DNA molecules reproduce through participation in chromosome mitosis, the normal process by which two parental sets of chromosomes are replaced by one set. Within the human chromosome the DNA molecule is a thing of remarkable length and complexity. Descriptions are only partial, but the Watson-Crick model introduced in 1953 has been the impetus to further discoveries (*34*).

In another vein, discoveries have been closely related to mental retardation through the demonstration of chromosome patterns associated with errors of development. The nature of the relevant chromosome patterns becomes progressively clearer, and the consistency and exceptionality of the symptoms in human beings become more accurately perceived.

We may start by observing that the normal complement of chromosomes in man is forty-six. It can be less, with generally fatal consequences, or it can be more, with serious but not always lethal consequences; for example, in the ever-expanding literature there is a report of a boy with sixty-nine chromosomes (*72*). Within the cells, chromosomes normally lie in a haphazard arrangement. Laboratory skills allow us to fix the materials during mitosis and to describe others according to their size; this method of description is called the Denver System and is further elucidated by the use of groupings within the twenty-three pairs—e.g., the chromosomes known as No. 13, No. 14, and No. 15, constitute a recognized entity, the D-group.

The most common error in the reproduction mechanism is *non-dis-*

junction, referred to as "abnormal segregation" by Lejeune and Turpin (*71*). Recall that humans have pairs of chromosomes and that union normally produces loss of one member of each pair. Normally, the process works well, and each parent pair yields a chromosome, allowing the resultant haploid cell-body to maintain the normal complement of two chromosomes. For reasons not clear to us, but to some extent more common in older females, the process may work improperly, and a chromosome from one pair may unite, not with one chromosome from another pair, but with two chromosomes, a pair which failed to separate. The result is three chromosomes, a *trisomy,* a chromosome plus a *pair* of chromosomes, in one cell, and one chromosome in another cell. When this happens to chromosome pair —21, the child has forty-seven instead of forty-six chromosomes, and the resultant pattern is mongolism or Down's syndrome. Day and Wright analyzed chromosome pattern in mongoloid offspring of forty-one young women (*27*); 85 per cent of these were examples of trisomy —21. This trisomy — 21 can be compared with other trisomies such as the intersex syndromes, but it is perhaps more relevant because of the clinical manifestations. Penrose believes that the chromosomal errors leading to mongolism are of two kinds (*100*); class A consists of four mechanisms largely independent of maternal age and due to a variety of causes, and class B consists of processes in which the age of the mother or the age of the ovum plays a part. This last possibility was explored in a study by Witschi presented in 1952 (*128*).

In addition to non-disjunction, we may mention *translocation.* This is the error in which chromosome materials are exchanged between different pairs of chromosomes. Usually, material from one of the smaller pairs is attached to a larger body. Since pair —21 is small, the probability of its being involved in translocation is increased; the result is one of the chromosomal patterns of mongolism (*10*). Deletion can have very serious effects, since it may exclude chromosomal elements whose genetic code is vital to life. Non-lethal effects occur, but they are generally serious (*99*).

It is wise to keep in mind that clinical expressions of chromosomal error including apparent normality (*49*) are possible and that there is a range of symptomatic expression among persons with the same genetic error. Trisomy —21 determines that Down's disease will appear, but afflicted persons still have other chromosomes each of which has its own genetic contribution to make. The over-all effect from the point of view of mental retardation may be mongolism, but within that facile observation, and between individuals, there are many normal items of growth. Each of these items of growth, the number of teeth, and the absence of dwarfism found in other chromosome syndromes, occurs within the normal range of growth. At the time of this writing there is speculation that translocation mongolism and trisomy mongolism may produce two patterns of development, sub-types of Down's disease.

Mental Retardation and Hereditary Diseases

Phenylketonuria is an error of metabolism first described by Folling in 1934. The parents of phenylketonuric children seem to have difficulty metabolizing phenylaniline, just as their children do. The condition may be controlled if a proper diet is introduced sufficiently early. Unfortunately, much of the ordinary diet of children—fish, meat, eggs, bread, etc.—must be omitted since they contain materials that elicit the faulty metabolic process.

Galactocemia is a genetically transmitted error in the metabolism of galactose. The condition seems to be recessive and therefore may or may not appear in given members of a family.

Skin disorders are sometimes seen in mental retardation. Such conditions as Von Recklinghausen's disease and tuberous sclerosis are due to genetically determined modes of development. While there is a definite incidence of mental retardation with these disorders, it is entirely possible for mental retardation to be absent. Koffman and Hyland have reported a series of cases of tuberous sclerosis in adults who were free from any intellectual inadequacies (69). This finding points out the endless variability of physical disorders. Relevant data occur in the many cases of "formes frustes," the conditions in which individuals present some of the characteristics that are normally associated with incapacitating disorders. Hurler's syndrome, mongolism, and tuberous sclerosis are entities some of whose distinctive characteristics may be found in normal people and specifically in relatives of handicapped people showing the full syndrome.

DEVELOPMENT

Fetal Loss

One of the realities of human development is that many processes are inefficient—that is, their outcomes can not be predicted with certainty. Reproduction must surely be included among these. The evidence for this assertion is the reality that a substantial number of conceptions produce an unfinished child, a small majority of such cases being males, in the proportion 58:42 (21). The proportion of conceptions failing to produce a live birth is high. Pregnancy wastage, as it is termed, varies according to the usual ecological and maternal variables

(84). Some of the mechanisms are the long-term consequence of early nutrition; for example, pelvic capacity may be adversely affected by poor diet during childhood (86). The condition may complicate pregnancy in a fashion which excludes relief. On the other hand, the best nutrition is no guarantee of a healthy outcome to pregnancy. The New York City (37) and Kauai pregnancy studies (8, 9) show that fetal wastage is high soon after conception and subsequently declines. In the Kauai (Hawaii) studies, Bierman et al. found that 1,311 four-week fetuses were required to produce 1,000 live births (8). The loss of 300 conceptions does not include live births with developmental defects, one of which would be mental retardation with and without disorders of the skeletal and nervous systems.

Fetal loss can be reduced, however. Fischer and Moloshok have drastically reduced fetal wastage in women with diabetes (40). Their intensive prenatal and perinatal care reduced fetal mortality from two out of each three conceptions to one out of four, approximately.

Raiha has reported from Finland that procedures based on reducing heart strain can be effective (102, 103). Women with a small heart volume were advised to rest during pregnancy. The results were positive, and the rate of perinatal mortality declined.

As welcome as such news is, we need to recognize that surviving a stormy gestation may not be without a price. Lillienfeld and Pasamanick have demonstrated that there is a "continuum of reproductive casualty" which extends from fetal mortality to survival with neuropsychiatric complications (78). Surviving children may be quite sound in every way, but the evidence indicates that mental retardation, cerebral palsy, and other disorders may be the minimal effects of reproductive inefficiency. The author has established by prospective means that instructional deficits occur with a significantly greater frequency in children with adverse early developmental experiences (59).

At present, research workers are exploring the role of the placenta in the problem of fetal loss (6). It continues to provide one of the great challenges to biological science for the nine months of gestation. Growth failure in that brief period increases the challenges to education and the social services which must care for the live and often damaged issue for many years.

Prematurity and Mental Retardation

During gestation the processes of growth take the organism from the microscopic stage of a fertilized ovum to the complex status of the neonate. During that period growth is characterized by (1) the accumulation of cells, and (2) the differentiation of cells. The result is that the full-term baby weighs about six pounds and presents a picture of complex functioning in complex organs.

It should be pointed out that of all young creatures man seems the most helpless. The implication is that even the full-term baby is far from complete and needs more time to grow. For example, the behavior of the newborn is not cortical in control but is determined by phylogenetically more primitive structures in the brain.

A necessary conclusion is that the baby needs to have reached the highest level of maturity possible before birth. The uterine environment is the best place to grow, although some have sketched alternatives. If the child is delivered prematurely, his growth can only proceed in a less-than-optimal environment. This poses two problems. First, there is the matter of survival. Depending upon the degree of prematurity, the child may not yet be equipped to breathe properly and to digest. Second, assuming that the child is mature enough not to succumb immediately, he must grow under conditions of explicit stress. Shock is possible, as are infections and nutritional disorders (73).

Prematurity is usually calculated on a developmental basis rather than on the basis of the calendar. This is understandable if only because predicted dates of birth probably should be ranked among the major works of fiction. On the other hand, individual differences in children's growth start long before birth, and developmental status—gauged by body weight—seems to be the most meaningful index. Usually infants weighing less than five pounds are considered premature and handled accordingly. Further specification is possible because a birth weight below three and a half pounds is almost invariably followed by serious consequences. These consequences are not unique to smaller babies but are more intense expressions of difficulties found in all premature infants. In this discussion, prematurity is conceived as limited gestation and is therefore to be discussed with the conditions whose common factor is the gestation period.

We may now consider some empirical evidence on prematurity (1, 30, 31, 50, 66). Most studies on prematurity are retrospective in design. They identify a group of individuals known as premature and go back to the circumstances of birth. A hazard in this approach is that the children considered may be those on whom there are fairly good records. This may partially reflect an accident of sampling, since adequate records would suggest adequate care, at least as opposed to poor care or no care, with a corresponding dearth of formal records.

An interesting study on the effects of prematurity has been offered by Alm (1). This is a retrospective study using records, going back over several decades, kept by three hospitals and various government agencies in Stockholm. The technique consisted of deriving two matched groups, one consisting of 999 premature boys, the other a control group consisting of boys born at full term; both groups were derived from Alm's analysis of 11,980 birth records. In the derivation of the sample, Alm eliminated some children, giving a slight bias towards legitimate middle-class urban children.

The children in the experimental sample all weighed less than 2,500 grams, about five and a half pounds; and the controls were between 2,760 grams and 3,750 grams. The more important results may be summarized as follows.

1. Being a premature increased the probability of manifesting some neurological disorder.

2. Being a premature increased the probability of dying in the first two years of life.

3. Being a plural-born premature increased still more the probability of dying in the first two years.

4. Being a premature increased the probability of being enrolled in a class for slow learners.

5. Being a premature increased the probability of manifesting disorders usually associated with birth injury.

6. Being a small premature increased the probability of adverse sequelae, as opposed to being a heavier, less premature, or a full-term baby

In the United States, Knobloch and associates reported evidence on the effects of prematurity (66). In this study, which is distinguished by being both retrospective and prospective, 500 single-born prematures below 2,500 grams were selected and compared with 492 full-term infants at developmental forty weeks. A finding which is now largely accepted as a rule-of-thumb was developed concerning the relationship between weight and susceptibility to damage. The babies below 1,501 grams had some discernible degree of neurological deficit in 50.9 per cent of the cases. This was discovered during the application of the Gesell Development Scale to these babies. Another finding, which may be relevant to the research proposal of Neel indicated previously (92), was that ethnic grouping did not produce any significant statistical differences. (Wortis and Freedman have since reported an increasing incidence of prematurity among Negro mothers (129). In stating their conclusions, Knobloch and her associates adjusted their figures and disclosed comparative rates of departure from the normal course of development. The figures were 12.8 per cent for the controls, 25.7 per cent for the prematures; the premature baby has twice the chance of manifesting developmental deviations as other youngsters. It has been found that prematurity occurs twice as frequently among mongoloid babies as among controls (81).

Confirming studies have been reported by Harper, Fischer, and Rider, who matched 460 prematures with 440 full-term babies at ages three to five (50). They found that a smaller proportion of the prematures could be considered neurologically normal. From England, Drillien reported essentially the same findings and confirmed the inverse relationship between cerebral injury and birth weight (30, 31). Drillien's findings will be discussed further in the next chapter.

The matter of intellectual status in prematures has been studied, and representative evidence on this issue was offered by Harper, Fischer, and Rider (50). They felt that the intellectual status of the prematures was lower than that of their controls.

A dissenting viewpoint can be found in the earlier work of Knehr and Sobol (65). However, these authors obtained subjects by means of one letter and required their S's to appear at the hospital for testing. The children were older, around six or so. The conclusion of essentially normal intelligence is understandable when one considers Alm's finding of higher mortality in the childhood years in a population of prematures.

More material on prematurity will be found in the next chapter.

Nutrition and Mental Retardation

Of considerable practical significance is the relationship between the health of the mother, in this case her level of nutrition, and the developmental progress of the child.

In a very moving paper Antonov has reported on maternal and child health during the siege of Leningrad, which lasted from August 1941 to January 1943 (2). During a particular period of great hunger the prematurity rate rose to 41.2 per cent and the stillbirth figure to 5.6 per cent. The course of development for those born alive was poor. Many of the children were lacking in vitality at delivery, and weight losses continued for several days. Mortality among the premature babies ranged from 50 per cent to 80 per cent. The average daily food allowance, largely bread, dropped to 250–350 grams for manual workers in December, 1941, and to 125–200 grams for "mental" workers. In addition to this, the women did their share of civil-defense duties.

The relationship between maternal diet and the child's course of development has been documented in the work of Coffey and Jessop (18). The investigators closely examined a sample of 204 children showing evidence of abnormality. The nutritional level of their mothers was checked by evaluating the hemoglobin concentration, and difference in the nutritional level of the mothers of the children with abnormalities was established at less than .05 probability.

A slightly different matter is nutrition in children and the relation of this to mental retardation. If the absence of protein in the diet of children is acute and chronic, this causes a regression in growth (95). Happily, the condition seems to be reversible, and the child returns to a higher level of intellectual functioning when the dietary deficiency is corrected.

Still another formulation of nutrition as a possible source of mental retardation lies in the mode of transmission prior to birth. Fetal distress in the later stages of pregnancy may arise from deficiencies in the placenta or from its premature separation. Both conditions reduce its effectiveness as the agent for transmitting nourishment and increase the probability of subsequent problems for the fetus. Uterine malnutrition, according to Gruenwald, may be short-term, but it may also be chronic (47). Further, according to Gruenwald, pregnancies terminated after thirty-six weeks sometimes show signs of placental disorders. In such cases fetuses show signs of nutritional deprivation.

An indirect connection between retardation and nutrition has been hazarded by Knobloch and Pasamanick (68). They studied the birth dates of 5,000 persons admitted to the Columbus State School over a period of thirty-four years; admissions were associated with winter births, and it appears that a decrease of protein intake in hot weather, among other possibilities, might coincide with nutritional needs during periods of cortical cell growth. Widespread use of air conditioning suggests re-examination in future years.

Maternal Health and Mental Retardation

In the minds of many people, virus infections pose a threat to the welfare of the child. The questions arise whether all virus infections produce damaged children and whether all children born to mothers who contacted dangerous viral infections are abnormal. The best way to answer such questions is in terms of evidence, since suppositions may be firmly grounded in ignorance.

In 1941 Gregg, an Australian, called attention to the relationship between maternal ill-health and the presence of developmental disorders in children. Rubella, or German measles, to use its more common name, is not one of the obvious illnesses that can strike a pregnant woman. Its impact on the child she carries may be decisive, however. The mechanism of transmission has been the subject of study. According to a *New*

York Times report (*96*), babies with illnesses traced to rubella acquired during gestation may themselves transmit the disease to others after birth. Outbreaks of rubella in recent years indicate the need to suppress possible contagion. Data developed by Coffey and Jessop describe the effects of rubella on women who contracted the disease while pregnant during an outbreak (*19*). The results indicated, in general, that women who were exposed to rubella or who actually contracted the disease gave birth to children with abnormalities four times more frequently than other mothers. On the other hand, not all the children had defects. There seems to be a significant relationship between the period in pregnancy and the effects of the disease. Thirty per cent of the women who contracted the disease in the first trimester gave birth to abnormal children, as opposed to 12 per cent who contracted the disease in the remaining six months of pregnancy. A very good study analyzing the occurrence of 24,825 cases of rubella in New York City between 1949 and 1955 has been reported by Greenberg, Pellitteri, and Barton (*46*). Apart from the scope of the study it is distinguished by its prospective nature. There were 104 cases of women having normal children, 3 per cent produced stillborn children, 12 per cent "nonviable" fetuses. Therapeutic abortions were performed on 46 per cent. These investigators commented that previous estimates of malformations were based on retrospective studies and were too high. They felt that blanket advocacy of therapeutic abortion is unjustified.

Dekaban, O'Rourke, and Cornman have analyzed the time sequence of developmental disorders precipitated by rubella (*28*). They believe that cataracts, heart-disease, and deafness occur when the disease is contracted before the fifth week of gestation.

The critical nature of the first three months of growth has been pointed out by a number of other people—for example, Warkany (*124*) and Benda (*4*) (*5*). More specifically, Liggins and Phillips have established probabilities of rubella damage in the early stages of gestation (*77*). They established their figures on the effects of rubella in New Zealand women and found that there was certainty of adverse effects in the first month of gestation. In the second month the probability dropped to 50 per cent, and then to 13 per cent for exposure in the third month of gestation.

According to Pasamanick and Lillienfeld there is a definite relationship between maternal health and mental retardation (*98*). In their materials, the medical histories of women whose children were later identified as mentally retarded showed a greater tendency towards abnormal incidents. Incidents such as toxemias and bleeding were more commonly reported.

In analyzing the importance of illness during pregnancy to women who delivered mongoloid babies, Levy and Perry analyzed the health of 148 mothers (75). It was their conclusion that intercurrent infections could be ruled out as the source of this particular form of mental deficiency.

The disease called Asian flu has recently created a world-wide health problem. In 1958 a prospective rather than retrospective study was initiated on the effect of this disease on pregnant women. Wilson and her associates identified seventy-five women judged by blood-sample to have contracted the disease and compared their offspring with those of non-infected mothers (127). The results did not justify the conclusion that Asian flu in mothers had an effect on the welfare of their unborn children. This study is in accord with the results offered by Walker and McKee (121).

In 1965 the Australian investigators Stoller and Collman reported the results of studies of Down's disease (114). Their work indicates that fluctuations in the incidence of mongolism in urban and rural areas from year to year conform to the epidemiological model of viral diseases. It seems that the incidence of —18 and —21 trisomy has peaks and cycles (52); also there are urban-rural differences in incidence which are interesting. This might explain an observation on mongolism made in 1876, to the effect that there were more instances of Kalmuc idiocy in some parts of Scotland than in others (42). Stoller and Collman did not say that the chromosomal aberrations of Down's disease are due to a virus. They did, however, establish a basis for experimental study of the problem and indicate that the hepatitis group might be a strategic virus to begin with.

Infections, then, cannot always be identified as the clear source of mental retardation. In some diseases there is an increased probability, but not a certainty, that infections can produce disorders while the mother is pregnant. There are also diseases which are blamed for disorders which do not affect the child. These may be relegated to the category of old-wives' tales about the effects of prenatal experiences on the growth of the child. Asian flu would seem to be one of these diseases.

A prospective investigation by Hedberg et al., has examined the effects of maternal health on the outcomes of pregnancy (51). Three thousand pregnancies provided the basis for observations, and sixty-one maldeveloped children from among these pregnancies were subsequently examined. Mothers of malformed infants had a higher proportion of previous abortions and a greater proportion of prior developmental anomalies in the family background.

Maternal diabetes seems to be a condition with implications for the development of unborn children. According to Driscoll, Benirschke, and Curtis, who examined ninety-five infants post-mortem, diminished brain weights were present, in addition to other adverse developments (32). In this series, death was most commonly due to hyaline membrane. A study on diabetic pregnancies by Fischer, Moloshok, and Rafton augments the observation that maternal diabetes is a threat to the fetus (40). They report fetal loss of 68 per cent in the previous histories of their patients. An intensive program of prenatal care reduced this figure to 23 per cent. A group of pre-diabetic women was also studied, and the results indicate that their health was also a source of abnormal fetal growth.

MENTAL RETARDATION AND THE PROBLEMS OF BIRTH

Some forms of mental retardation may be traced to the operation of genetic factors *in utero* and to the impact of non-genetic factors, also, during the process of gestation. There are some forms of mental retardation which originate in the problems attendant on delivery. An important point to be considered is that such forms of mental deficiency are due to injuries to an otherwise normal child. The result is that the disorder in no way reflects on the family's genetic heritage, nor is it likely to occur, except by coincidence, in other issue.

Mental Retardation and Obstetric Problems

The process of delivery consists essentially of the child who has developed in a symbiotic relation with the mother (1) being deprived of a protective environment, (2) changing his status to one of independence, and (3) using his own physiological processes to survive. The mechanical act of being delivered to the external world involves explicit physical problems, but it also involves less obvious but no less important matters of physiology.

The hazards of a physical order consist of damage to the child. A breech birth involves displacement of blood to the head. This is obviously a threat to the integrity of the circulatory system in the brain. Other procedural problems may involve damage to the skull. Claireaux has indicated that in his analysis of 1,056 post-mortems, direct mechanical trauma to the brains of babies was prominent (16). In his series the usual lesion was a rupture of the *tentorium cerebelli*. Serious hemorrhages may follow, leading to death. The great vein of Galen is also threatened in a similar manner.

An equally valuable contribution to the nature of damage during delivery has come from Courville (22). He examined a series of 446 (N = 446) babies who were stillborn or died within 7 days after delivery. The final conclusions, based on a smaller number (N = 401), largely discount the comparative frequency of physical injury. Anoxia was more common by a ratio of 5:1. Only 20 of 401 cases were due unequivocally to mechanical injury, according to Courville.

A disorder that may produce a variable picture, depending on the length of time involved, is premature separation of the placenta. In this instance the placental separation means a reduced supply of oxygen with a corresponding degree of deprivation in the cells of the brain. This would be brief, as opposed to the chronic placental distress mentioned earlier, in the discussion of nutrition.

Perhaps the most important of all medical discoveries, at least from the viewpoint of the sick, is the development of techniques to ease pain. In the process of delivery, anaesthetics are commonly used to help the mother. Such is the physiological nature of anaesthetics that if they are absorbed by the mother, they are also absorbed by the child. Levinson has indicated that the injudicious use of anesthetics can produce anoxia in the child, with corresponding brain damage and mental retardation (74). Experimental evidence on this problem in guinea pigs has been offered by Becker, Flannagan, and King, which supports Levinson's findings (3). According to Yacorzynski and Tucker, labor lasting less than two hours is associated with later intellectual deficit (130).

Crome and Kirman have reported that diabetes has an indirect role in mental retardation (55). They have indicated that diabetic mothers have larger babies and that this presents additional problems in the mechanics of delivery.

While the birth process can produce serious and obvious damage to an infant, it can also produce damage which is less obvious and minimal. The sequel to such damage may be learning and behavior disturbances, as well as tics. Thus, cerebral damage attendant to a difficult birth may produce mild neurological disorders that appear as less overt but no less serious problems in later years (67).

It may be that the obstetrics team is too much the victim of idle talk. Certainly, many people, with great facility, ascribe cerebral palsy to obstetric error. Malzberg, however, was able to identify only about one in every twenty institutionalized retardates as the victims of birth trauma (85). In his analysis of the causes of mental retardation, Jervis offered an observation which also suggests that obstetric accidents may be overly blamed for mental retardation. "It should be noted that more than half of the children showing clinical evidence of birth injury are not mentally defective" (57, p. 30).

MENTAL RETARDATION AND OTHER FACTORS

Maternal Age

On an empirical basis maternal age emerges as a salient variable in the background of women who have delivered children who show some deviation from normal development. The age of the father does not seem to be important. The task of relating this finding to the condition of the child is not an easy one. The basic data simply show, on an inspection basis, that if one arranges children with and without mental retardation, the ones with mental retardation and related disorders have older rather than younger mothers.

On the other hand, the youth of the mother does not protect her child absolutely. According to Pasamanick and Lillienfeld, the relation of maternal age and child welfare is non-linear (98). The result is that there is a period when maternal age is least likely to relate to disorders in the offspring. Before age twenty-five and after age twenty-nine, a woman is more likely to produce a retarded child. Between those years she is less likely to do so.

Maternal age cannot be considered a primary factor as, for example, genetic elements may. The reason is that the pattern of disorders that relate to maternal age is wide. Mongolism and cerebral palsy are related to maternal age (4, 5, 48). The developmental failure known as a hare lip, which may or may not be associated with mental retardation, occurs four times more commonly in children whose mothers are over thirty-eight (83). The more serious congenital disorders which occur in about 1.6 per cent of a series of births are also related to maternal age (18). In a report which drew on data accumulated over twenty years, Davis and Potter found that congenital disorders occurred most commonly in offspring of mothers in the beginning or end of the child-bearing period (26).

Blood Disorders

A finding which is only about a quarter of a century old is the identification of a blood characteristic which distinguishes various groups of people. Using the rhesus monkey, it was possible to demonstrate that in about a dozen people, roughly two would have a blood incompatibility with the rest. These people are described as rh-negative.

The crucial arrangement of parent and rh-factor is when the mother is rh-negative and the father is rh-positive. The consequence of this in a child is that the blood may be affected, and the infant at delivery may be subject to jaundice and to a range of other disorders, if he survives (101). According to Claireaux, infants with the haemolytic disease show jaundice shortly after birth (16). In those cases where transfusion therapy is not initiated, damage to the brain may follow. The basal ganglia of the brain seem to be quite vulnerable (106), and cerebral palsy of the athetoid variety is a common result.

Rarely there may be mental retardation also due to blood problems of a different sort. It is possible that apart from the iso-immunization problem of the blood, the blood itself may be incapable of using available oxygen. Gibson has described a rare case in which a child presented mental retardation with a persistent cyanosis originating in a defect of blood chemistry (45). Of two siblings, one has the condition and is also mentally retarded; the other has neither the mental retardation nor the blood disorder.

Teratogenic Agents and Developmental Disorders

The problem of investigating the sources of mental retardation and the other disorders in human beings is generally a matter of making shrewd guesses about what went wrong and how it went wrong. Lucey has listed thirty agents which a pregnant woman might ingest with harmful consequences (79). Some, but not all, are known to affect all unborn creatures, but the processes are not clear. The processes of gestation are largely hidden in human beings, and the investigator can only make observations with great difficulty.

An obstetrician analyzing the processes of growth in a pregnant woman can come to direct knowledge of growth in only restricted areas. He cannot see the child, but he can feel the child. He can check the over-all size of the child *in utero* by measuring, and he can listen to the heart beat. The process of growth is not open to direct examination. In other circumstances the use of X-rays can help disclose things invisible to the naked eye, but this is quite hazardous to the welfare of the unborn child (41). However, although the problems are great, they have been largely sidestepped in recent years.

"Since the development of prenatal defects is not accessible to direct observation in man, teratologic experiments in mammals can contribute greatly to a better understanding of the mechanism leading to congenital structural errors" (123, p. 322). This dictum by Warkany applies to mental retardation. Waisman and his associates have been able to produce phenylketonuria in infant monkeys, and the value of this development is clear (120). Biochemical and behavioral studies can be made, and the symptomatic expression of the disease otherwise produced by genetic error can be manipulated by investigators.

Some of the agents that have been used to produce congenital malformations in mammals are radiation, anoxia, hypothermia, vitamin deficiency and excess, cortisone, nitrogen mustard, starvation, and trypan blue (90). This last agent is a dye which has been reported by Wilson as capable of producing congenital abnormalities in 50 per cent or more of young rats (126).

The mechanisms involved are, of course, the heart of the animal studies in malformation. Experimental evidence offered by Runner and Dagg suggests that various agents may share a common metabolic pathway (110). Several comments which may serve as additional remarks on this issue have been offered by Millen and Woollam (89). They point out that the specific type of malformation which occurs in animals may be developed by a variety of teratogenic agents. This means that the single cause mentioned in the part of this chapter called "Formulating the Problem" is ruled out. These investigators also point out that the interference of these agents in the biochemistry of the animals is not necessarily direct, that they may act by disturbing some intermediary such as the pituitary gland. Also, the time at which the agent is introduced plays a role in determining which congenital disorder will appear.

Thalidomide

In November 1961, a German pediatrician, Lenz, brought to the attention of the scientific community an unparalleled tragedy, the "Saga of Thalidomide," as Mellin and Katzenstein styled it in their classic paper (87). The significance of the Thalidomide experience for this chapter lies partially in the drug's role as a source of mental retardation; about one-third of forty-three Swedish children affected by Thalidomide are reported to be retarded (25). Thalidomide is also, however, an analogue for the study of serious developmental error, because mental retardation can be a secondary consequence of maldevelopment.

It seemed that Thalidomide was an excellent chemical for purposes of sedation, and it was in wide use throughout the world. Experiments on animals showed that the drug produced largely innocuous results, and in humans its teratogenic possibilities went unsuspected. As a sedative it defied abuse. Attempted suicide with massive doses produced only deep sleep; prescribed for pregnant women it was quite satisfactory. Most pregnant women, especially those more than two months pregnant, found it beneficial. Fourteen women in Illinois took Thalidomide; all were in the ninth month of pregnancy, and no malformations were found in their children (94). Those between the twenty-eighth and forty-second day of pregnancy were not immune, however. According to the 1963 federal report on the drug, sixteen women took Thalidomide at the time when the human fetus was susceptible; and the drug, a species-, as well as time-, specific teratogen, produced phocomelia in their children. Acting roughly a month after conception, a period when limb buds are perceptible in the one-inch fetus, Thalidomide caused arms and legs to be misformed. Intelligence, however, has been generally thought normal in affected children, though cases of hydrocephalus have been reported, and the Swedish study just cited (25) suggests that intelligence is affected. Taussig, whose paper merits attention along with that of Mellin and Katzenstein, reported that there seems to be no relationship between the size of the dosage and the severity of maldevelopment (117).

The relevance of the Thalidomide tragedy has several aspects. First, the normal process of testing the drug on animals produced insignificant effects. There may be other drugs whose action is specific to the human species. There can be no guarantee the problem will not recur, because there may be other drugs whose bad effects are equally narrow. The absence of more serious consequences in the United States was purely fortuitous. But for the alertness of Dr. Frances Kelsey of the Food and Drug Administration, cases of phocomelic children would have been far more numerous. The relevance of the entire episode lies in its illustrative value; intelligence is an epiphenomenon of the central nervous system, which can be moved from the normal course of development by a variety of factors. The Thalidomide experience illustrates how delicate the interaction is between teratogens and the susceptibility in time of a given human creature. A human may live three-score years and ten from the moment of conception. The course of that life, and indeed the entire premise of viability, may well hinge on highly fortuitous events.

The general lesson to be learned is that minimal interference with the normal course of gestation, except when absolutely necessary, remains a sound maxim. A more specific lesson is that gestation is a remarkably delicate process; its complexity is illustrated in the paradox of a drug which was harmless and indeed beneficial to pregnant women and their unborn children for all but a few of the miraculous weeks of gestation. Sober reflection suggests that our appreciation of prenatal growth based on the Thalidomide experience might well lead to more emphasis on prenatal biology and experimental teratology.

MENTAL RETARDATION AND THE GROWING CHILD

Cerebral Trauma

The number of cases of mental retardation that are due to physical disorders beginning after the time of birth is small. While exact figures on the total problem are lacking, the incidence of postnatally acquired intellectual inadequacy is certainly less than the incidence of disorders whose locus in time is during gestation or at delivery. An estimate of the number of cases of postnatal cerebral trauma resulting in mental retardation has been offered by Boldt (11). On the basis of 1,000 cases in an institutional setting, he offered a figure of 1.6 per cent.

Infectious Diseases

Poliomyelitis. This condition is generally associated with paralyses; but more profoundly analyzed, it emerges as a disease whose effects are focused on the central nervous system. While polio does not cause a large number of cases of mental retardation—and indeed it may well be disappearing if public health techniques are fully accepted—it can cause a disturbance of intellectual functioning. The Soviet scientist Reznick has commented on disturbances of what is termed in the Russian idiom "higher nervous activity" (105). Findings of weakness and inertia in the "cortical dynamics" of children recovering from this disease were reported. A report of intellectual functioning in post-polio adults has been reported by Wendlund, Urmer, and Safford (125). Using the *Wechsler Adult Intelligence Scale* they found a difference in ability suggesting lower scores after polio. They temper their conclusions by noting that the hospital environment of their study might have a dulling effect on the performance of their subjects.

Pertussis. Whooping cough is a disease which is usually associated with childhood. In those cases where it occurs in the young and is quite acute, mental retardation is a possible aftereffect. Twenty children out of 120 investigated having a history of pertussis were mentally retarded, according to Levy and Perry (75). These investigators felt that their 15.6 per cent incidence of mental retardation was attributable to the whooping cough. Berg identified the mechanism as cerebral anoxia due to severe apnoea during the paroxysmal stage of the illness (7).

Encephalitis. There are many diseases which produce the various inflammatory states of the brain. Sleeping sickness—encephalitis lethargica—is often included in discussions of etiology. Certainly cases of inadequate intellectual functioning in previously normal people who succumb to the disease may be logically ascribed to it. A dissenting opinion was expressed by Bourne on the role of virus encephalitis; he felt, on the basis of applying strict criteria, that the condition has been overrated as a cause of mental defects (13).

Assorted Acquired States. Meningitis is a disease which poses a serious threat to the integrity of the brain. When one considers that the word describes an inflammation of the covering of the brain, it becomes apparent that the disease can pose a real threat. That it has been fatal, and is still considered serious, is clearly a rational estimate of the significance of the disease. The mechanisms leading to brain damage consist of interference with the venous system and the development of exudates (113).

Lead poisoning is a rarely encountered condition in which an individual absorbs lead from some source. Toy soldiers, paints, and other items provide a source of this toxic substance. The occurrence is rare (44). Thallium sulphate, a common ingredient of pesticides, has occasionally been ingested by children when combined with food (112). The results are serious, and mental retardation and psychosis have been found to result.

Radioactive fallout is at this point a source of danger to all forms of life. Perhaps its role as the origin of gene mutation will in the future emerge more clearly. Since most mutations are maladaptive, it remains to be seen whether radioactivity will produce a large-scale change in the intellectual and physical integrity of mankind.

Cretinism. In some infants who show no obvious defects, the passage of several months may reveal changes in appearance and metabolism that indicate a change in the effectiveness of the thyroid gland. The word *cretin* is used to describe such children. The word has varying interpretations depending on one's etymological skill. Some people relate the word to a Teutonic stem and say it meant chalky, while others point to the similarity with *chrétien,* saying that the afflicted fell under the care of the church in the Middle Ages.

Generally speaking, this condition is remediable. The procedures are more appropriately considered in a later chapter, but they consist of providing the hormones that the defective gland does not provide. The results of such therapy are quite striking, and the child simply may not be recognized on a before-and-after basis.

Cultural Factors. Not all conditions of mental retardation acquired after birth are biological in basis. Growth under unfavorable circumstances produces a definite drop in levels of ability as the years go by. In Chapter 4 this issue is covered more fully. The essential data are the findings of Gordon on the growth of the canalboat children, Sherman's

and Key's data on children in the Appalachians, and the other environmental studies.

Largely worthless are the often-quoted studies on Kaspar Hauser,
the boy who was discovered on the continent and raised in an urban
setting until his death in mysterious circumstances; accounts of feral
children, children abandoned and raised by animals, are also not very
reliable. The reservations expressed reflect uncertainties about the
conditions of life prior to abandonment and discovery.

Recent studies have shed some light on what a change in environment can mean to a child known to be retarded. Centerwall and Centerwall have reported some data on mongoloid children raised at home
and in foster homes (15). The intelligence and social quotients of children reared at home were higher than the quotients of children reared
in foster homes. The mean IQ of the home-reared children was seven
points higher than that of the other S's; although a small difference, it
was significant at the $p < .01$ level. Lyle has reported a positive change
in the language development of children moved from a large institution to a smaller, more personalized setting (80). Although the children
remained retarded, their level of functioning indicates that we need to
translate into functional terms whatever developmental error nature
produces rather than erroneously equating biological development
with behavioral development.

Tarjan has conceptualized the place of the environment as a causative factor by pointing out that intelligence grows as an ego-function
(116). He has also pointed out that the analysis of physiological and
chemical problems is analogous to investigating the way a computer
works. Significantly, he adds that the computer has to be programmed
in order to function. The environment may be said to act in this capacity.

SUMMARY

In this chapter we have considered (1) the formulation of the problem of how mental retardation develops, (2) the disciplines involved
in the investigation of sources of the problem, (3) techniques of investigation, and (4) specific sources of mental retardation organized
around (a) the period of gestation, (b) the processes of birth, and (c)
the postnatal biological and environmental issues.

BIBLIOGRAPHY

1. Alm, I., "The Long-Term Prognosis for Prematurely Born Children: A
   Follow-Up Study of 999 Premature Boys Born in Wedlock and of 1002
   Controls," *Acta Paediat. Suppl.*, 1953, No. 94.

2. Antonov, A. N., "Children Born during the Siege of Leningrad in 1942," *J. Pediat.*, 1947, *30*, 250-259.

3. Becker, R. F., Flannagan, E., and King, J. E., "The Fate of Offspring from Mothers Receiving Sodium Pentobarbital before Delivery: A Study in the Guinea Pig," *Neurol.*, 1958, *8*, 776-782.

4. Benda, C. E., *Developmental Disorders of Mentation and Cerebral Palsies*, Grune and Stratton, 1952.

5. _____, "Mongolism: A Comprehensive Review," *Arch. Pediat.*, 1956, *73*, 391-406.

6. Bergsma, D. (ed.), "Symposium on the Placenta," *Birth Def. Orig. Art. Series*, 1965, *1*, 1.

7. Berg, J. M., "Neurological Sequelae of Pertussis with Particular Reference to Mental Defect," *Arch. Dis. Childhood*, 1959, *34*, 322-324.

8. Bierman, J. L., *et. al.*, "Analysis of the Outcome of all Pregnancies in a Community," *Amer. J. Obstet. Gynec.*, 1965, *91*, 37-45.

9. Bierman, J. L., *et al.*, "The Community Impact of Handicaps of Prenatal or Natal Origin," *Pub. Hlth. Rep.*, 1963, *78*, 837-855.

10. Biesele, J. J., Schmid, W., Lee, C. H., and Smith, P. H., "Translocation Between Acrocentric Chromosomes in a 46-Chromosome Mongoloid and his 45-Chromosome Mother," *Amer. J. Hum. Genet.*, 1962, *14*, 107-124.

11. Boldt, W. H., "Postnatal Cerebral Trauma as an Etiological Factor in Mental Deficiency," *Am. J. Ment. Def.*, 1951, *55*, 345-365.

12. Book, J. A., Fraccaro, M., and Linsten, J., "Cytogenetical Observations in Mongolism," *Acta Paed.*, 1959, *48*, 453-468.

13. Bourne, H., "Does Virus Encephalitis Cause Mental Defect?" *Am. J. Ment. Def.*, 1956, *61*, 198-203.

14. Case, R. A. M., and Lea, A. J., "Mustard Gas Poisoning, Chronic Bronchitis, and Lung Cancer," *Brit. J. Prev. Soc. Med.*, 1955, *9*, 62-72.

15. Centerwall, S. A., and Centerwall, W. R., "A Study of Children with Mongolism Reared in the Home Compared to Those Reared Away from the Home," *Pediat.*, 1960, *25*, 678-685.

16. Claireaux, A., "Cerebral Pathology in the Newborn," *Guy's Hosp. Rep.*, 1959, *108*, 2-18.

17. Clarke, A. M., and Clarke A. D. B., *Mental Deficiency, The Changing Outlook*, London, Methuen, 1958.

18. Coffey, V. P., and Jessop, W. J. E., "Congenital Abnormalities," *Irish J. Med. Sci.*, 1955, *349*, 30-48.

19. _____, "Rubella and Incidence of Congenital Abnormalities," *Irish J. Med. Sci.*, 1959, *397*, 1-11.

20. Cohen, B. H., Lillienfeld, A. M., and Sigher, A. T., "Some Epidemological Aspects of Mongolism: A Review," *Amer. J. Pub. Hlth.*, 1963, *53*, 223-236.

21. Conway, H., and Wagner, K. J., "Congenital Anomalies Reported on Birth Certificates in New York City," *N. Y. J. Med.*, 1965, *65*, 1087-1090.

22. Courville, C. B., "Birth and Brain Damage: Traumatic Versus Ànoxic Damage to the Fetal Brain," *Bull. L. A. Neurol. Soc.*, 1963, *28*, 209-216.

23. Cowie, V., and Coppen, A., "Protein-Bound Iodine in Phenylketonuria," *J. Ment. Def. Res.*, 1959, *3*, 94-95.

24. Dancis, J., "Phenylketonuria and Maple Sugar Urine Disease," *Bull. N.Y. Acad. Med.*, 1959, *35*, 422-432.

25. d'Avignon, M., Hellgren, K., and Juhlin, I. M., "Thalidomide Damaged Children, Experiences from Eugeniahemmet," *Acta Paed. Scand. Suppl.*, 1965, No. 159.

26. Davis, M. E., and Potter, E. L., "Congenital Malformations and Obstetrics," *Pediat.*, 1957, *19*, 719-724.

27. Day, R. W., and Wright, S. W., "Down's Syndrome at Young Maternal Ages: Chromosomal and Family Studies," *J. Pediat.*, 1965, *66*, 764-771.

28. Dekaban, A., O'Rourke, J., and Cornman, T., "Abnormalities in Offspring Related to Maternal Rubella during Pregnancy," *Neurol.*, 1958, *8*, 387-395.

29. Dennis, W., "Causes of Retardation among Institutional Children: Iran," *J. Genet. Psych.*, 1960, *96*, 47-59.

30. Drillien, C. M., "A Longitudinal Study of the Growth and Development of Pre-Maturely and Maturely Born Children," *Arch. Dis. Childhd.*, 1959, *34*, 37-45.

31. _____, *The Growth and Development of the Prematurely Born Infant*, Edinburgh, E. and S. Livingstone, 1964.

32. Driscoll, S. G., Benirschke, K., and Curtis, G. W., "Neonatal Deaths Among Infants of Diabetic Mothers. Postmortem Findings in Ninety-Five Infants," *Am. J. Dis. Child.*, 1960, *100*, 818-835.

33. Dunn, L. N., "A Comparison of the Reading Processes of Mentally Retarded and Normal Boys of the Same Mental Age," *Mon. Soc. Res. Ch. Dev.*, 1954, No. 58.

34. Dunn, L. C., "Old and New in Genetics," *Bull. N.Y. Acad. Med.*, 1964, *40*, 325-333.

35. Dutton, G., "The Neutral 17-Ketosteroid and 17-Ketogenic Steroid Excretion of Mongol and Non-Mongol Mentally Defective Boys," *J. Ment. Def. Res.*, 1959, *3*, 103-107.

36. ———, "The Size of Mental Defective Boys," Arch. Dis. Childhd., 1959, 34, 331-333.

37. Erhardt, L. L., "Pregnancy Losses in New York City, 1963, Amer. J. Pub. Hlth., 1963, 53, 1337-1352.

38. Essen-Möller, E., "Individual Traits and Morbidity in a Swedish Population," Acta Psychiat. Neurol. Scand., Suppl. 1956, No. 100.

39. Farber, B., "Family Organization and Crisis: Maintenance of Integration in Families with a Severely Retarded Child," Mon. Soc. Res. Ch. Dev., 1960, No. 75.

40. Fischer, A. E., Moloshok, R. E., and Rafton, E. H., "Diabetic and Prediabetic Pregnancies with Special Reference to the Newborn," J. Pediat., 1960, 57, 704-714.

41. Ford, D. D., Patterson, J. C. S., and Treuting, W. L., "Fetal Exposure to Diagnostic X-Rays and Leukemia and Other Diseases in Childhood," J. Nat. Cancer Inst., 1959, 22, 1093-1104.

42. Fraser, J., and Mitchell, A., "Kalmuc Idiocy: Report of a Case with Autopsy and Notes on 62 Cases," J. Ment. Sci., 1876, 22, 161-162, 169-179.

43. Gentry, J. T., Parkhurst, E., and Bulin, G. V., "An Epidemiological Study of Congenital Malformations in New York State," Am. J. Pub. Hlth., 1959, 49, 1-22.

44. Gibb, J. W. G., "Arrested Mental Development Induced by Lead Poisoning," Brit. Med. J., 1955, 4909, 320-323.

45. Gibson, R., "Familial Idiopathic Methaemoglobinaemia Associated with Oligophrenia," Am. J. Ment. Def., 1956, 61, 207-209.

46. Greenberg, M., Pellitteri, O., and Barton, J., "Frequency of Defects in Infants Whose Mothers Had Rubella during Pregnancy," J. Am. Med. Ass., 1957, 165, 675-678.

47. Gruenwald, P., "Chronic Fetal Distress and Placental Insufficiency," Biol. Neonat., 1963, 5, 215-265.

48. Hansen, E., "Cerebral Palsy in Denmark," Acta Psychiat. Neurol. Scand. Suppl., 1960, No. 146.

49. Harnden, D. G., and Williams, J. A., "Chromosome Rearrangements in Apparently Normal Individuals," Heredity, 1962, 17, 299-300.

50. Harper, P., Fischer, L., and Rider, R. V., "Neurological and Intellectual Status of Prematures at Three to Five Years of Age," J. Pediat., 1959, 55, 679-690.

51. Hedberg, E. et al., "On Relationship between Maternal Conditions during Pregnancy and Congenital Malformations," Acta Paed., 1963, 52, 353-360.

52. Heinreichs, E. H., Allen, S. W., and Nelson, P. S., "Simultaneous 18-Trisomy and 21-Trisomy Cluster," Lancet, 1963, 2, 468.

53. Hicks, S. P., "Radiation as an Experimental Tool in Mammalian Development Neurology," *Physiol. Rev.*, 1958, *38*, 337-356.

54. Higgins, J. V., "A Study of Intelligence of the NAM Family in Minnesota," *Am. J. Ment. Def.*, 1959, *64*, 491-504.

55. Hilliard, L. T., and Kirman, B. H., *Mental Deficiency*, Little, Brown, 1957.

56. Inghe, C., "Mental and Physical Illness among Paupers in Stockholm," *Acta Psychiat. Neurol. Scand. Suppl.*, 1958, No. 121.

57. Jervis, G., "The Mental Deficiencies," *Ann. Am. Acad. Polit. Soc. Sci.*, 1953, *286*, 25-33.

58. Johnston, A. W., and McKusick, V. A., "A Sex-Linked Recessive Form of Spastic Paraplegia," *Amer. J. Hum. Genet.*, 1962, *14*, 83-94.

59. Jordan, T. E., "Early Developmental Adversity and Classroom Learning: A Prospective Inquiry," *Amer. J. Ment. Def.*, 1964, *69*, 360-371.

60. ———, "Retrospective versus Prospective Technique in Research on Learning Disability," unpublished paper, Southern Illinois University, 1965.

61. Kanner, L., "A Miniature Textbook on Feeblemindedness," *Ch. Care Mon.*, 1949, No. 1.

62. ———, "Feeblemindedness, Absolute, Relative and Apparent," *Nerv. Ch.*, 1948, *7*, 365-397.

63. Khosrovani, H., "Malformations Des Mains et Des Pieds (Ectrodactylie) A Travers Cinq Générations Successives Dans Une Grande Famille Vaudoise," *J. Genet. Hum.*, 1959, *8*, 1-59.

64. Klein, A., and Franceschetti, A., "Le Depistage Des Conducteurs de Genes Pathologiques," *Rev. Med. Suisse Rom.*, 1959, *79*, 369-399.

65. Knehr, C., and Sobol, A., "Mental Abilities of Prematurely Born Children at Early School Age," *J. Psych.*, 1949, *27*, 355-361.

66. Knobloch, H., et al., "Neuropsychiatric Sequelae of Prematurity: A Longitudinal Study," *J. Am. Med. Ass.*, 1956, *161*, 581-585.

67. Knobloch, H., and Pasamanick, B., "Syndrome of Minimal Cerebral Damage in Infancy," *J. Am. Med. Ass.*, 1959, *170*, 1384-1387.

68. ———, "Seasonal Variations in the Birth of the Mentally Deficient," *Am. J. Pub. Hlth.*, 1958, *48*, 1201-1208.

69. Koffman, O., and Hyland, H. H., "Tuberous Sclerosis in Adults with Normal Intelligence," *Arch. Neurol. Psychiat.*, 1959, *81*, 43-48.

70. Kratter, F. E., "Mental Deficiency and Its Causations," *Dis. Nerv. Syst.*, 1960, *21*, 163-164.

71. Lejeune, J., and Turpin, R., "Chromosomal Aberrations in Man," *Amer. J. Hum. Genet.*, 1961, *13*, 175-184.

72. Lennox, B., "Chromosomes for Beginners," *Lancet*, 1961, *1*, 1046-1051.

73. Levine, S. Z., and Gordon, H., "Physiologic Handicaps of the Premature Infant, I. Their Pathogenesis," *Am. J. Dis. Child.*, 1942, *64*, 274-296.

74. Levinson, A., "Medical Aspects of Mental Deficiency," *Am. J. Ment. Def.*, 1950, *54*, 476-483.

75. Levy, S., and Perry, H. A., "Pertussis as a Cause of Mental Deficiency," *Am. J. Ment. Def.*, 1948, *52*, 217-226.

76. ————, "The Role of Maternal Illness during Pregnancy in the Etiology of Mongolism," *Am. J. Ment. Def.*, 1948, *53*, 284-293.

77. Liggins, G. C., and Phillips, L. I., "Rubella Embryopathy: An Interim Report on a New Zealand Epidemic," *Brit. Med. J.*, 1963, *5332*, 711-713.

78. Lillienfeld, A. M., and Pasamanick, B., "The Association of Maternal and Fetal Factors with the Development of Cerebral Palsy and Epilepsy." *Am. J. Obst. Gynec.*, 1955, *70*, 93-101.

79. Lucey, J. F., "Drugs and the Intrauterine Patient," *Birth Def. Orig. Art. Series*, 1965, *1*, 46-51.

80. Lyle, J. G., "A Study of the Verbal Ability of Imbecile Children," unpublished Ph. D. dissertation, University of London, 1959.

81. McIntire, M. S., Menolascino, F. J., and Wiley, J. H., "Mongolism—Some Clinical Aspects," *Amer. J. Ment. Def.*, 1965, *69*, 794-800.

82. MacMahon, B., Pugh, T. F., and Ipsen, J., *Epidemiologic Methods*, Little, Brown, 1960.

83. MacMahon, B., and McKeown, T., "The Incidence of Hare Lip and Cleft Palate Related to Birth Rank and Maternal Age," *Am. J. Hum. Gen.*, 1953, *5*, 176-183.

84. McDonald, A. D., "Maternal Health in Early Pregnancy and Congenital Defect: Final report on a Prospective Inquiry," *Brit. J. Prev. Soc. Med.*, 1961, *15*, 154-166.

85. Malzberg, B., "Statistical Aspects of Mental Deficiency Due to Birth Traumas," *Am. J. Ment. Def.*, 1950, *54*, 427-433.

86. *Mechanisms of Congenital Malformation*, Association for Aid to Crippled Children, 1954.

87. Mellin, G. W., and Katzenstein, M., "The Saga of Thalidomide," *N. Engl. J. Med.*, 1962, *267*, 1184-1193, 1238-1264.

88. Menkes, J. H., "Maple Syrup Disease," *Neurol.*, 1959, *9*, 826-835.

89. Millen, J. E., and Woollam, D. H. M., "Observations on the Experimental Production of Malformations of the Central Nervous System," *J. Ment. Def. Res.*, 1959, *3*, 23-32.

90. Millen, J. W., "Some Aspects of the Relationship between Environment and Congenital Malformations," *Irish J. Med. Sci.*, 1959, *397*, 22-29.

91. Munson, S. E., and May, A. M., "Are Cleft Palate Persons of Subnormal Intelligence?" *J. Educ. Res.*, 1955, *48*, 617-621.

92. Neel, J. V., "Genetics and Human Congenital Malformations," *Pediat.*, 1957, *19*, 749-754.

93. Nelson, M. M., "Production of Congenital Anomalies in Mammals by Maternal Dietary Insufficiencies," *Pediat.*, 1957, *19*, 764-776.

94. "No Illinois Thalidomide Deformities," *Chicago Tribune*, 1963.

95. Onesti, S. J. (ed.), *Etiologic Factors in Mental Retardation*, Report of the Twenty-Third Ross Pediatric Research Conference, 1956.

96. Osmundsen, J. A., "Rubella's Spread is Laid to Babies," *New York Times*, February 14, 1965.

97. Pasamanick, B., "Research on the Influence of Sociocultural Variables upon Organic Factors in Mental Retardation," *Am. J. Ment. Def.*, 1959, *64*, 316-320.

98. _____, and Lillienfeld, A. M., "The Association of Maternal and Fetal Factors with the Development of Mental Deficiency II," *Am. J. Ment. Def.*, 1956, *60*, 557-569.

99. Patau, K., Opitz, J. M., and Dewey, W. J., "A Multiple Congenital Anomaly in Man Presumably Caused by a Minute Deletion in Chromosome," *Sci.*, 1964, *147*, 429.

100. Penrose, L. S., "Mongolism," *Brit. Med. Bull.*, 1961, *17*, 184-189.

101. Pentschew, A., "The Genesis of Encephalopathia Posterica Infantum (Kernicterus)," *Am. J. Ment. Def.*, 1948, *53*, 145-152.

102. Raiha, C.-E., "The Possibilities of Reducing Perinatal Mortality," *Ann. Paed. Fenn.*, 1963, *9*, 152-167.

103. _____, and Kauppinen, M., "An Attempt to Decrease Perinatal Mortality and the Rate of Premature Births," *Devpm. Med. Child. Neurol.*, 1963, *5*, 225-232.

104. Reed, S. C., Reed, E. W., and Palm, J. D., "Fertility and Intelligence Among Families of the Mentally Deficient," *Eugen. Quart.*, 1954, *1*, 44-52.

105. Reznick, B., "Characteristic Features of the Higher Nervous Activity of Children in the Recovery Period after Poliomyelitis," *Pavlov. J. Higher Nerv. Activit.*, 1958, *8*, 45-51.

106. Richards, B. W., "Kernicterus," *Am. J. Ment. Def.*, 1951, *55*, 529-534.

107. _____, and Rundle, A. T., "A Familial Hormonal Disorder Associated with Mental Deficiency, Deaf Mutism and Ataxia," *J. Ment. Def. Res.*, 1959, *3*, 33-55.

108. Ridler, M. A. C., and Shapiro, A., "The Longitudinal Study of the Leucocyte Count in Infants with Mongolism," *J. Ment. Def. Res.*, 1959, *3*, 96-102.

109. Runner, M. N., "Inheritance of Susceptibility to Congenital Deformity," *J. Nat. Cancer Inst.*, 1959, *15*, 637-647.

110. _____, and Dagg, C. P., "Metabolic Mechanisms of Teratogenic Agents during Morphogenesis," in "Symposium on Normal and Abnormal Differentiation and Development," *Nat. Cancer Instit. Mon.*, 1960, No. 2.

111. Schlesinger, E., *et al.*, "Survivorship in Cerebral Palsy," *Am. J. Pub. Hlth.*, 1959, *49*, 343-349.

112. "Scientists Would Ban A Common Rat Poison from Household Use," *Wall Street Journal*, February 15, 1963.

113. Smith, J. F., and Landing, B. H., "Mechanisms of Brain Damage in H. Influenzae Meningitis," *J. Neuropath. and Exp. Neurol.*, 1960, *19*, 248-265.

114. Stoller, A., and Collman, R. D., "Patterns of Occurrence of Births in Victoria, Australia, Producing Down's Syndrome (Mongolism) and Congenital Anomalies of the Central Nervous System: A 21 Year Prospective and Retrospective Survey," *Med. J. Austral.*, 1965, *7*, 1-4.

115. Svejcar, T., Frankenberger, Z., and Burian, F., "Contribution a l' étude De l'Action Tératogene Des Hormones Cortico-surrenales," *Arch. Franc. Ped.*, 1959, *16*, 215-217.

116. Tarjan, G., "Research in Mental Deficiency with Emphasis on Etiology," *Bull. Menninger Clin.*, 1960, *24*, 57-69.

117. Taussig, H., "The Thalidomide Syndrome," *Sci. Amer.*, 1962, *207*, 29-35.

118. Tredgold, A. F., *A Textbook of Mental Deficiency*, Williams and Wilkins, 1952.

119. Van Pelt, J. F., and Huizinga, J., "Some Observations on the Genetics of Gargoylism," *Acta Genet. (Basel)*, 1962, *12*, 1-11.

120. Waisman, H. A., *et al.*, "Phenylketonuria in Infant Monkeys," *Nature*, 1960, *188*, 1124-1125.

121. Walker, W. M., and McKee, A. P., "Asian Influenza in Pregnancy: Relationship to Fetal Anomalies," *Obst. and Gynec.*, 1959, *13*, 394-398.

122. Wallace, H. W., "Phenylpyruvic Oligophrenia," *Bull. Tufts N. Engl.*, *Med. Cent.*, 1959, *5*, 16-27.

123. Warkany, J., "Experimental Production of Congenital Malformations," *Internat. Rec. Med.*, 1956, *169*, 320-322.

124. _____, "Some Factors in the Etiology of Congenital Malformations," *Am. J. Ment. Def.*, 1945, *50*, 231-241.

125. Wendlund, L. V., Urmer, A. H., and Safford, H. W., "The Intellectual Functioning of Post Poliomyelitic Patients," *J. Clin. Psych.*, 1960, *16*, 179-181.

126. Wilson, J. G., "Is There Specificity of Action in Experimental Teratology?" *Pediat.*, 1957, *19*, 755-763.

127. Wilson, M. G., *et al.*, "Teratogenic Effects of Asian Influenza," *J. Am. Med. Ass.*, 1959, *171*, 638-641.

128. Witschi, E., "Overripeness of the Egg as a Cause of Twinning and Teratogenesis," *Cancer Res.*, 1952, *12*, 763-786.

129. Wortis, H., and Freedman, A., "The Contribution of Social Environment to the Development of Premature Children," *Amer. J. Orthopsychiat.*, 1965, *35*, 57-67.

130 Yacorzynski, G. K., and Tucker, B. E., "What Price Intelligence?" *Am. Psychol.*, 1960, *15*, 201-203.

131. Zellweger, "L'Hérédité dans La Maladie de Hurler," *J. Genet. Hum.*, 1958, *7*, 308-314.

Chapter 8

PATTERNS OF DEVELOPMENT

Since there are many sources of mental retardation, there are many forms which the condition may take. In those cases where the intellectual status of the retarded individual is attributable to an acquired pathology, we may expect to see a set of corresponding signs. In those cases where a dull individual grows in a non-stimulating environment, we may see a narrowed, underdeveloped intellect without either neurological or biochemical correlates. The way in which retarded individuals grow depends largely on the basis for their intellectual inadequacy. Since there are many sources of intellectual inadequacy, there are many patterns of growth that may emerge.

Generally speaking, there are some consistent patterns in those cases where individuals share a common pathology or cause. Individuals who have suffered injury to a previously sound brain tend to manifest some commonalities. On the other hand, these are commonalities and not uniformities. The point is that there are individual differences even among those sharing many common physical and psychological signs. Each cluster of characteristics, or *syndrome,* presents consistencies and also presents inconsistencies.

A much overstated type is the "classic case." Skeptics have remarked that classic cases are found only in the textbooks. We must take care to avoid excessive stereotyping of the patterns of mental deficiency.

Traditionally, scientific phenomena are named for their investigators —even when the descriptions later prove inadequate and when the entities themselves seem less than precise. The terminology used in this chapter will reflect that tradition. We will consider the more important syndromes, or patterns of development; some particularly obscure entities will not be discussed. The reader may wish to consider some of the medically oriented texts in order to pursue the more uncommon syndromes. Excellent summaries by medical specialists may be found in Hilliard and Kirman (83), Benda (11), Kugelmass (105), Paine (128), and Illingworth (88).

MIND, MENTAL RETARDATION, AND DEVELOPMENT

Mental retardation has been discussed in Chapter 1 as a cognitive problem. This is one of many ways to approach the problem, and its value emerges once more in a context of human growth.

The cognitive functions of man are related to his development and growth. As he grows older, his abilities increase; as he matures, his cognitive skills also mature. Clearly, intellect is a correlate of organic growth. The use of the word *correlate* is deliberate, because it suggests the probability that two phenomena will occur together frequently. In this instance, the two phenomena are physical growth and intellect. This issue is usually presented in a more general way as the traditional problem of mind and body and the nexus of problems surrounding these two phenomena.

Historically, the problem of relating intellect of various degrees to the biology of man has been perplexing. The traditional formulation of the problem has been a dualism—mind and its sphere, and body and its sphere. The two have existed interdependently, and they have been regarded as correlates, rather than as manifestations of one another. The problem of relating mind (in this context, various degrees of intellect) and body (the patterns of physical growth) is still perplexing. Several investigators have attempted to shed new light on the problem. Halstead's analysis of brain pathology has particularly considered "biological intelligence." It will be recalled that "psychometric intellgence," as investigated by testers and factor analysts, has also made valuable—though not transcendentally valuable—contributions to understanding intellect. The clinical ideas of intellect—remembering, solving problems, adjusting, and the like—have also been vital. In a very interesting paper, Reitan has attempted to connect the varying constructions of intellect and has found that Halstead's biological intelligence has much in common with Wechsler's psychometric formulation (135). Study shows brain cells and mind are still far apart (172).

In all fairness, these empirical formulations complement rather than revoke previous formulations of mind and intellect. The metaphysician's penchant for categories and logic is not really basically threatened. Two philosophers, one the physiologist Sherrington (146), the other the Jesuit Teilhard de Chardin (41), have written moving essays on the historical problem of mind. For Teilhard, mind in a context of creative evolution is a key to understanding nature. To Sherrington, the flashing of synaptic connections in a physiological structure is the sign of an awakening mind. In the Wayneflete Lectures, Eccles has given an explicit picture of mind as a manifestation of the brain (55). This position assumes a monism, that mentation—intellect—is a phenomenon of the awakening cerebrum.

There are commonalities between the dualists and the monists. To Teilhard and the physiologists, the end of development is not in sight. To Teilhard there is the increasing "hominization" of man, which has a counterpart in the emerging evolution of man acknowledged in Sherrington and Eccles.

To the student of mental retardation, the consideration of metaphysical formulations of mind may seem strained. On the other hand, to consider intellect—even deficient intellect—is to assay the problem tackled by philosophers over the centuries. If the tool of the investigator is as sophisticated as factor analysis (70), the result is a contribution to the nature of things metaphysical as surely as the writings of Aquinas. To digress, but only slightly: mental retardation poses epistemological questions every bit as keen as those just referred to. The entire problem of definition mentioned in Chapter 1 is epistemological; the nature of retardation is commonly formulated as if it were ontologically a reality independent of afflicted persons and the modes by which it is studied.

A consideration of patterns of physical development is required in this chapter by two lines of reasoning. First, a text should treat the phenomena encountered systematically. As we encounter inadequate intellect, so may we encounter inadequate physique. Second, if we construe mental retardation as a phenomenon of intellect, of mind, we must respect the historic counterpart, the physical body.

THE MECHANISMS OF MENTAL RETARDATION

A problem in the study of mental retardation is that we tend to view it as the central issue. This is a common-sense view insofar as mental retardation is a problem to social-service personnel and to parent When the intellectually inadequate human being exhibits his behavic to such people, his actions usually appear to be the sole issue. As Chap ter 1 indicated, however, there are alternative formulations. Mental re tardation may be considered, not so much as a basic problem, but as symptom of still another problem. We may say that mental retardatio is a behavioral deficit which is visible much as the smallest portion c an iceberg is visible. To pursue the metaphor, there is also a less ob vious component—the physical disorder which projects a set of beha ioral and social problems.

In this chapter, we will consider the basic somatic components c mental retardation insofar as they exist and are identifiable. The focu of the discussion is the biological correlate of behavioral deficit. T that end we will consider the somatic disorders encountered and a tempt to sketch the characteristics involved.

We will try to understand the physical problems as, *first,* disorde of body structure and, *second,* disorders of body chemistry. This div sion is an alternative to most of those shown in Table 8·1. The divisic does not mean that the biological correlates of mental retardatic neatly align themselves as wholly disorders of body structure or whol disorders of body chemistry. In some cases of mental retardation, virt ally all body organs are disturbed, so that the physical signs are bot chemical and structural.

In this discussion, the conditions which show both disturbances for example, mongolism—will be considered primarily affections structure *or* chemistry. This more simple schema is possible since mar presentations use the patterns of growth to illustrate the vario causes. Since the preceding chapter covered that issue, the more simp fied presentation seems appropriate. The disease entities are listed a phabetically.

TABLE 8·1

SCHEMATA FOR PRESENTATION OF SYMPTOMS IN MENTAL RETARDATION

	Schema	*Author*
I. a.	Malformation	Malamud (*110*)
b.	Destructive processs	
c.	Metabolic disorders	
d.	Neoplastic disorders	

II.	a.	Development varieties	Kugelmass (*105*)
	b.	Metabolic varieties	
	c.	Neuromotor varieties	
	d.	Psychological varieties	
III.	a.	Antenatal disorders	Benda (*11*)
	b.	Metabolic disorders and degenerative disease	
	c.	Total personality disorders	
IV.	a.	Mongolism	Hilliard and Kirman (*83*)
	b.	Metabolic syndromes	
	c.	Morphological syndromes	
V.	a.	Sub-cultural defect	Clarke and Clarke (*26*)
	b.	Genetic defects—dominant	
	c.	Genetic defects—recessive	
	d.	Defects of obscure origin	

DISORDERS OF BODY STRUCTURE

Arnold-Chiari Syndrome

This is a condition in which there is a downward displacement of the medulla and cerebellum. A concomitant disorder at the other end of the spine is *meningocele,* a structural disorder which usually interferes with the innervation of bowel or bladder control. Since the flow of cerebro-spinal fluid is blocked, hydrocephalus may occur. It is not impossible for the condition to respond to surgery, and it is possible to encounter cases in which intelligence may be only mildly affected.

Daniel and Stritch have reported evidence based on twenty-six cases (*36*). It is their judgment that the Arnold-Chiari malformation exemplifies the early developmental disorders. The condition probably has its origins in the embryonic period of growth. It represents a basic error of development present from the time when bodily organs began to emerge as discrete structures. Recent evidence on this problem, the problem of *morphogenesis,* has been offered by Runner and Dagg. Their experimental studies on animals demonstrate that in all probability *teratogenesis,* the maldevelopment of creatures, occurs through common metabolic pathways (*139*). This formulation demonstrates the need to structure our thinking about etiology in a very careful way. Developmental disorders, such as the Arnold-Chiari malformation, do not occur for simple reasons. The origin of the condition demonstrates the complexity of human growth and development.

Brain Injury

In another place we have considered the tenuous relationship between mind and the nervous system. There are a few cases where that relationship is not tenuous; but, as crucial as they are, they are weakened by their largely negative nature.

Pribram approached the problem directly and has reported experiments "On the Neurology of Thinking" (133). In his writing bearing that title, he gives an account of selective destruction of the frontal lobes in monkeys. The animals were presented with tasks whose operations he describes as "differentiative" and "intentional." The results constitute a concrete description of what selective destruction of tissue in the frontal lobes can mean to cognitive operations in primates.

Other investigators have called attention to the role of the brain stem in behavior (97, 104, 124). The Soviet scientists Kreindler, Ungher and Volanskii have observed the disruption of "higher nervous activity" when lesions have been produced in the reticular formation in dogs (104). The *reticular formation* is the name given to the cell assemblies in the brain stem that act as an arousal system for the cortex (124). This is an area of emerging interest, since, as Hebb pointed out, the cortical processes of thought cannot exist by themselves. Hebb has also commented that "no account of intellectual processes and their relation to the brain can be taken seriously today when this (the reticular formation) is omitted from the reckoning" (77, p. 267). This observation is apt when we recall Rimland's formulation of the autistic state, mentioned in Chapter 6.

The result of this and other contributions is to cause us to reconstrue the total problem of brain functions. The author has heard it stated that Sigmund Freud's writings are not read with enough respect for Freud's established reputation in neurology. Investigation of the disseminative (associative) effects of the reticular mechanism may constitute a rapprochement between the psychoanalytic work and the earlier neurologic work of Freud. This is not offered as fact, nor is it offered as a basis for rejecting the primacy of the cortex as the locus of cognition. Rather, it suggests the range of yet-unexplored matters when one tries to connect brain and mind.

It is when one returns to a consideration of the traditional locus of mind, the cortex, that the effects of brain injury become clearer. Beginning with Goldstein's work in World War I and continuing through the several volumes of Strauss and his associates (154, 155), we see the description of various consequences of brain damage.

When using the term *brain injury,* we refer primarily to the disturbances of motor and cognitive processes. There seem to be no real cures for damage to brain tissue as yet, so that the condition has practical implications primarily to teachers and therapists. These specialists do not work directly with the brain pathology of the individual but work with the functional correlates of neurology. They deal with the processes, the functions, that have a non-specific origin. The result is that they treat a functionally disabled child, not an impaired nervous system. Therapists do not base their work on the precision of the neurologist's findings. There is in fact no little manual specifying "What to Do 'til the Neurologist Comes"; rather they work on the basis of degree of functional disability. Thus, the term *brain injury* misses the point, since the focus of treatment is on peripheral, rather than central (i.e., cortical) disorders. In all probability the neurologist would not feel that therapeutic plans for reading and speech would be improved by mapping Brodman's areas of the cortex. There is a profound hiatus between the taxonomy of disorders and the tactics of instruction in all areas of handicapping. Recent work by Stevens and by Jordan suggests that this problem may yet be solved (*91, 95, 151*).

An equally disquieting incongruence exists between early anoxia with its implied brain damage and subsequent developmental status. For the last several years, prospective longitudinal study of anoxic children has been underway at the Washington University Medical School. One hundred and one anoxic children have been studied over a period of years, together with controls. At age seven the anoxic children were studied by Corah *et al.* (*30*) in order to extend work done perinatally and at age three. Sample shrinkage, an inescapable problem in prospective inquiry, was minimal, allowing conclusions to be developed *ad hoc*. At age seven the anoxic children were generally comparable to their controls in intelligence. *WISC* vocabulary was impaired to some extent, as was reading ability. The anoxic group of seven-year-olds did comparatively poorly on tests of perceptual motor functioning and perceptual attention. A significant finding was that competence may be reduced, but the possibility of the classic hyperkinetic syndrome was not substantiated. A fundamental conclusion was that predictions of development based on evidence of early anoxia cannot be made with confidence.

Stevens and Birch suggest that the term "Strauss Syndrome" be used to describe behavior which (1) is erratic and inappropriate, (2) consists of excessive motor response to stimuli, (3) is poorly organized, (4) may be described as distractable, (5) includes perceptual disorders, (6) is hyperactive, and (7) demonstrates poor motor coordination (*152*).

In recent years, gross, observable damage of the sort mentioned by Stevens and Birch has been augmented by attention to minimal damage, a degree of insult inferred more than observed. In a variety of studies—particularly those of Knobloch and Pasamanick (*102*), Daryn

(38), Clement and Peters (27), and Myklebust and Boshes (123)—
we have descriptions of children whose development has been abnormal in minor ways. In some instances growing children demonstrate essentially normal IQ's but show behavioral and emotional disturbances. Such damage need not be traumatic but may date from
growth error in early fetal life. Such damage (developmental) may
lead to further insult (traumatic) when it suppresses immediate respi-
ration in newborns (101). Generally speaking, the concept of developmental and traumatic brain damage accounts for the decreasing
emphasis on classical heredity as the source of retardation. The Scottish physician, Browne, seems to have been among the first to develop
this line of reasoning (20).

Prematurity

There was a time when early termination of gestation, premature
delivery, was an explicit threat to the lives of all but the healthiest
babies. Today the mortality rate for children under 2,500 grams is 1.3
per cent in Sweden (82), a figure which rises as one deviates from the
health standards of Sweden and from the conventional criteria of 2,500
grams. The origins of premature delivery are subject to increasing scrutiny. It seems that infertility and fetal wastage are common physical
antecedents (46), and psychological factors, while less well studied,
may contribute to the end of pregnancy (17). Much of the current
attention to premature children is concentrated, increasingly, on a
sub-population of babies weighing less than 1,500 grams. In this group
mortality is high, 72 per cent according to Hesseljo and Anberg (82),
and survival is not without a price. Survival is of course the principal
issue when children are born, but it broadens into persistent problems
of growth in the remaining years of childhood. The chief mechanism is
neurological damage, and it is well documented in the studies of
Bandera and Churchill (9); Drillien (46–49); and Heimer, Cutler, and
Freedman (79). Low IQ's are also usually found, but not uniformly:
children above 2,000 grams seem to escape most of the serious consequences, both neurological and psychological (49); but those below
that level generally incur several disabilities which produce further
problems (113, 137). We may now consider the persistent problems
which are largely secondary to neurological damage and which create
long-term problems to be faced after the neonatal period has passed.

Hearing. Campanelli, Pollock, and Henner examined the incidence
of hearing loss in forty-four survivors of premature birth (21). Seven
children, about 16 per cent, had losses, and their birth weights were on
the average considerably below those of the other children (p. < .05).

McDonald's series was a group of children with birth weights below four pounds (114). About 2 per cent had moderate to severe losses, and most of them had been delivered after no more than thirty-three weeks of gestation.

Vision. The relationship of visual damage to prematurity has been twofold. Originally, unrestricted use of oxygen during incubation produced retrolental fibroplasia, an irreversible form of damage to the eye. According to Genn and Silverman, this disease and its essential mechanism of hypoxia may produce further neurological damage. Since estimates of ability were employed, the question is still open (63). Even with the modification of oxygen administration, eye problems persist. Dann, Levine, and New (37), as well as Drillien (46), have found persistent visual deficiencies. Eames found visual acuity consistently associated with degree of prematurity (53, 54).

School Achievement. The long-term effects of prematurity are well illustrated in the presence of school problems. The form they take includes a discrepancy between mental age and the presumptions of the curriculum. Several studies reveal a significant relationship between prematurity and enrollment in special-education classes (6, 47). Other symptoms ascertained in classroom investigations are pervasive disorders such as reading problems, poor concentration, motor disabilities, shyness, and immaturity (44).

Over-all Development. We may now hazard a sketch of the development of premature babies over a period of years, based on partial evidence continued in a number of studies. In the first two years, the picture is one of delayed development, a condition proportional to degree of prematurity and lower social-class standing. A high incidence (< 20 %) of neurological abnormalities is found at this age (79). Walking and talking are less likely to be present at the usual point in the first twenty-four months of life (48). Three years after birth, evidence of cognitive impairment may well be present, as well as perceptual motor limitations (68). Between ages three and five, according to Harper, Fischer, and Rider, depressed intellectual and neurological signs are found in premature children (76). Examining the same children at age six, Wiener *et al.* found the usual proportional relationships between prematurity and dysfunction (169); although children under IQ 60 were excluded, perceptual-motor problems were found, as were immaturity of speech comprehension and reasoning. Barlow found a threefold increase in the incidence of retardation at this age (10). At age eight to ten years Robinson and Robinson found the smaller of three groups of premature children likely to be considered aggressive, subject to distractions, and capable of inadequate relationships, in the eyes of their teachers (137). In the years of middle childhood and adolescence, Howard and Worrell found twenty-two small premature children included seven with low IQ's (87).

We may now venture a few observations on the nature of prematurity as a subject of study. A particularly pressing problem is the use of birth weight below 2,500 grams as the criterion of prematurity. The facts seem to indicate that birth weight 100 grams below the conventional figure may be followed by few adverse effects. On the other hand, a birth weight of 1,500 grams clearly poses a threat to the integrity of children. The use of 2,100 grams as a criterion by Heimer, Cutler, and Freedman may be more defensible than the figure now commonly used.

Occasionally one encounters in the literature a straw man: the proposition that prematurity can be harmful when no specific damage to the child is involved. It is wise to keep in mind that damage, and damage proportional to degree of immaturity, is the essential concept in prematurity.

Social class should be recognized as one of the great concomitants of prematurity (171). This applies in two ways. First, lower-class mothers are more likely to see a doctor only when they present themselves for delivery; their prenatal health may be quite unsupervised, and we know that prematurity is frequently preceded by prenatal complications (79). Second, and more pervasive, is the effect of maternal child-care practices among disadvantaged persons. The preemy born to a lower-class mother, let us say a mother in an urban slum, is subject to the adversity which affects siblings of normal birth weight. However, social adversity is far more threatening to children who started life in a marginally competitive degree of health. We shall continue to see lower social classes contribute a disproportionate number of children of low birth weight. Action programs such as Project Headstart should help such children considerably, but they come after the fact of social, biological and cultural adversity. As we see social intervention develop as a part of the federal program against poverty and its progeny, we may expect to see support for research into bio-social issues such as prematurity. There is room, in particular, for studies with greater sophistication. The model, granted an eclectic one, would take the rigor of the explorations of Wiener and associates (169), the long-term commitment of Drillien—who has recently summarized a decade of work on the problem (46)—and add to it the sophistication introduced by Robinson and Robinson (137). The result would be a major contribution to the welfare of children.

Congenital Malformations

Most mentally retarded individuals are not profoundly retarded, nor are they grossly different in appearance. Sometimes, however, severe disturbances are apparent at birth and, while it is rare, this problem merits attention.

The range of congenital malformations is broad, and the severity ranges from mild to extreme (43). Reporting on 543 autopsies, Malamud reported congenital malformations in 74 per cent of the cases (110). According to Davis and Potter, deaths due to congenital malformations occurred in the proportions of four to six per 1,000 births over a twenty-year period (39). The incidence was highest in disorders of the nervous system; cardiac disorders came next, with problems of the gastro-intestinal and gastro-urinary system about equally divided. The problems were most common in male whites whose mothers were at the beginning or end of the child-bearing period. The presence of disorders of an extreme sort in non-whites has been documented in Muir's discussion of hydranencephaly and allied disorders in Chinese children in Singapore. The disorders were traced to a variety of causes —viral, vascular, and chemical (122).

Experimental work by Runner and Dagg, previously cited, has suggested that a variety of agents can produce malformation by using a common metabolic pathway. In such circumstances, the search for specific human teratogenic agents may represent a naive formulation of the problem of congenital disorders.

Craniostenosis

A term used to describe the condition in which the bones of the skull fuse prematurely is *craniostenosis.* In this condition, the mental retardation is secondary to the skull deformity. In those cases where the skull deformity is prevented, no mental retardation need occur. On the other hand, there is no necessary correspondence between skull irregularities and intellectual status. Daniel Webster had a large skull, while that of Immanuel Kant was quite small. This further aggravates the mind-brain problem mentioned previously.

Comparable disorders are the various -cephalies—*scaphocephaly, brachycephaly* and *oxycephaly*. The prefix in each case simply describes the shape of the skull as a consequence of growth following the line of least resistance along the suture lines. In scaphocephaly, the head is long; in brachycephaly, it is primarily broad; and in oxycephaly, it is distinctively high.

Craniostenosis is one of those physical disorders that may be treated, thus avoiding mental retardation which is secondary to the skull disorder. This condition has a familial incidence. Its therapy is discussed in Chapter 9.

Ectodermal Disorders

Among the developmental problems encountered in the study of mental retardation are those whose prime characteristics are skin disorders. The skin problems are not superficial but illustrate growth problems originating in the ectoderm and occurring from the earliest weeks of fetal life.

Tuberous Sclerosis is the condition which is characterized by some degree of mental retardation (though there are exceptions), epilepsy, and adenoma sebaceum. The condition is sometimes identified as *epiloia* and has the appearance of a "butterfly" rash on the cheeks. It is possible to confuse this with acne. At post-mortem, tumors are encountered in the brain, and the organs of the body may be affected. The condition is found consistently in specific families (*111*).

Von Recklinghausen's Disease is the condition in which there are multiple tumors of the nerves. This gives rise to an alternate name, *neurofibromatosis*. In some cases, there may be physical giantism, as in the case reported by the author (*94*), and the mechanism may be attributable to disorders of the pituitary gland. This is not clear, however. In other cases, the spinal cord may be affected (*3*).

Sturge-Weber Syndrome is a condition in which there is a discoloration on the face due to tumors of the blood vessels. According to Benda, the description of the condition is almost entirely the contribution of Sturge, and supplementary contributions have come from Weber, Oppenheim, and Kufs. The extent of disorders is not confined to the skin and brain. Seizures have been reported, and disorders of the internal organs are not unknown. Sometimes this syndrome is known as *naevoid amentia*.

Hurler's Disease (Gargoylism)

This is a rare condition in which mental retardation is part of an over-all disturbance of body functioning. Having its origin mainly in heredity (*173*), the condition is largely unresponsive to treatment. A concomitant frailty may limit the life expectancy quite sharply.

The physical signs of the condition are obviously skeletal. In this respect, the condition is similar to Morquio's disease, and Benda has commented on the essential similarity between the two conditions. People who show this syndrome are dwarfs. They usually have heads of normal size, a fact which emphasizes the disparity of the trunk and limbs. The over-all appearance is a rather ugly one, giving rise to the name *gargoylism*. Other characteristics are masculine appearance in women and a protruding abdomen. The condition is accompanied by a fairly recognizable facial type, the bridge of the nose being depressed and the mouth large. The spine is often abnormal, and this contributes to the over-all grotesque appearance. While mental retardation is common, the author has observed one apparent case of Hurler's disease on a university campus. This is noteworthy if only because it demonstrates the inadvisability of jumping to conclusions of mental retardation on the basis of physical evidence alone.

Hydrocephalus

The brain sits in a bath of fluid. The liquid courses along the spinal column and is therefore called *cerebro-spinal* fluid. Within the head, the fluid passes through well-described passages which constitute the ventricular system. In those cases where an accident causes the ventricles to be blocked (see Arnold-Chiari Syndrome) (*36*), the fluid is not permitted to continue to its usual place of absorption, and an excess accumulates. It should be noted that this is not the same as saying that the quantity of fluid is the result of excessive production. In some cases, the condition is arrested. The result is damage to the brain and an enlarged skull. In other cases, the disease is progressive, and usually the result has been increasing dysfunction and death (*172*).

Communicating hydrocephalus is the form in which the fluid may pass into the ventricles from the spine. In some cases the opposite condition exists; it is called, correspondingly, *non-communicating hydrocephalus*. It should be noted that this condition is not associated with the word *communicable*.

As an example of the uncertainties relating mind and brain, the author saw, a few years ago, a severe case of hydrocephalus with attendant paraplegia in a child whose verbal intelligence quotient was well above average. The performance quotient was well below normal. It is interesting to consider that the child was about to be placed in a classroom for mentally retarded youngsters when, in fact, a consideration of his academic aptitude would suggest quite the opposite disposition of the case. The child's physical status indicated that, if schooling were to be provided, the youngster would have better belonged in a room for the physically handicapped. A recent investigation shows the boy to be quite debilitated; his condition has now become much worse.

The previously negative picture of the course of the disease has been modified by the development of surgical techniques. While not all cases of hydrocephalus are necessarily amenable to surgery, there is less pessimism about the condition than in former years. Ultimately, chemical control of production of cerebro-spinal fluid may be the most effective form of management (60).

Mongolism (Down's Disease, Acromicria)

Scientific analysis of mental retardation began in the last century. The tenor of nineteenth-century science was optimistic. Herbert Spencer and his associates had begun a systematic advancement of learning which drew much of its vitality from progress in the physical and biological sciences. One example of the Spencerian ambition was the initiation of studies in comparative ethnology and anthropology. During this period, Down attempted to formulate a concept of mental retardation which is highly consonant with, if not a part of, the Spencer movement (45). Down felt that one particular form of mental deficiency showed a definite resemblance to the appearance of Asian peoples, hence the word *mongolism*. On the face of it, this connection is absurd, but hindsight is a wonderful protection. Such a concept of mental retardation probably seemed eminently reasonable in the days of the "white man's burden." While the concept has been rejected, the label has stayed to plague us. Warkany has pointed out that no less than thirty-nine different explanations have been offered for the origins of mongolism (167). He grouped them in four categories: (a) reversion to primitive type, (b) genetic origin, (c) environmental disturbances, and (d) changes within the child—e.g., endocrine dysfunction.

The present state of our knowledge is that we are as uncertain as Down was a hundred years ago—but at a higher level. In this generation, our uncertainties are at least attributable to a surfeit of ill-digested fact, while Down's were attributable to a lack of facts.

Perhaps the first thing that should be said about mongolism, or *acromicria* as it is sometimes called, is that it is a total disturbance of development. This means that the entity is an affection of many parts of the body. The distinctive facial appearance of such children is only one aspect of the disorder, and the mental retardation is one manifestation of the pervasive pathology. An incidence of one to two cases per thousand births has been reported from Denmark (126) and from Australia, where fluctuations in annual incidence have been quite pronounced.

The syndrome of mongolism does not exist on an all-or-none basis.

The signs are so many that they can be expected to occur in different proportions from child to child. On the other hand, many cases are fairly clear-cut, with many signs being obvious.

At birth, a large anterior fontanel and open sutures are present. The neck is usually short, and the features may appear compressed. In some cases, the convolutions of the ear seem unusual. Often the palm of the hand has one transverse fissure, and there may be a large gap between the first and second toes (13). The oral cavity is unusual, with the palate being high and the tongue commonly being fissured. Voice pitch is *not* abnormal, as it sometimes stated (117). The sexual organs may be malformed, as may the heart. Hilliard and Kirman have called attention to Fallot's tetralogy in about 10 per cent of the cases of mongolism (83). Since this is a heart disorder, it seems clear why some mongoloid children do not survive the period of infancy. Hall found that fifteen of thirty-eight infants died in the first six months; seven of ten autopsies showed cardiac defects (73). The life expectation for children surviving infancy is not normal; however, Penrose has observed an increase from nine to twelve years over a period of a decade and a half (130), and Collman and Stoller have confirmed in detail the reduced life expectancy for persons with Down's disease (29).

Less obvious components of mongolism are coarseness of the hair, incurving of the little finger, special finger-print patterns, speckling of the iris, abnormal interpupillary distance, dental disorders, poor circulation, and a fragile respiratory system. Recent studies in hematology have disclosed a number of unusual blood characteristics. Sobel and associates have found increased concentrations of serum gamma globulin (149), a finding that was also reported by Carver, Wilson, and Wittse (24). A lower output of adrenalin has been reported by Bergsman (16). High concentrations of gamma-globulin and low concentrations of albumin are reported by Appleton and Pritham (4).

A high incidence of spinal disorders has been observed by Mautner (112). In his series of eighty mongoloids, thirty had malformations of the lower spine. A slightly broader investigation of development in cases of the acromicria syndrome has been offered by Dutton (52). He found a generally normal rate of growth for the skeleton; but he found that height, when used to derive quotients of development, produced a picture of retarded rate of growth. Studies of the leucocytes in the blood of mongoloids have indicated abnormalities. Kluge found evidence of immaturity (100), a finding substantiated on a longitudinal basis by Ridler and Shapiro (136). Analyses of the endocrine system are common. Benda has called attention to disorders of the pituitary and the thyroid and has also found abnormalities of the thymus (14).

In view of the distinct appearance and well-documented physical anomalies, it is appropriate to ask if severity of physical development is parallel to intellectual retardation. Kääriäinen and Dingman examined the issue by analyzing intelligence and ten cardinal signs of mongolism (96). Factor analysis increased the depth of the investigation which concluded that physical and mental signs were not associated in degree of severity. A similar study by Johnson and Barnett employed twenty-three signs and a different methodology but produced essentially comparable findings (90). In eighty-eight subjects the mean number of stigmata was 13.6, and it did not fluctuate as a correlate of intelligence.

An interesting series of papers has examined reproduction in mongolism. There seem to be no sex differences in incidence (28). In a pair of studies, Sawyer has recorded the growth of a child born to a mongoloid female (140, 141). The child is now in early adulthood and had been in nursing training for some time at last report. The child is apparently normal and has made progress in professional training. Forssman and Thyssell reported findings in a boy born to a mongoloid female in Sweden (59). The child was born in 1954 and is essentially normal in appearance, intellect, and chromosomes (58). Mongolism in both of monozygotic twins has been reported by MacGillivray (108), while Rehn and Thomas have given a pedigree of a mongoloid who bore a mongoloid child (134). Interestingly, all the accounts seem to be of fertile females. This reflects both a problem in pathology and a problem in accountability, since sexual maturity in mongoloid females is generally quite delayed (121). Mortality in young mongoloid females is reported by Gruenberg to be high (69).

It seems certain that development of mongolism takes place early in gestation. Some workers specify the point in time and say that a deviation of the growth pattern begins around the eighth week (14). Others use the development stage of the child and indicate that mongolism is a disorder of the thirty-five millimeter embryo (83). A further consideration of the work of Runner and Dagg suggests that perhaps the development of mongolism is the metabolic consequence of a number of factors which act by producing a similar disturbance of the body's chromosomes (139). Apart from the relevance of the Runner and Dagg paper to this particular problem, the science of experimental embryology illustrates how broad our intellectual perspective must be when we study a problem as gross as mental retardation.

A correlate of mongolism is advanced maternal age, which has been observed for a hundred years. In a series reported by Fraser and Mitchell in 1876, nine Scottish women were between ages forty and fifty years at the delivery of the afflicted child (62). As in Hansen's study of cerebral palsy in Denmark, the condition is associated with increased age in the mother. Dysfunction of the thyroid and pituitary glands (13, 56), disorders of the chromosomes (18), and errors of vitamin absorption (149) are factors which are associated with mongolism.

Down's disease has been found all over the world (29, 160, 163, 170), and it has been known for centuries. We can be sure of the early occurrence from the observations made on a skeleton found in a Saxon grave by Bothwell (19). The earliest scholarly reference known to the writer which might be liberally interpreted as a description of the condition is found in a book published by Giovanni Batista della Porta in 1618 (42). It is not likely that knowledge of the condition as a unique clinical entity or syndrome goes back more than a hundred years. For example, as recently as 1876 experts seem to have considered Kalmuc idiocy a special form of cretinism (62).

Current formulations are still incomplete. We know that *pku* can be produced in monkeys; is it possible to produce mongolism in animals? What are the sufficient biological errors needed? Indeed, to return to the epistemological issue, what is mongolism? One might say it is a trisomic condition, but one might say it is a disorder of the fifty- to sixty-day embryo. Could, should, a child with growth fixated within the thirty-five-millimeter stage, with or without chromosomal error, be considered mongoloid? The practice has been to rely on cytological evidence in the face of variation in the phenotype, as Hall put it (73). This provides no unique evidence, since the chromosomal count may be normal, as in the case of three mongoloid siblings studied by Atkins, O'Sullivan, and Pryles (8) and in the case discussed by Schmid, Lee, and Smith (143). Mongolism, or Down's disease, continues to be a scientific enigma. Knowledge accrues, as in studies of caloric intake (33), and the quality of our questions improves; but the answers continue to be incomplete. As Hallenbeck has pointed out, we have seen a spurt in research on mongolism (74). We hope that the passage of time will unearth new findings about the origins of this disease and also that diligent study will allow us to place a meaningful interpretation on existing knowledge. An example of this is the possibility that two behavorial syndromes of mongolism will emerge as extensions of the cytological patterns of trisomy and translocation.

Rud's Syndrome

This is a condition which is infrequently encountered but which shows how pervasive the bodily disturbances may be in mental retardation. Rather than consisting of a simple defect of the thinking processes, this condition has concomitant elements which are unique. The full syndrome consists of low-grade mental deficiency and epilepsy. Also, infantilism and the scale-like thickening of the skin called ichthyosis are present. MacGillivray gave an account of this pattern of development several years ago (109).

Cerebral Palsy

In 1861 William Little published a classic paper on the "mental and physical derangements," as he termed them, of children injured by the processes of "abnormal parturition" (107). Since that time an increasingly precise literature has accrued on the problems of children whose motor and intellectual deficits can be ascribed to cerebral damage due to specific insult or developmental failure (92). The condition has been inclusively defined by Perlstein: "Cerebral Palsy, by definition, is a condition characterized by paralysis, weakness, in-coordination, or any other aberration of motor function due to pathology in the *motor control centers of the brain*" (93). This definition points to the motor disorders as the primary symptoms; the reference to brain damage as the source puts the entire condition in the same class with other conditions which may follow or accompany brain damage, such as aphasia, the agnosias, and convulsions. The condition may be clinically described as follows.

Spasticity. This in an abnormal contraction of the muscles. It usually occurs when the muscles are subjected to stretching. If the stretching occurs quickly in the more severe spastic, the contracture will also occur quickly.

Athetosis. Totally unlike spasticity, this condition is characterized by uncontrollable twisting movements in the extremities. The movements are often slow and continuous, almost wave-like in appearance.

Ataxia. In some cases the motor difficulties are revealed in an inability to maintain a normal gait. Balance and coordination are involved.

Rigidity. In rare cases the cerebral palsied exhibit a high degree of muscle tension. The condition may resemble spasticity very closely, but it is due to damage in areas of the brain outside the pyramidal tracts.

While these conditions can be sub-divided quite extensively, both by overlapping of the conditions and by creating fine distinctions within the categories, generally the motor picture is sufficient to lead to a generalized conclusion about the extent and nature of the disorder.

Phelps has pointed out some of the more obvious aspects of palsies

(*132*). He has indicated that in spastic paralysis the problem is one of hyperirritability of the muscles in response to stimuli. The hyperirritability means that attempts to contract muscles lead to arousal of the extensor system, with an attendant failure of the normal reciprocal action of extensors and flexors.

Commenting on the athetoses, Phelps points out that there are no signs of pyramidal involvement in muscle action; the increased reflexes, the hyperirritability, of the spastic disorder are absent. (At the risk of redundancy we may point out that this neurological distinction indicates that it is unnecessary to confuse the two conditions if one considers not the words *spasticity* and *athetosis* but, appropriately, their significance.) Rather, the symptoms of the athetoid are superimposed on normal movements. Commonly, one may see contractures of muscles in athetoids, but this should be considered not evidence of the basic problem but a condition resulting from physical confinement to wheel chairs, and the like. Contractures are therefore secondary to athetosis, rather than prime manifestations of the disorder.

The palsies have their origin in physical damage. It follows that they may be profitably understood as consequences of brain lesions. Perlstein has discussed the cerebral palsies in terms of the site of the damage.

A. *Pyramidal Tract Involvement*—Clinically, patients with pyramidal tract involvement, either in cortical regions in the precentral gyrus, or subcortically in the region of the internal capsule, are the true spastics, and the clinical syndromes are presumably due to removal of the inhibitory effects of the pyramidal tract.

B. *Extrapyramidal Tract Involvement*—This covers involvement primarily of the basilar nuclear areas and/or their connections. Clinically, this classification covers patients with abnormalities of motion, such as athetosis, choreas, tremors, ballismus, dystonias and rigidities. . . .

C. *Involvement of the Cerebellum and/or its its Connections*—Clinically, this classification would include primarily ataxias and the atonic forms of cerebral palsy. (*93*)

Perlstein's presentation gives a picture of the structural problem. This is the basis of the disorder and therefore important. Still another way to approach cerebral palsy is to realize that it is the functional side of the problem, the operational correlate of the structural damage, that one observes. An equally obvious point is that the level of functioning in people with cerebral palsy varies from slight malfunction to severe.

It follows that the condition may be profitably approached by considering the functional ability of the individual with cerebral palsy. The following classification has been proposed by Minear.

Class I.   Patients with cerebral palsy with no practical limitation of activity.

Class II.   Patients with cerebral palsy with slight to moderate limitations of activity.

Class III.   Patients with cerebral palsy with moderate to great limitation of activity.

Class IV.   Patients with cerebral palsy unable to carry on any useful physical activity. (119)

Minear supplements this presentation by ordering the conditions in a therapeutic idiom:

Class A.   Patients with cerebral palsy not requiring treatment.

Class B.   Patients with cerebral palsy who need minimal bracing and minimal therapy.

Class C.   Patients with cerebral palsy who need bracing and apparatus, and the services of a cerebral palsy treatment team.

Class D.   Patients with cerebral palsy limited to such a degree that they require long term institutionalization and treatment. (119)

One more physical consideration of cerebral palsy is the recognition that it need not be an all-or-nothing condition, either involving all the subject's motor functioning or none of it. Actually, the existence of cerebral palsy may be restricted to a part of the body. The occurrence of the condition in the various quadrants of the body is described by the suffix -*plegia* and is shown in Figure 8·1. *Monoplegia* means the involvement of one extremity, a leg for example. *Paraplegia* refers to the involvement of the lower limbs. *Hemiplegia* involves one side of the body; both the arm and the leg are typically involved. *Triplegia* is the term covering damage that affects three extremities, leaving the fourth unimpaired. *Quadriplegia* is the involvement of all four limbs.

Generally, hemiplegia is associated with spasticity. Quadriplegia is more commonly found in athetosis. Triplegia, which is less common, is associated with spasticity, as is paraplegia. Monoplegia, a rare condition, is found about equally in spasticity and athetosis.

An excellent study of the incidence of patterns of physical involvement and neurological disorders in cerebral palsy is contained in the work of Hopkins, Bice, and Colton (86). In their New Jersey study of 1954, they reported data substantiating the observations offered in the

Type	Involvement	Description
Monoplegia		one limb is involved
Hemiplegia		one side is involved
Paraplegia		legs and lower trunk involved
Triplegia		three limbs are involved
Quadriplegia	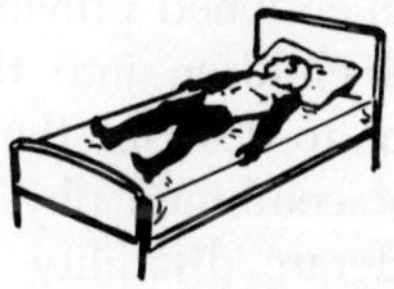	all four quadrants involved

Figure 8·1
Topology of Cerebral Palsy

preceding paragraph. Table 8·2 shows the distribution of the -plegias in spasticity, athetosis, and rigidity.

TABLE 8·2

TOPOLOGY AND TYPES IN CEREBRAL PALSY

(Hopkins, Bice, and Colton, 86)

	Spastic	Athetoid	Rigid	Ataxic
Quadriplegia	160	292	88	—
Triplegia	55	2	7	—
Hemiplegia	299	35	73	—
Paraplegia	124	3	9	—
Monoplegia	7	1	—	—
TOTAL	645	333	177	

The occurrence of the various forms of cerebral palsy suggests that spasticity is more likely to be found in an individual than athetosis. Also, both of these forms of cerebral palsy are more likely to occur than rigidity or ataxia. When one attempts to coordinate the data to validate such a view, a curious finding emerges—namely, that the demographic studies are not consistent in their enumeration of the types.

Asher and Schonell, examining 400 English cases, found the proportion of spastics to athetoids about 8:1, with other conditions occurring much less frequently (7). Schonell studied 340 children and found a similar proportion (145). According to Hopkins, Bice, and Colton, the spastic-to-athetoid ratio is closer to 2:1 (86). O'Reilly has offered data which is closer to the New Jersey data of Hopkins and associates. He gives frequencies of the types of cerebral palsy as spasticity 50 per cent, athetosis 25 per cent, rigidity 13 per cent, ataxia 6 per cent, other kinds 6 per cent (125). In their excellent work on cerebral palsy, Cruickshank and Raus accept the New Jersey data on incidence (32). The inconsistency of these data probably does not describe national differences in the pattern of the disease; the differences are probably in the standards of classification.

One further consideration is the frequency of degree of handicap. Minear's classification has been mentioned previously. A grouping by Schonell of 345 cerebral-palsied children into the categories slight, moderate, severe, and very severe, to describe the degree of handicap, shows the following incidence of combined physical and mental disability: slight disability 87, moderate disability 148, severe 87, very severe 21 (145). The picture is one of significant handicap and limitations in the majority of cases (> 70 per cent).

Growth. In general the pattern of growth in cerebral palsied children is slow. The normal developmental mileposts are reached late, and the routine emergence of sitting, walking, and talking is significantly delayed. Walking may never really be established, while talking may be characterized by poor articulation even when syntax is good (91, 92).

There is more to growth than emergence of specific functions. Other events are increases in height and weight and the establishment of normal processes of nutrition. In this last instance the work of Ruby and Matheny is valuable (138). They evaluated growth and nutrition in 137 children, virtually all of whom were seriously handicapped. Individual records were developed and maintained on the children, who ranged in age from two to eighteen years. Athetoids were smaller than spastic children, and in general all clinical types showed disturbances of long-term growth. The authors cite unpublished data on wrist X-rays which revealed a serious lag in bone maturation in thirty-six cerebral-palsied children. Sterling's work on growth in height and weight is a useful contribution based on characteristics of forty spastic, fifty-five athetoid, and five "other" cases of cerebral palsy (150). When data were evaluated by means of the *Wetzel Grid,* about three-quarters of the congenital cases were below the thirtieth percentile for height (N=77) and for weight (N=73). Postnatal cases did not have equally deviant height and weight, although the number of cases, six, did not permit broad observations and conclusions.

It is wise to keep in mind that the fragile health of many cerebral-palsied children is a constant source of problems. Colds become serious illnesses rather than the transient irritations which lower the energy of normal children for a few days. Further, there seems to be no change in this condition of chronic susceptibility to poor health. It has been suggested that adolescence may bring more rather than fewer health problems and that deterioration may begin quite early (89). Certainly this is compatible with what we know about the lowered life expectancy in the cerebral-palsied. Even with the best care the general disability of cerebral-palsied children reduces their chances of living to an advanced age. In all probability the relationship between severity and life expectancy is direct; namely, the most severe cases have the least chance of living into the years of middle adulthood (142, 165).

Intelligence. In 1948 Phelps published a paper which has been used by other writers as a starting point in the study of intelligence in the cerebral-palsied. Commenting on the level of intellect in a population of cerebral-palsied individuals, he asserted that in 70 per cent of the cases, ". . . the mentality may be described as 'normal' using the word in the sense that these individuals show the normal spread of intelligence level seen in the population at large. The remaining 30 per cent are mentally defective, and the deficiency is directly the result of brain damage involving intelligence" (132, p. 11).[1]

The conclusion which people drew from this study, rightly or wrongly, was that Phelps believed intelligence to be largely intact in the cerebral-palsied. The note of optimism, as opposed to total pessimism, struck by this study has been echoed by others. Heilman, for example, pointed out in 1951 that cerebral palsy did not preclude adequate intelligence, that not all cerebral-palsied individuals are retarded (78).

One of the earlier attempts to give a rational account of intelligence in the cerebral palsied came from Burgmeister and Blum in 1949 (93). They reported that in thirty-eight children with a median CA of four years and four months there was "more serious retardation among our group of cerebral palsied children sample than is generally reported in the literature." Twenty of the thirty-eight children in this sample were of border-line intelligence or less. Fifteen of the thirty-eight were of good intelligence. While this sample is small, the results may be considered fairly representative.

Specific evidence has come from several sources. According to Miller and Rosenfeld, significantly more cerebral-palsied children fall below the average level of intelligence than at or above it (118). Their results were derived from administration of the Binet or the *Cattell Infant Intelligence Scale* and indicated that 73 per cent of the children tested were below IQ 89.

Lamm and Fisch examined eighty-four children and found that a difference of twenty-three points in IQ separated those children making satisfactory therapeutic progress from those who were not (106). Their data are presented in Figure 8·2 and indicate that sixty-six of their eighty-four cases were below IQ 90. This means that only about 22 per cent were in the average range or better.

English data by Schonell derived from 354 children between three and fifteen years of age gives a slightly more positive picture. Nevertheless, it does indicate a distribution centered on a mean about two standard deviations below average (145). Fifty per cent of the cases fell between IQ 50 and IQ 89. Only about 25 per cent of the cases were above IQ 90.

An interesting paper by Fouracre and Thiel put together data collected by Bice, Hopkins, and Colton; Miller and Rosenfeld; Asher and

---

[1]Phelps uses the word normal here to mean "unaffected by brain damage."

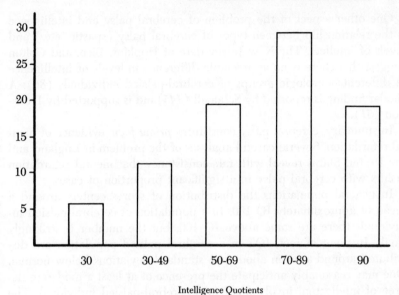

Intelligence Quotients

Figure 8·2

Range and Distribution of IQ's in 84 Children with
Cerebral Palsy. (Lamm and Fisch, 106)

Schonell; and Fouracre, Jann, and Mortorana (*61*). Table 8·3 shows
the summary of the four studies. In each case there is a significant de-

TABLE 8·3

SUMMARY OF STUDIES OF INTELLIGENCE IN
CHILDREN WITH CEREBRAL PALSY
(Fouracre & Thiel) 61

	IQ 0-69		IQ 70-89		IQ 90-109		IQ 109+		
	No.	%	No.	%	No.	%	No.	%	Total
Bice *et al.*	487	49.0	224	22.5	212	21.9	69	6.6	992
Miller	104	50.0	74	22.5	77	23.0	15	4.5	330
Asher	160	45.2	75	16.8	71	20.1	14	4.0	354
Fouracre	27	41.5	15	23.1	16	24.6	7	10.8	65

gree of consistency in the percentage of cases below IQ 69. It is just
about 50 per cent for all four studies combined. A glance at the data
in the IQ range above 90 indicates that only about 10 per cent of the
cases fall in the normal range or better. There are usually about seven
times as many cases in this intelligence level.

One other aspect of the problem of cerebral palsy and intelligence is the relationship between types of cerebral palsy (spastic, etc.) and levels of intellect. The New Jersey data of Hopkins, Bice, and Colton suggest that there is no appreciable difference in levels of intelligence in different neurologic groups of cerebral-palsied individuals (86). A similar finding is reported by Schonell (145) and is supported by Dunsdon (51).

In summary, cerebral palsy constitutes *prima facie* evidence of mental retardation. Several careful analyses of the problem in England and the United States reveal with fair consistency that mental retardation occurs with cerebral palsy in a significant proportion of cases.

In general populations the distribution of scores centers around a mean of approximately IQ 100. In a population of cerebral-palsied individuals there are some above IQ 100, but the number is strikingly small. In point of fact, IQ's in a cerebral palsied population are distributed around a mean about two standard deviations below normal. One may reasonably anticipate the presence of at least a moderate degree of intellectual involvement in a cerebral-palsied individual. The stipulation must be observed, however, that there will be some cerebral palsied persons of average intelligence and, rarely, some of above average intelligence. For more extended discussions of cerebral palsy the reader is referred to Items 31 and 32 in the bibliography.

DISORDERS OF BODY CHEMISTRY

Cretinism

The general opinion of experts maintains that there is little room for radical progress in those forms of mental deficiency which may be traced to some physical disorder. What amelioration is possible occurs within limits largely resistant to change. Cretinism seems to be the classic exception to this principle. It is entirely possible to produce a radical change in the physiology of the cretin, and this change is usually reflected in a more alert and inquiring intellect.

The basis of cretinism is a low level of excretion by the thyroid gland. Usually the condition is recognizable by the time the child is about six months of age. The basal metabolism is low, the temperature is low, and the child's features may seem coarse. Left untreated for a long time, the slowness of intellectual and physical processes may prove less responsive to therapy than it would otherwise. In those cases where thyroid therapy is instituted early, and is well supervised, the course of the resulting changes is quite impressive. The child may grow several inches and may present a strikingly altered appearance.

In other cases where hypothyroidism is only postulated, non-cretinous children may be treated. The changes are usually minimal in such cases. Perhaps a good way to phrase this observation is to say that thyroid therapy is a specific and can be expected to produce change only when thyroid metabolism is the source of the disorder. As Benda has pointed out, even then we must be cautious in our expectations; no one was ever lifted above the intellectual level determined by his heredity (14).

Degenerative Disorders

One of the considerations offered in a previous chapter was that mental retardation is a significant problem involving the lives of people other than the afflicted individual. The validity of this proposition is clear when one considers the degenerative disorders. In such cases of mental retardation, the family sees regression climaxed by the death of the victim. Genetic metabolic errors are often suggested as mechanisms in these disorders (15).

The symptoms of the degenerative disorders vary in degree, speed of development, and extent. The result is that a variety of clinical pictures emerges, each having some distinctive elements. The commonalities are many, however, since the conditions do not seem to be arrestable, let alone curable. In general, the course is regression: seizures, obliteration of the senses, the various -plegias, and finally death. An account of the stages of degenerative process has been given by Guiraud and Roualt de la Vigne (71).

Tay-Sachs Disease was once felt to be a hereditary disease in Jewish families; this is no longer entirely the case (50, 127). A familial incidence has been documented by Aronson, Aronson, and Volk (5). The disease has been known for about eighty years and is most commonly thought to occur among Ashkenazic families originally living near the Baltic Sea (66). Benda and Melchior have given an account of three cases in which the disease was evident before four months of age. Schneck's series of fourteen children were generally normal in the first ten months of life (144). However, in the next four months they exhibited spontaneous and pathological laughter associated with lapses of consciousness. Two to six months later convulsions were evident. Death often follows tetraplegia, blindness, and seizures, at ages ranging up to four and a half years (15). This condition involves degeneration of the retina, and is accordingly sometimes called *cerebromacular degeneration*. The mechanism is failure to metabolize fat deposited in nerve cells. A diagnostic test has been developed by Volk, Aronson, and Saifer (158).

Niemann-Pick Disease is quite comparable to the preceding condition but is different in that the spleen and the liver are involved. The course of this disorder is generally predictable, and death is the usual outcome. No treatment is really known, although optimism is aroused in some cases by treatments based on injecting the dessicated glands of animals into afflicted children; the author has come across instances of children in relatively advanced states of deterioration who received such treatment. No acceptance of this procedure seems evident, however, in conventional medical circles.

Kernicterus

One of the more recently analyzed problems in children is the condition in which there is a blood-group incompatibility between a mother and her child. Usually the child is rh-positive, meaning that its red cells are agglutinated by rh typing serum; the mother is rh-negative, meaning that this reaction does not take place. When the child's red cells infiltrate the mother's circulation, she develops antibodies. The antibodies enter the fetal blood, and the red cells are rapidly destroyed.

The unborn infant may have been able to produce enough red cells to replace those destroyed. At birth, however, jaundice may appear. The mechanism of this is not fully understood. Allen and Diamond have speculated on the effect of *light* on the development of jaundice in the skin (1).

The most important consequence is probably the development of *kernicterus*. This is the condition in which pigment is deposited in the brain, and the result is the development of mental retardation and also cerebral palsy of the extra-pyramidal type. The condition is at least partially remediable by the use of blood transfusions (64). In the next chapter, evidence is presented on the effects of the condition on children who survived erythroblastosis by this technique.

Phenylketonuria (Folling's Disease, Phenylpyruvic Amentia, pku)

In 1934, Folling described a disease one of whose prominent characteristics was the excretion of phenylpyruvic acid. This condition, which has received much attention in recent years, is quite rare and may account for 1 per cent of the cases of mental deficiency; Moore, McGee and Sindzinski, for example, found eight cases of pku in 757 residents of the Arizona State Institution at Coolidge (120). There seems to be a familial incidence of the disease (23); and it has been found in most divisions of humanity including, for example, Jewish (25), Ojibwa Indian (129), and Chinese (161) families.

The condition is due to a disorder of metabolism and involves an error in the conversion of phenylaniline to tyrosine. If the condition is detected by a simple chemical test before a child is two or three, it seems possible to avoid many consequences of the disease, including the disorder of intellect. Tapia (156) and Allen and Gibson (2) have found normal intelligence in children with biochemical signs of the disorder.

According to Wallace, the symptoms of the condition, apart from that revealed by urinalysis, are seizures in about 30 per cent of the cases (166); Wallace has documented other neurological signs such as "brisk reflexes, increased muscle tone, short-stepped gait, epileptic fits, and hyperkinetic movements with stereotyped digital mannerism" (166, p. 16). Kratter has called attention to a series of consistent behavioral traits in victims of this disease. He has reported distractability and allied symptoms in eleven of twelve cases of phenylketonuria (103). Similar behavior occurred in Partington's series (129). Waisman and Harlow produced pku by dietary means in six monkeys (164). The outstanding behavioral change they encountered was a drop in the level of motivation shown by the affected infant monkeys during testing sessions. As we shall see in the next chapter, prompt diagnosis and treatment can be effective.

As Paine has pointed out, this disease may be classified with some other even less frequently encountered diseases (128). Maple Syrup disease, with a characteristic smell, is a related disorder (35, 115, 116). It is quite obscure but is of interest because biochemical advances now permit early identification, and the condition presents the rare opportunity to consider seriously the possibility of successful treatment. Menkes has described symptoms in the first week of life (116). Previously healthy children began to breath irregularly; opisthotonos-arching of the back, a high-pitched cry, and presence of a diagnostically significant odor in the urine are observed. Death may follow within the first two months of life, according to Menkes, although he has indicated that survival is not unknown. Indeed, survival to age seven years has been reported by Silberman, Dancis, and Feigin (147). Hartnup disease (81) and Oasthouse disease are conditions which have much in common (148). All typify the biochemical errors found in various metabolic forms of mental retardation. Discussions of errors of metabolism that are inborn have been presented by Gutman (72) and Hooft (85).

It should be noted that biochemical variability has applications to intellect beyond the syndromes of retardation. We know, from the work of King, Bowman, and Moreland (99), that a series of connections can be established between the amino-acids and intellectual factors. Those investigators established a canonical correlation between twenty-one amino-acids and a series of cognitive measures in fifty-eight teenagers of normal intelligence. This fact is mentioned as a way of illustrating the observation that research on retardation can contribute to our understanding of human nature in general.

As a final note to this chapter, it is helpful to observe that not all physical disorders in retarded children are inseparable from intellectual deficit. Child-rearing practices have much to do with development. An inappropriate diet, one in which milk is fed to a child well beyond the point when solids are the usual staple items, can produce a fussy child. The iron deficiencies in such children are biochemical problems, but they are concomitants rather than antecedents to the degree of retardation. Similarly, obesity in retarded children is a serious health problem. In many cases it, too, reflects parental modes of rearing children. A fat child, as well as a malnourished child, may be the result of poor diet. As with the unfortunate child whose social history was presented in Chapter 6, dietary errors are encountered. Not necessarily all disorders in the retarded are inevitable expressions of biological error.

SUMMARY

In this chapter, we have considered the biological correlates of mental retardation. Patterns of growth have been presented as examples of (1) disorders of body structure and (2) disorders of body chemistry. Attention has been called to the historic problem of coordinating mind and brain, indicating that mental retardation presents problems of a special sort in this area.

BIBLIOGRAPHY

1. Allen, F. H., and Diamond, L. K., Erythroblastosis Fetalis, Little, Brown, 1958.

2. Allen, R. J., and Gibson, R. M., "Phenylketonuria with Normal Intelligence," Amer. J. Dis. Child., 1961, 102, 115-122.

3. Allibone, E. C., Illingworth, R. S., and Wright, T., "Neurofibromatosis (Von Recklinghausen's Disease) of the Vertebral Column," Arch Dis. Childhd., 1960, 35, 153-158.

4. Appleton, M. D., and Pritham, G. H., "Biochemical Studies in Mongolism II: The Influence of Age and Sex on the Plasma Proteins," Amer. J. Ment. Def., 1963, 67, 521-525.

5. Aronson, S. M., Aronson, B. E., and Volk, B. W., "A Genetic Profile of Infantile Amaurotic Family Idiocy," *J. Dis. Child.*, 1959, *64*, 50-71.

6. Asher, C., and Roberts, J. A. F., "A Study of Birth Weight and Intelligence," *Brit. J. Soc. Med.*, 1949, *3*, 56-68.

7. Asher, P., and Schonell, F. E., "A Survey of 400 Cases of Cerebral Palsy in Childhood," *Arch. Dis. Childhd.*, 1950, *25*, 360-379.

8. Atkins, L., O'Sullivan, M. A., and Pryles, C. V., "Mongolism in Three Siblings with 46 Chromosomes," *N. Engl. J. Med.*, 1962, *266*, 631-635.

9. Bandera, E. A., and Churchill, J. A., "Prematurity and Neurological Disorders," *H. Ford Hosp. Bull.*, 1961, *9*, 414-418.

10. Barlow, A., "Prognosis in Prematurity," *Arch. Dis. Childhd.*, 1945, *20*, 184-185.

11. Benda, C. E., *Developmental Disorders of Mentation and Cerebral Palsies*, Grune and Stratton, 1952.

12. _____, "Empiric Risk Figures in Monogolism," *Am. J. Ment. Def.*, 1951, *55*, 539-545.

13. _____, "Mongolism: A Comprehensive Review," *Arch. Pediat.*, 1956, *73*, 391-406.

14. _____, *Mongolism and Cretinism*, Grune and Stratton, 1946.

15. Benda, C. E., and Melchior, J. C., "Progressive Deteriorating Diseases of Infancy," *J. Neuropath. Exp. Neurol.*, 1958, *17*, 205-239.

16. Bergsman, A., "The Urinary Excretion of Adrenaline and Noradrenaline in Some Mental Diseases," *Acta. Psychiat. Neurol. Scand. Suppl.*, 1959, No. 133.

17. Blau, A., *et al.*, "The Psychogenic Etiology of Premature Births: A Preliminary Report," *Psychosomat. Med.*, 1963, *25*, 201-211.

18. Book, J. A., Fraccaro, M., and Lindsten, J., "Cytogenetical Observations in Mongolism," *Acta Paed.*, 1959, *48*, 453-468.

19. Bothwell, D. R., "Possible Case of Mongolism in a Saxon Population," *Ann. Hum. Genet.*, 1960, *24*, 141-150.

20. Browne, J., "Psychical Diseases of Early Life," *J. Ment. Sci.*, 1860, *6*, 284-320.

21. Campanelli, P. A., Pollock, F. J., and Henner, R., "An Oto-Audiological Evaluation of 44 Premature Children," *Arch. Otolaryng.*, 1958, *67*, 609-615.

22. Carson, N. A. J., *et al.*, "Homocystinuria: A New Inborn Error of Metabolism Associated with Mental Deficiency," *Arch. Dis. Childh.*, 1963, *38*, 425-436.

23. Carter, C. O., and Woolf, L. I., "The Birthplaces of Parents and Grand-Parents of a Series of Patients with Phenylketonuria in South-East England," *Ann. Hum. Genet.*, 1961, *25*, 57-64.

24. Carver, M. J., Wittse, H., and Wilson, C. L., "Basic Studies in Mongolism," *Dis. Nerv. Syst.*, 1959, 70, 162-164.

25. Centerwall, W. R., and Neff, C. A., "Phenylketonuria: A Case Report of Children of Jewish Ancestry," *Arch. Pediat.*, 1961, 78, 379-384.

26. Clarke A., and Clarke, A., *Mental Deficiency: The Changing Outlook*, Methuen, 1958.

27. Clement, S., and Peters, J. E., "Minimal Brain Dysfunctions in the School-Age Child," *Arch. Gen. Psychiat.*, 1962, 6, 185-197.

28. Cohen, B. H., Lillienfeld, A. M., and Sigler, A. T., "Some Epidemiological Aspects of Mongolism: A Review," *Amer. J. Pub. Hlth.*, 1963, 53, 223-236.

29. Collman, R. D., and Stoller, A., "Data on Mongolism in Victoria, Australia: Prevalence and Life Expectation," *J. Ment. Def. Res.*, 1963, 7, 60-68.

30. Corah, N. L., *et al.*, "Effects of Perinatal Anoxia after Seven Years," *Psych. Mon.*, 1965, 79, No. 3.

31. Crothers, G., and Paine, R. S., *The Natural History of Cerebral Palsy*, Harvard University Press, 1959.

32. Cruickshank, W. M., and Raus, G. M., *Cerebral Palsy: Its Individual and Community Problems*, Syracuse University Press, 1955.

33. Culley, W. J., *et al.*, "Caloric Intake of Children with Down's Syndrome," *J. Pediat.*, 1965, 66, 772-775.

34. Daae Blegen, S., "The Premature Child. The Incidence, Aetiology, Mortality and the Fate of the Survivors," *Acta Paed. Suppl.*, 1952, No. 88.

35. Dancis, J., "Phenylketonuria and Maple Sugar Urine Disease," *Bull. N. Y. Acad. Med.*, 1959, 35, 427-432.

36. Daniel, P. M., and Stritch, S. J., "Some Observations on the Congenital Deformity of the Central Nervous System Known as the Arnold-Chiari Malformation," *J. Neuropath. Exp. Neurol.*, 1958, 17, 255-266.

37. Dann, M., Levine, S. Z., and New, E. V., "The Development of Prematurely Born Children with Birth Weights or Minimal Postnatal Weights of 1,000 Grams or Less," *Pediat.*, 1958, 22, 1037-1053.

38. Daryn, E., "Problem of Children with Diffuse Brain Damage," *Arch. Gen. Psychiat.*, 1961, 4, 299-306.

39. Davis, M. E., and Potter, E. L., "Congenital Malformations and Obstetrics," *Pediat.*, 1957, 19, 719-724.

40. Davis, D. C., "A Comparative Study of the Growth and Development of Premature and Full-Term Children with Special Reference to Oral Communication," doctoral dissertation, Northwestern University, 1951.

41. Teilhard deChardin, P., *The Phenomenon of Man*, Harper & Brothers, 1959.

42. Della Porta, G. B., *De Physiognomonia Humana*, Frankfurt, 1618.

43. Donohue, W. L., and Uchida, I., "Leprechaunism: Euphemism for Rare Familial Disorder," *J. Pediat.*, 1954, *45*, 505-519.

44. Douglas, J. W. B., "Mental Ability and School Achievement of Premature Children at 8 Years of Age," *Brit. Med. J.*, 1956, *1*, 1210-1214.

45. Down, J. H. L., "Observations on an Ethnic Classification of Idiocy," *Rep. Observ. London Hosp.*, 1866, *3*, 259-262 (to be found in Jordan, T. E., *Perspectives in Mental Retardation*, Southern Illinois University Press, 1966).

46. Drillien, C. M., *The Growth and Development of the Prematurely Born Infant*, Edinburgh, C. and S. Livingstone, 1964.

47. _____, "The Incidence of Mental and Physical Handicaps in School-Age Children of Very Low Birth Weight," *Pediat.*, 1961, *27*, 452-464.

48. _____, "A Longitudinal Study of the Growth and Development of Prematurely and Maturely Born Children: III Mental Development," *Arch. Dis. Childhd.*, 1959, *34*, 37-45.

49. _____, "Physical and Mental Handicap in the Prematurely Born," *J. Obstet. Gynec. Brit. Emp.*, 1959, *66*, 721-728.

50. Duke, J. R., and Clark, D. B., "Infantile Amaurotic Familial Idiocy (Tay-Sachs Disease) in the Negro Race," *Amer. J. Ophthalm.*, 1962, *53*, 800-805.

51. Dunsdon, M. I., *The Educability of Cerebral Palsied Children*, London, Newnes, 1954.

52. Dutton, G., "The Physical Development of Mongols," *Arch. Dis. Childhood*, 1959, *34*, 46-50.

53. Eames, J. H., "Correlation Between Birth Weight and Visual Acuity," *Amer. J. Ophthalm.*, 1954, *38*, 850-852.

54. _____, "The Relationship of Birth Weight, Speed of Object and Word Perception and Visual Acuity," *J. Pediat.*, 1955, *47*, 603-606.

55. Eccles, J. C., *The Neuro-physiological Basis of Mind*, Oxford University Press, 1953.

56. Ek, J. I., "Thyroid Function in Mothers of Mongoloid Infants," *Acta Paed.*, 1959, *48*, 33-42.

57. Farber, B., "Family Organization and Crisis: Maintenance of Integration in Families with a Severely Mentally Retarded Child," *Ch. Dev. Mon. Soc. Res. Ch. Dev.*, 1960, No. 75.

58. Forssman, H., Lehmann, O., and Thyssell, T., "Reproduction in Mongolism: Chromosome Studies and Re-Examination of a Child," *Amer. J. Ment. Def.*, 1961, *65*, 495-498.

59. Forssman, H., and Thyssell, T., "A Woman with Mongolism and Her Child," *Am. J. Ment. Def.*, 1957, *62*, 500-503.

60. Fost, W. H., Wood, F. A., and Ross, C. S., "Hydrocephalus: Two Cases," *Pediat. Conf.*, 1960, *3*, 3, 15.

61. Fouracre, M. H., and Thiel, E. A., "Education of Children with Mental Retardation Accompanying Cerebral Palsy," *Am. J. Ment. Def.*, 1953, *57*, 401-414.

62. Fraser, J., and Mitchell, A., "Kalmuc Idiocy: Report of a Case with Autopsy and Notes on 62 Cases," *J. Ment. Sci.*, 1876, *22*, 161-162, 169-179.

63. Genn, M. M., and Silverman, W. A., "The Mental Development of Ex-Premature Children with Retrolental Fibroplasia," *J. Nerv. Ment. Dis.*, 1964, *138*, 79-86.

64. Gerver, J. M., and Day, R., "Intelligence Quotients of Children Who Have Recovered From Erythroblastosis Fetalis," *J. Pediat.*, 1950, *36*, 342-348.

65. Gibson, D., and Frank, H. F., "Dual Occurrences of Mongolism in Two Sibships," *Am. J. Ment. Def.*, 1959, *63*, 618-620.

66. Goldschmidt, E., and Cividalli, L., "Metabolic Defects in Some Isolates of Israel," *J. Genet. Hum.*, 1964, *13*, 25-31.

67. Goldstein, H., "Congenital Acromicria Syndrome," *Arch. Pediat.*, 1956, *73*, 115-124.

68. Graham, F., *et al.*, "Development Three Years after Perinatal Anoxin and Other Potentially Damaging Newborn Experiences," *Psych. Mon.*, 1962, *76*, No. 3.

69. Gruenberg, E., "Epidemiology," in Stevens, H. A., and Heber, R. (eds.), *Mental Retardation: A Review of Research*, University of Chicago Press, 1964.

70. Guilford, J. P., "The Structure of Intellect," *Psych. Bull.*, 1965, *53*, 267-293.

71. Guiraud, P., and Roualt de la Vigne, A., "Maladie de Hallevorden-Spatz, Maladie de Friedreich et Troubles Mentaux Cachexie Nerveuse Progressive" *L'Encephale*, 1959, *38*, 317-324.

72. Gutman, A. B., "Inborn Errors of Metabolism," *Bull. N. Y. Acad. Med.*, 1959, *35*, 419-426.

73. Hall, B., "Mongolism in Newborns: A Clinical and Cytogenetic Study," *Acta Paed. (Stockh.)*, 1964, *53*, 478-483.

74. Hallenbeck, P. N., "A Survey of Recent Research on Mongolism," *Am. J. Ment. Def.*, 1960, *64*, 827-834.

75. Hansen, E., "Cerebral Palsy in Denmark," *Acta Psychiat. Neurol. Scand. Suppl.*, 1960, No. 146.

76. Harper, P., Fischer, L., and Rider, R. V., "Neurological and Intellectual Status of Prematures at Three to Five Years of Age," *J. Pediat.*, 1959, *55*, 679-690.

77. Hebb, D. O., "Intelligence, Brain Function and the Theory of Mind," *Brain*, 1959, *82*, 260-275.

78. Heilman, A. E., "Appraisal of Abilities of the Cerebral Palsied Child," *Am. J. Ment. Def.*, 1949, *53*, 606-609.

79. Heimer, C. B., Cutler, R., and Freedman, A. M., "Neurological Sequelae of Premature Birth," *J. Dis. Child.*, 1964, *104*, 122-133.

80. Heinreichs, E. H., Allen, S. W., and Nelson, P. S., "Simultaneous 18-Trisomy and 21-Trisomy Cluster," *Lancet*, 1963, 2, 468.

81. Henderson, W., "Case of Hartnup Disease," *Arch. Dis. Childhd.*, 1958, *33*, 114-117.

82. Hesseljo, R., and Anberg, A., "Perinatal Mortality," *Acta Obstet. Gynec. Scand. Suppl.*, No. 5, 1962.

83. Hilliard, L. T., and Kirman, B. H., *Mental Deficiency*, Little, Brown, 1957.

84. Holt, S. B., "Finger Print Patterns in Mongolism," *Ann. Hum. Genet.*, 1964, *27*, 279-282.

85. Hooft, C., *et al.*, "Etude de l'aminocidurie d'un Groupe d'enfants Presentant de l'arrièration Mentale," *Acta Paed. Belg.*, 1963, *17*, 77-104.

86. Hopkins, T., Bice, H. V., and Colton, K., *Evaluation and Education of the Cerebral Palsied Child*, Washington, D. C., Council for Exceptional Children, 1954.

87. Howard, P. J., and Worrell, C. H., "Premature Infants in Later Life: Study of Intelligence and Personality of 22 Premature Infants at Ages 8-19 Years," *Pediat.*, 1952, 9, 577-584.

88. Illingworth, R. S., *The Development of the Infant and Young Child: Normal and Abnormal*. Edinburgh, E. and S. Livingstone, 1963.

89. James, R. E., "Deterioration of the Cerebral Palsied at Adolescence," *Develop. Med. Child Neurol.*, 1963, 5, 531-532.

90. Johnson, C. D., and Barnett, C. D., "Relationship of Physical Stigmata to Intellectual Status in Mongoloids," *Am. J. Ment. Def.*, 1961, *66*, 435-437.

91. Jordan, T. E., "Data Language and Constructs in Special Education," in *Perspectives in Mental Retardation*, Southern Illinois University Press, 1966.

92. _____, *The Exceptional Child*, Chapter 7, "Cerebral Palsy," Charles E. Merrill Books, Inc., 1962.

93. _____, *The Mentally Retarded*, Chapter 10, Charles E. Merrill Books, Inc., 1961.

94. _____, "Psychological Findings in a Case of Von Recklinghausen's Disease and Hyperpituitarism," *J. Clin. Psych.*, 1956, *12*, 389-391.

95. _____, *et al.*, *Rehabilitation of the Adult with Cerebral Palsy*, St. Louis University, 1961, 38 pp.

96. Kääriäinen, R., and Dingman, H. F., "The Relation of the Degree of Mongolism to the Degree of Subnormality," *Amer. J. Ment. Def.*, 1961, *66*, 438-443.

97. Kahn, E., and Cohen, L. H., "Organic Driveness, A Brain-Syndrome and an Experience," *N. Engl. J. Med.*, 1934, *210*, 748-756.

98. Kastein, S., and Fowler, E., "Language Development Among Survivors of Premature Birth," *Arch. Otolaryng.*, 1959, *69*, 131-135.

99. King, F. J., Bowman, B. H., and Moreland, H. J., "Some Intellectual Correlates of Biochemical Variability," *Behav. Sci.*, 1961, *6*, 297-302.

100. Kluge, W., "Leucocytic Shift to the Left in Mongolism with Some Observation on Segmentation Inhibition and the Pelger-Haet Anomaly," *J. Ment. Def. Res.*, 1959, *3*, 56-62.

101. Knobloch, H., and Pasamanick B., "Mental Subnormality," *N. Engl. J. Med.*, 1962, *266*, 1045-1051, 1092-1097, 1155-1161.

102. _____, "Syndrome of Minimal Cerebral Damage in Infancy," *J. Amer. Med. Assoc.*, 1959, *170*, 1384-1387.

103. Kratter, F. E., "The Physiognomic, Psychometric, Behavioral, and Neurological Aspects of Phenylketonuria," *J. Ment. Sci.*, 1959, *105*, 421-427.

104. Kreindler, A., Ungher, I., and Volanskii, D., "Effect of a Circumscribed Lesion of the Reticular Formation in the Brain Stem on the Higher Nervous Activity of Dogs," *Sechenov Physiol. J. U.S.S.R.*, 1959, *45*, 247-256.

105. Kugelmass, I. N., *The Management of Mental Deficiency in Children*, Grune and Stratton, 1954.

106. Lamm, S., and Fisch, M., "Intellectual Development of the Cerebral Palsied Child as a Factor in Therapeutic Progress," *Am. J. Ment. Def.*, 1955, *59*, 452-457.

107. Little, W. J., "On the Influence of Abnormal Parturition, Difficult Labours, Premature Birth, and Asphyxia Neonatorum, on the Mental and Physical Condition of the Child, Especially in Relation to Deformities," *Trans. Obstet. Soc. Lond.*, 1861 *3*, 293-360.

108. MacGillivray, R. C., "Mongolism in Both of Monozygotic Twins," *Am. J. Ment. Def.*, 1959, *64*, 450-454.

109. _____, "The Syndrome of Rud." *Am. J. Ment. Def.*, 1954, *59*, 67-72.

110. Malamud, N., Recent Trends in Classification of Neuropathological Findings in Mental Deficiency," *Am. J. Ment. Def.*, 1954, *58*, 438-447.

111. Marshall, D., Saul, G. B., and Sachs, B., "Tuberous Sclerosis. A Report of 16 Cases in Two Family Trees Revealing Genetic Dominance," *N. Eng. J. Med.*, 1959, *761*, 1102-1105.

112. Mautner, H., "Abnormal Findings on the Spine in Mongoloids," *Am. J. Ment. Def.*, 1950, *55*, 105-107.

113. McDonald, A. D., "Deafness in Children of Very Low Birthweight," *Arch. Dis. Childhd.*, 1964, *39*, 272-277.

114. ———, "Intelligence in Children of Very Low Birthweight," *Brit. J. Brev. Sol. Med.*, 1964, *18*, 59-74.

115. Menkes, J. H., "Maple Syrup Disease," *Neurol.*, 1959, *9*, 826-835.

116. ———, "Maple Syrup Disease and other Rare Disorders of Amino Acid Metabolism," *Clin. Proc. Child. Hosp. D. C.*, 1964, *20*, 152-160.

117. Michel, J. F. and Carney, R. J., "Pitch Characteristics of Mongoloid Boys," *J. Sp. Hear. Dis.*, 1964, *29*, 121-125.

118. Miller, E. A., and Rosenfeld, G., "Psychological Evaluation of Children with Cerebral Palsy and Its Implications in Treatment," *J. Pediat.*, 1952, *41*, 613-621.

119. Minear, W. L., "A Classification of Cerebral Palsy," *Pediat.*, 1956, *18*, 841-852.

120. Moore, B. C., McGee, E. S., and Sindzinski, R. M., "Prevalence of Phenylketonuria in an Institution for the Mentally Retarded," *Arizona Med.*, 1964, *21*, 715-717.

121. Mosier, H. D., Grossman, H. J., and Dingman, H. F., "Secondary Sex Development in Mentally Deficient Individuals," *Child Devpm.*, 1962, *33*, 273-286.

122. Muir, C. S., "Hydranencephaly and Allied Disorders," *Arch. Dis. Childhd.* 1959, *34*, 231-246.

123. Myklebust, H. R., and Boshes, B., "Psychoneurological Learning Disorders in Children," *Arch. Pediat.*, 1960, *77*, 247-256.

124. Olds, J., and Peretz, B., "A Motivational Analysis of the Reticular Activating System," *EEG Clin. Neurophysiol.*, 1960, *12*, 445-454.

125. O'Reilly, D. E., "Evaluation of Cerebral Palsy Treatment," *Mo. Med.*, 1954, *51*, 38-40.

126. Oster, J., *Mongolism*, Copenhagen, Danish Science Press, 1953.

127. Otsuka, K., "Clinicopathological Studies on Three Cases of Tay-Sachs Disease," *Jap. J. Child Psychiat.*, 1961, *2*, 44-74.

128. Paine, R. S., "Evaluation of Familial Biochemically Determined Mental Retardation in Children with Special Reference to Aminoaciduria," *N. Eng. J. Med.*, 1960, *262*, 658-665.

129. Partington, M. W., "Observations on Phenylketonuria in Ontario," *Canad. Med. Ass. J.*, 1961, *84*, 958-991.

130. Penrose, L. S., "Mongolism," *Brit. Med. Bull.*, 1961, *17*, 184-189.

131. ———, "Observations on the Aetiology of Mongolism," *Lancet*, 1954, *267*, 505-509.

132. Phelps, W. M., "Characteristic Psychological Variations in Cerebral Palsy," *Nerv. Child.*, 1948, *7*, 10-13.

133. Pribram, K., "On the Neurology of Thinking," *Behav. Sc.*, 1959, *4*, 265-287.

134. Rehn, A. T., and Thomas, E., "Family History of a Mongoloid Girl Who Bore a Mongoloid Child," *Am. J. Ment. Def.*, 1957, *62*, 496-499.

135. Reitan, R. M., "Investigation of Relationships between 'Psychometric' and 'Biological' Intelligence," *J. Nerv. Ment. Dis.*, 1956, *123*, 536-541.

136. Ridler, M. A. C., and Shapiro, A., "Longitudinal Study of the Leucocyte Count in Infants with Mongolism," *J. Ment. Def. Res.*, 1959, *3*, 96-102.

137. Robinson, N. M., and Robinson, H. B., "A Follow-up Study of Children of Low Birth Weight and Control Children of School Age," *Pediat.*, 1965, *35*, 425-433.

138. Ruby, D. O., and Matheny, W. D., "Comments on Growth of Cerebral Palsied Children," *J. Amer. Diet. Ass.*, 1962, *40*, 525-527.

139. Runner, M. N., and Dagg, C. P., "Metabolic Mechanisms of Teratogenic Agents during Morphogenesis," *Symposium on Normal and Abnormal Differentiation and Development, Nat. Cancer Inst. Mon.*, 1960, No. 2.

140. Sawyer, G. M., "Case Report: Reproduction in a Mongoloid," *Am. J. Ment. Def.*, 1949, *54*, 204-206.

141. ———, and Shafter, A. J., "Reproduction in a Mongoloid: A Follow-up," *Am. J. Ment. Def.*, 1957, *61*, 793-795.

142. Schlesinger, E. R., Allaway, N. G., and Peltin, S., "Survivorship in Cerebral Palsy," *Amer. J. Pub. Hlth.*, 1959, *49*, 343-349.

143. Schmid, W., Lee, C. H., and Smith, P. M., "At the Borderline of Mongolism," *Amer. J. Ment. Def.*, 1961, *66*, 449-455.

144. Schneck, L., "The Early Electroencephalographic and Seizure Characteristics of Tay-Sachs Disease," *Acta Neurol. Scand.*, 1965, *41*, 163-171.

145. Schonell, F. E., *Educating Spastic Children*, New York, Philosophical Library, 1956.

146. Sherrington, C. S., *Man On His Nature*, Cambridge University Press, 1951.

147. Silberman, J. Dancis, J., and Feigin, I., "Neuropathological Observations in Maple Syrup Urine Disease," *Arch. Neurol.*, 1961, *5*, 351-363.

148. Smith, A. J., and Strang, L. B., "Inborn Error of Metabolism with Urinary Excretion of α-Hydroxy-butyric Acid and Phenylpyruvic Acid," *Arch. Dis. Childhd.*, 1958, *33*, 109-113.

149. Sobel, A. E., *et al.*, "Vitamin A Absorption and Other Blood Composition Studies in Mongolism," *Am. J. Ment. Def.*, 1958, *62*, 642-656.

150. Sterling, H. M., "Height and Weight of Children with Cerebral Palsy and Acquired Brain Damage," *Arch. Phys. Med.*, 1960, *41*, 131-135.

151. Stevens, G. D., "Taxonomy in Special Education for Children with Body Disorders," unpublished Ph.D. dissertation, Columbia University, 1962.

152. _____ and Birch, J. W., "A Proposal for Clarification of the Terminology Used to Describe Brain-Injured Children," *Excep. Ch.*, 1959, *23*, 346-349.

153. Stoller, A., and Collman, R. D., "Patterns of Occurrence of Births in Victoria, Australia, Producing Down's Syndrome (Mongolism) and Congenital Anomalies of the Central Nervous System: A 21 Year Prospective and Retrospective Survey," *Med. J. Australia*, 1965, *7*, 1-4.

154. Strauss, A. A., and Lehtinen, L. A., *Psychopathology and Education of the Brain-Injured Child*, Grune and Stratton, 1947.

155. _____, and Kephart, N. E., *Psychopathology and Education of the Brain-Injured Child*, Vol. II, Grune and Stratton, 1955.

156. Tapia, F., "Phenylpyruvic Oligophrenia; Report of a Case with Normal Intelligence," *Dis. Nerv. Syst.*, 1961, *22*, 465-466.

157. "Test gives Baby a Chance at Life," *New York Times*, Sunday, April 14, 1965.

158. "Test Gives Hope in Rare Disease," *New York Times*, Sunday, April 14, 1963.

159. Tredgold, A. F., *A Textbook of Mental Deficiency*, 8th ed., Williams and Wilkins, 1952.

160. Tsuang, M. T., and Lin, T.-Y., "A Clinical and Family Study of Chinese Mongol Children," *J. Ment. Def. Res.*, 1964, *8*, 84-91.

161. Tu, J., *et al.*, "Studies on Phenylketonuria in a Chinese Family," *Acta Paediat. Sinica*, 1964, *5*, 56-64.

162. Vera Cruz, P. G., "Crainostenosis," *Clin. Proc. Ch. Hosp. Wash., D. C.*, 1959, *15*, 11-18.

163. Wagner, H. R., "Mongolism in Orientals," *A.M.A. J. Dis. Child.*, 1962, *103*, 706-714.

164. Waisman, H. A., and Harlow, H. F., "Experimental Phenylketonuria in Infant Monkeys," *Sci.*, 1965, *147*, 685-695.

165. Wallace, H. M., *et al.*, "Cerebral Palsy in Minnesota," *Am. J. Pub. Hlth.*, 1961, *51*, 417-426.

166. Wallace, H. W., "Phenylpyruvic Oligophrenia," *Bull. Tufts N. Eng. Med. Cent.*, 1959, 5. 16-27.

167. Warkany, J., "Etiology of Mongolism," *J. Pediat.*, 1960, 56, 412-419.

168. Wiener, G., "Psychologic Correlates of Premature Birth: A Review," *J. Nerv. Ment. Dis.*, 1962, 134, 129-144.

169. _____, *et al.*, "Correlates of Low Birth Weight: Psychological Status at Six to Seven Years of Age," *Pediat.*, 1965, 35, 434-444.

170. Wilton, E., "Chromosome Investigation of Bantu and Coloured Patients with the Langdon Down Syndrome," *Med. Proc.*, 1964, 10, 171-176.

171. Wortis, H., *et al.*, "Growing Up in Brooklyn: The Early History of the Premature Child," *Amer. J. Orthopsychiat.*, 1963, 33, 535-539.

172. Yashon, D., Jane, A., and Sugar, O., "The Course of Severe Untreated Infantile Hydrocephalus: Prognostic Significance of the Cerebral Mantle," *J. Neurosurg.*, 1965, 23, 509-516.

173. Zellweger, H., "L'Hérédité Dans La Maladie De Hurler," *J. Genet. Hum.*, 1958, 7, 308-314.

Chapter 9

THERAPEUTIC
CONSIDERATIONS

There is reason to believe, as the author has previously noted, that the way in which an issue is considered is a reflection of the times and the society. For example, since there seems to be a great deal of the obvious in attempts to measure intellect, this ambitious undertaking is held by many to be quantifiable and fit for analysis and description. Another issue which catches the ethos of the times and the society is disease. The earlier acceptance of sickness and disability as an inescapable part of life has largely disappeared. Beginning with the dismissal of pain, probably the greatest of our advances, we have slowly eliminated some diseases and prevented others. Consequently, people bring to any health problem the consideration—if not the expectation—of relief and, ultimately, cure. The techniques of preventive medicine have banished previously endemic diseases, and may be able to reduce the frequency of premature

317

births (*101*). The current vogue of chemotherapy has revolutionized our thinking with regard to the prevention and cure of emotional disorders.

It is only understandable that considerations of relief be applied to mental retardation. What is not evident is that our recent advances in the treatment of disease have not been panaceas, cures for all conditions. More carefully understood, they appear as well-chosen weapons to be used selectively and judiciously to effect the maximum relief. A consideration of a public health problem of diminished proportions will illustrate the point. Diabetes has been a fatal disease within living memory. The development of insulin left the diabetic with a way to come to terms with his disease. Oral forms of therapy have recently been developed. Nevertheless, careful consideration suggests that orally administered therapies are not applicable to all; some people must still give themselves daily injections of insulin. In other words, *selectivity* rather than *generality* characterizes effective treatment of the disease.

Having considered the subtlety of techniques, consideration of their application remains. Perhaps a way of doing this is to consider the plurality of the conditions labeled mental deficiency. Some clinical syndromes are metabolic; others are affections of the nervous system. Using another of several dimensions, some entities are genetic and deteriorating, while others are acquired and typically non-fatal. The only thing common to Tay-Sachs disease and cerebral palsy, for example, is the phenomenal disability loosely described as mental retardation.

Still another consideration clouds our thinking. The stereotype of mental retardation would suggest a discernible pathology. Nevertheless, there are human beings who are intellectually inadequate for the demands of contemporary life who show no pathology whatever. Such people may be analogous to those children who have small parents and who will therefore always be ineligible for some school sports. It is no defect of the physique but a height significantly below average that accounts for their limitations.

This last analogy has the weakness of all analogies: its imagery may bemuse the reader and trap the writer. Still, in this case the analogy serves to suggest that some who are poor competitors may have nothing wrong with them in the sense of manifest pathology. With no identifiable defect clearly related to the relevant behavioral deficit, there can be no physical treatment. This issue can be rephrased as follows: Therapeutic considerations predicate tissue needs; in those cases where deprivation or simple inheritance are the problems, it may be that no physical treatment can be considered.

TERMS

Before proceeding further, it would be well to define those terms which are appropriate to the problem of therapy for the mentally retarded.

Cure. This is a small word of large import. The essential idea it expresses is that sick people receive some treatment that restores them to a previous state of normality. Obviously, this is a limited term for two reasons: (1) we have few cures for those conditions acquired after birth, and (2) the hereditary conditions preclude the original normality predicated by the idea of a cure.

Treatment. This is a more modest term. It covers those procedures that are invoked in the attempt to help the sick. The word does not describe the efficacy of any procedure but suggests the point in time when the disabled individual is the recipient of attention which, it is hoped, will improve his condition.

Therapy. Since the word *treatment* conjures images of physical manipulation or at least some suggestion of a physical act, the word *therapy* may be considered. In this context, the word describes procedures used with the disabled that may or may not work and that may or may not be medicines and physical techniques. By *physical techniques* we mean either procedures that require one person to do something to another person or procedures based on a physical change within the constitution of the individual.

Therapy, then, may describe anything intended to alleviate the condition of the disabled—in this case, the intellectually inadequate.

Therapy and the Term *Mental Retardation*

Words are tools; they signify ideas in a communicable way. What we understand about a problem is clearly determined by the terms employed in the discussion. Of vital significance over the years has been the issue of whether or not mental retardation is curable.

Generally speaking, there are few things as irrelevant as formal definitions of mental retardation. In Chapter 1, the discussion was intended to build various concepts of mental retardation. In that discussion definitions of mental retardation were included; they can function as summaries after concepts of retardation have been acquired.

Ultimately, any extended discussion requires that a summary of ideas be offered. A point which can create much confusion is the attempt at formal definition without a prior and necessary discussion of the basic concepts. Too often people begin with the definition, when, in fact, such a summary should come last, if at all.

The relevance of these ideas to the study of mental retardation is the fact that many definitions of the condition make reference to the impossibility of "cure," using that word in the sense propounded a little earlier. To many people it is vital that the stability of the condition be acknowledged in the definition. This has traditionally been the stand, with the emergence of many problems as a direct consequence (30, 53).

Now let us turn to the conceptual core of this chapter, the extent to which therapy can significantly alter the status of a human being initially and carefully diagnosed as intellectually inadequate. First we will consider the issue *conceptually,* and then we will consider it operationally—that is, in light of the experimental evidence.

In many cases the evidence of change is a discrepancy of some sort. It may be a discrepancy between performance predicted at diagnosis and level of performance at a later date. In this case we must examine the nature of the prediction and the stability of measurement.

If the nature of the prediction is negative, it is no great problem to account for later discrepancies. To say that child "will not be able to . . ." may be exactly the challenge needed to motivate a parent with the desire to refute the specific prediction. A comparable source of later embarrassment is the phrasing of predictive statements to include the word *never.* Perhaps, as Gilbert and Sullivan said it, "well, hardly ever" would be more discreet, since the statements of clinicians and physicians are in no way binding on the future.

It is indicative of a person's sensitivity to the plasticity of human nature, and the whims of chance, when he utters or accepts statements in terms of probability rather than as absolutes. Inferior schools may permit very dull children to earn diplomas, but this is no causal link in a chain of events beginning with a prediction about a child's school work. If anything, it shows how irreverently chance may deal with absolute statements by clinicians about the future.

A more identifiable source of discrepancies is the stage at which diagnostic procedures are initiated. At such times judgments are usually requested or offered about later achievement by youngsters. If the issues arise when a child is small, say about age three, we immediately run into the problem studied by Honzik—namely, the stability of test scores over a large span of time. This is particularly a problem when there is a wide range of prediction open. Where education and training are careful, the eventual status may be quite encouraging. The same level of ability shaped under conditions that are adverse will not create an adequate child later. When children are seriously disabled, positive home and school experiences will also produce improvement, but they will not be able to raise the child up to the level of adequacy.

A further consideration is the discomfort of physicians and diagnosticians. There is much safety in including the idea of incurability in a definition of mental retardation; probably the safest thing insecure and uninformed counselors can do is build a concept of incurability into their formulation of the condition. Consider what the concept of incurability does for the counselor's batting average. Should the child confound his judge by later high achievement, his performance violates the "incurability clause" in the diagnostician's judgment. Clearly such a child does not meet the vital condition; *ergo,* he was not mentally retarded to begin with. The parent is happy, and the clinician is still unsullied as a seer.

Another source of discrepancies between predictions and eventual levels of performance is the use of the IQ as the conceptual core of mental retardation. It is a truism that we measure to predict. It follows that the prediction will be as sound as the predictive value of the IQ. An examination of the basic texts on measurement will reveal that IQ and school performance, two relatable propositions, do not coincide. In fact, IQ and achievement, expressed as correlational statements, frequently do not exceed .50 with large samples, although this does represent statistical significance at $< .05$, or even $< .01$ occasionally. Were more consideration given to this notion, there would be less use of psychometric data as an operational definition of retardation. Still another source of error exists in the use of tests, and one in particular. The Binet scale is our best scale for individual measurement, and it will continue to be held in high regard. It must be pointed out that the early years of the Binet have a markedly different content from the later years; that is, there is a profound shift to verbal content at the upper levels. The implication of this is that Binet scores gathered after treatment requiring several years may tap a pool of skills quite removed from that drawn upon prior to application (*107*).

How may we summarize the extent to which children judged inadequate later prove to be adequate? It would seem best to accept the fact that truly different levels of performance exist in children at different times. This applies to all children, normal and retarded. In the case of the retarded we may say that situational factors can produce a better picture than anticipated, even when the child is truly functioning below average at diagnosis; but we must also recognize that the change is one of amelioration, of improvement, rather than of restoration to normality (cure).

Doll has suggested that those cases where the change is to adequacy rather than to partial adequacy are traceable to (1) errors in terminology, (2) the uncertainties of diagnosis, (3) optimistic inferences unwisely derived from behavior (30).

THE NATURE OF THERAPEUTIC AGENTS

We return now to the question of public expectations in disease. For most of us, diseases are no longer a matter to be left to time and the wisdom of the body. Most of us expect a physician to do something. The essence of this expectation is that the physician will intervene and do what nature cannot do alone. The mechanism of this intervention is an agent of some sort, some item from the resources of the little black bag or the local pharmacy. From the point of view of the patient, the drug (or placebo) has powers that relate directly to his personal perception of his symptoms.

There is a more objective and sophisticated way to view medication, and it can help our understanding of the issues and problems in the therapy of mental retardation. The issue may be approached obliquely, as follows.

In some cases people expect that medical research will produce a single "cure" for mental retardation. Our current awareness of the contributions of biology and medicine has suggested that science will announce the development of a "magic bullet." The term is taken from the radical change in the outlook on disease introduced by Ehrlich. His work made a striking change in concepts of cure (remission of symptoms and reversion to a previously healthy state). To the extent that mental retardation is analogous to disease caused by a biological entity, this sort of thinking is appropriate.

Another consideration is akin to the "fillet of a fenny snake" in *Macbeth,* the idea that a blending of drugs will produce an effect not found in the several ingredients alone. The feeding of vitamins and the routine application of endocrine therapies are often greeted by the public with the expectation of radical change. There can be no doubt that all could profit from a careful attention to diet, but it does not follow that miracles should be expected from regimens intended to relieve dietary insufficiencies (94).

A third consideration is based on the analogy between growth patterns and their often deviant nature and the path of a rocket or missile. As a rocket may be returned to its planned trajectory by intervention, so growth in a retarded child may be moved in a better direction by procedures often unspecified but nonetheless posited. The analogy suggests that we may be able to alter the course of growth, its direction and velocity (IQ), by some chemotherapeutic means. In some cases, as we shall see, conditions based on identifiable endocrine disorders may be amenable to this procedure (45, 59).

The approaches to treatment just discussed are alike in that they take a short-term position and look to the help of individuals. A more objective and sophisticated approach is to consider the prevention of mental retardation primarily by delineating the mechanisms in the development of the condition. Advances in obstetrics and sensitivity to the problems in rh incompatibility demonstrate the basic soundness of this proposition (24, 142).

Implicit in this idea is the careful selection of therapeutic technique and condition. Not all retarded children are the result of rh incompatibility, nor are all cases of mental retardation helped by blood exchange. Generalizing further, it seems reasonable to anticipate progress by means of careful matching of condition and cure. Such has been the progress of medicine to date; such would seem to be the hope for mental retardation.

SCHOOLS OF THERAPY

It is satisfying to realize that it is possible to discuss experiments in the treatment of the intellectually inadequate. Not all the studies which follow report success, and some that do are contrary to fact.

The number of studies is large, and they are grouped under the following headings.

1. *Functional therapies.* This term is used to describe those procedures of a non-medical sort which report changes in intellectual status through instruction and a proper environment.

2. *Psychotherapies.* These are the methods which are highly skilled attempts to influence the functioning self of the retardate primarily by resolving conflicts and building positive values and perceptions.

3. *Surgical therapies.* In some cases there have been attempts to alter the intellectual status of retarded persons by using surgical techniques to change their physiology or anatomy.

4. *Chemotherapies.* The last few years have seen the introduction of drugs which act on the nervous system in such a way as to alter manifest behavior. Their effects are temporary, but they precipitate radical and significant changes in temperament.

FUNCTIONAL THERAPIES

The use of the phrase *functional therapy* is a cautious one. It is an attempt to classify a number of issues by identifying common factors among them. Common factors may be interpersonal interaction involving tasks of a roughly instructional nature and formal provisions of a quasi-educational sort. In some cases the issues will be curricular; in other cases they will be somewhat broader, reflecting an institutional program.

The functional therapies have a long history. The treatment of the "Wild Boy of Aveyron" by Itard was an attempt to take a half-wild and conceivably retarded child and change him into a "civilized" or adequate child by instruction and tutoring. Kaspar Hauser is also an example of a child whose inadequacies were obvious but whose remediation was not completely successful. It should be kept in mind that we really do not know what sort of problem these children represented or what formulation of their disorders a diagnostician would make today. On the basis of precedent and the accounts of their difficulties, it may be safe to say that they acted in a significantly inadequate way; they were phenomenally inadequate, and we can only guess at the condition and circumstances of their lives prior to the attempts to help them.

A more recent example of this sort of problem was the study of Amahla and Kamala, the feral children, some forty years ago in India. This case exemplifies all the difficulties of retrospective studies. We simply do not know the circumstances which led to the abandonment of these children, and the result is that the accounts of such cases of isolation amentia can deal only with slight amounts of fact and large amounts of fancy. It is worth pointing out that none of these classic cases showed significant improvement. We have very little basis on which to evaluate the modest gains they did make, and a satisfactory evaluation can be made only in light of a great deal of information—a problem which has plagued investigators to this day.

We may continue consideration of attempts to produce change in the level of intellectual functioning by phrasing a broad question: Does instruction change children intellectually and personally? Several possible lines of response to the question are open.

We can consider what changes are noted in IQ subsequent to an optional school experience. In some places kindergarten is an integral part of school; in others it is not. Consequently, by chance, we have children of the same age subjected to two treatments—in the design sense—in conceivably adjacent school districts. There is the task of matching by control variables—some of which are socio-economic status, ethnic group, intelligence, and social age—and we have the beginnings of a study.

Fortunately, as it happens, the problem was examined in 1940 by Page (97). The issue of whether IQ improves subsequent to pre-school experience is usually presented in terms of the effect of kindergarten experience on primary-grade performance. Page considered the issue over a period of one to five years and used nursery-school experiences. The children were quite young at the time of the special experience. The results of this study were that the seventy-two children considered did not show higher intelligence quotients in the subsequent years.

Page's data used IQ; this measure is convenient and objective. Of a less scientific order is the observation that very few children fail to profit from exposure to a new situation and to attention from new friends and adults. Again, to use subjective evidence, exclusion from school has a detrimental effect. This effect can be seen in normal children who lose interest when excluded from school by arbitrary entrance-age requirements. The retarded have been excluded from school largely because they appeared inadequate; but their inadequacies are partially the result of having been excluded. The parents of trainable children have seen this vicious circle time and time again. The child is held to be markedly unable to relate effectively to others; yet he has been denied the opportunity to grow in that direction. One might burlesque the point to make it clearer; typical children in a classroom are "typical" because they have had the opportunity to learn typical classroom behavior. More precisely, they have been given the opportunity to learn the relevant norms of behavior, the ground rules of being a pupil. While this argument is intended to identify the role-playing component of school behavior, it should not be interpreted to mean that role-playing can be learned by all children. Any learning activity is partially limited by constitutional factors.

An interesting study has been reported from Toronto by Francey (37). A group of children six to twelve years of age with IQ's between 40 and 50 were educated for up to four years. The effects on the Stanford-Binet IQ's were negligible. However, the *Vineland Social Maturity Scale* demonstrated a remarkable degree of growth in level of functioning. A mean increment in social quotient of nearly eleven points was registered. The program to which the children responded, according to Francey, used several teachers, maintained small class enrollments, and provided a counseling service for parents.

Another study which relates the previous issues, school experience and mental retardation, is Hill's account of the effect of schooling (53).

Using the IQ, he found that there were changes in the performance of children in special classes; but, as Table 9·1 indicates, the changes are both positive and negative.

TABLE 9·1

IQ VARIATIONS IN RETARDATES EXPOSED TO A
SPECIAL CLASS CURRICULUM

IQ Variation	+18 to +22	+13 to +17	+8 to +12	+3 to +7
Percent	1	5	8	12

IQ Variation	+2 to −2	−3 to −7	−8 to −12	−13 to −17	−18 to −22
Percent	30	24	8	5	1

There is a tendency for the number of negative cases slightly to exceed the number of positive changes. We may generalize from these data, keeping in mind the matter of re-test reliability, by saying that while changes did occur in individual cases there was no basis for generalizing an upward or downward shift of significant size.

It should be pointed out that the author regards as redundant the question of whether IQ's do in fact fluctuate. The Iowa studies two or three decades ago make that clear. Evidence has recently come from England of apparently "spontaneous" changes in IQ as a result of the shift from depriving homes to a more pleasant residential setting (20, 21). The Clarkes have called attention to this phenomenon. Using a rating of the home, they have been able to distinguish between those S's who showed subsequent IQ increment primarily in the next two or three years and those who did not. Only six of fifty-nine subjects came from "good" homes, and the investigators accordingly sound a cautious note about generalizing from their data.

The evidence considered so far is of modest proportion. The issues are narrowly defined, and the discussion has been in a minor key. It would be well to keep in mind, however, that the problem of the effects of special experiences on retarded individuals is not intrinsically a mild one. It is really an explosive issue.

In the last half of the 1940's, a serious controversy was precipitated, and its effects are still evident. A monograph on the personal, social, and intellectual changes occurring in mentally retarded children who had been in special classes was published. At the same time, popular journals published accounts and wide interest was aroused. The significance of the study lay in the wave of expectations aroused in parents of retarded youngsters. The claims advanced resulted in much attention to the problem of whether or not children could in fact be made normal, in the literal sense of the word, by functional procedures. Clearly what was needed was a study that would attempt to assess the same basic problem but with more attention to the specification of details and a careful formulation of the goals. In 1949 Kirk began an investigation of a parallel problem which he described fully in 1958 (67). The purpose of the study was to consider what pre-school education would do for the mental and social development of young educable children. The children generally were between three and six years of age and had IQ's between 45 and 80. In order to avoid losing subjects, an attempt was made to select children who would remain in the community for several years.

The instructional program has not been discussed extensively by Kirk in his account of the study, but it seems to have followed that described in his other statements about pre-school education (66)— namely, the development of emotional and physical health, maturation through self-help, expression, and intellectual, social, and motor development. Complementary programs were parent education and clinical help for special instructional problems.

Generally speaking, the data substantiate the idea that pre-school work for the retarded produces gains that are significant. The Clarkes' findings about removal from a depriving setting are paralleled in Kirk's study. An enriched environment seems to make a significant contribution to the development of young retardates, with non-organic cases showing better progress.

It would be naive to conclude that the formal content of a program for the retarded is the component that produces changes in children. Further, it would be naive to think that it is the procedures that create the limited but defensible changes that can occur. In all probability, the particular role of the people who teach may turn out to be vital. This is not an easy issue to clarify, since contemporary education does not work from a particular conception or model of the relationship of teacher and student. Were there such a model—and in Chapter 10 attention is called to the possibility—we might delineate the comparative contributions of people and programs.

Evidence has come from a study by Oliver in England (96). Oliver selected two groups of "educationally sub-normal boys." The experimental group received ten weeks of physical conditioning. Intelligence- and achievement-test results indicated a degree of positive change in these boys. Fortunately, we are not faced with the option of believing that one can raise his abilities by raising weights.

Oliver points out that there was a high degree of attention focused on the boys and that interpersonal factors may well account for the greater effectiveness and better adjustment in his experimental subjects.

Oliver's study demonstrates in a circuitous way the importance of the climate in which a child works. Lee has provided data indicating that the low intelligence-test ratings of Negro children born in the rural South rose as a function of the amount of time they had resided in Philadelphia (74).

If the larger environment contributes to intellectual growth, the restricted environment of the home must also play a part. The formative years of childhood are spent within the home, and the larger setting affects children only indirectly.

In 1946 Despert and Pierce published a monograph in which the relationship of emotional adjustment to significant gains in IQ was examined (28). Their results indicated that school had a positive and significant effect on children who were shy. All came from good homes, rather than from indifferent or poor homes.

Lyle (79) moved sixteen children of elementary-school age from the Fountain Hospital to a large house and built a program around warm affective relationships and socialization. A significant shift in the direction of emotional and social maturity emerged, and a statistically significant shift in verbal intelligence appeared. Interestingly, Lyle considered the *Hawthorne effect* a valuable therapeutic agent. The small-group, interactive effect undoubtedly was augmented by the home-like environment.

The author applied a measure of maternal values to mothers of retarded youngsters (62). The measure used, the *Parent Attitude Research Instrument* of Schaefer and Bell, has twenty-three sub-tests which measure various components of mothers' attitudes and values concerning the rearing of children. The results of the study indicate that the value system guiding the growth of children affects their intellectual status.

A comparable attempt was reported by Stoddard, who related the perceptions of parents of retarded children to the youngsters' growth (126). On the basis of the data obtained from parents of thirty-two severely retarded children, Stoddard concluded that there was an insignificant correlation between the child's growth and parental perceptions. In considering the material further, Stoddard added that she did not feel the matter was closed, despite her data, since she had reservations about the scaling instruments she had used.

Reinforcement Systems

An interesting innovation has been the development of token systems designed to produce desirable behavior. Originally, workers at Anna

State Hospital, Illinois, found that the behavior of patients with serious regression syndromes could be modified. The work has been extended to retarded persons, particularly at Parsons State Hospital and Training Center. The procedure places the traditional use of stars and bribes in classrooms on a firmer footing. It takes classroom rewards, deleting punishment, and replaces them with substitutes. Plastic or metal tokens can be exchanged promptly for objects such as candy, cosmetics, and soft drinks (46). The price for the objects is manipulated, and the token-wages are earned for specified performance. The wages are varied for performance reasons and for economic reasons. The system has been helpful with quite inadequate persons—e.g., IQ 20-50 (46), or IQ below 40 (11) Dayan has described application of the system to toilet training (26), placing stress on the strategic role of Ellis' rationale (32). The cost of the system is an excellent aspect. Girardeau and Spradlin believe the cost can be minimal (46), and Dayan has reported a substantial drop in laundry costs in the case of toilet training (26).

Language Training

Among the functional therapies which can do a great deal to alter the performance of children, a prominent place must be allotted to language training. *Language training* means speech therapy, language stimulation, and the improvement of psycholinguistic skills. All three topics are implicit in Chapter 5's treatment of language, but they are placed here in order to consider them in the context of ameliorative processes of all types. In doing so, the author is conscious of truncating the prior discussion of language but feels that the greater value is realized by synthesizing a cautiously optimistic case for ameliorative programs.

Speech Therapy and Language Stimulation. One of the more unfortunate problems in language training has been fragmentation of work among the professions and disciplines. As we have divided the modalties among workers—eyes for the nurse, wits for the psychometrist, and ears for the audiologist—so we have given written language to the remedial teacher and spoken language to the speech therapist. Traditionally, speech pathologists have been averse to therapeutic work with retarded children. This attitude was partially the result of indoctrination during training and partially the need to produce tangible results. It was also the result of overgeneralization about the basis for speech development; statements may be found at several points in the literature showing the comparative importance of intellectual development in language growth, while even more studies have shown the intimate relationship between language retardation and mental retardation. The situation has evolved in recent years so that mental retardation is no longer automatically considered a contraindication for speech therapy (119).

Speech therapy is the process of improving speech by attending to pitch, intelligibility, accent, and most of all to articulation. In this section, whose goal can only be to present the principal matters, improvement of articulation is particularly relevant.

Articulation is generally but not always poor in retarded children. Its specific forms are the substitution of sounds, their omission from words, and also their distortion. Specific patterns of defective articulation do not necessarily arise from developmental syndromes (43), although Blanchard has shown that oral language is less developed among mongoloid children than among those who have had serious postnatal infections (12).

Brain injury acts as an intervening factor in many cases. It can produce cerebral dysfunction with symptoms such as limited auditory discrimination and disturbances of syntax; it can also produce motor dysfunction whose symptoms are best illustrated by the articulation of cerebral-palsied children (35, 75). Whatever ability and motor equipment children possess can result in speech only when the family culture rewards it and when stimulation and motivation encourage it. Aserlind has shown that language growth among the poorest segment of the population, usually called "disadvantaged," is reduced when the sibship is large and the mother verbally impoverished (2). In addition, adequate speech depends on sensory development. Many retarded children have hearing losses (40), and this disability produces serious language disruption even in bright children. It can also lead to serious errors of diagnosis in normal children (10). Frisina conducted a series of studies on mentally retarded deaf children and came to some interesting conclusions (39). He found that his subjects used vision in a compensatory way; and, more interestingly, he found a wide variety of performance on a number of tests despite the consistency and severity of the double-disability state.

The procedures of therapy for articulation disorders in retarded children are not unique (27, 8). As it does for all children, the process begins with an account of the children's personal assets and liabilities and an accurate description of the sounds of the English language as they occur in actual use. Usually this last stage consists of eliciting words either by showing pictures or by showing pictures and asking for repetition of the appropriate word. A problem which has been given little serious study in the presentation of pictures for diagnosis of articulation is the resemblance of the task to pictorial tests of intelligence;

that is, the ideational content of a picture has significance for some but not all levels of mental maturity.

After clinical description and appraisal, therapists specify objectives. These usually take two forms. The first consists of statements designed to justify the expenditure of resources on retarded children (10, 56, 114); the second is the set of behavioral objectives to be realized by training. The latter provide a basis for deciding whether remedial work has been successful. Representative behavioral goals include demonstrably better articulation and useable transfer from practice situations to everyday social contexts. The procedures consist of selecting phonemes which can be worked on first with a high probability of improvement. This is done by adding experience in hearing correct and incorrect articulation to work on production of the phoneme in isolation. As quickly as possible, the phoneme is practiced in actual words, and then sentences, in order to facilitate transfer and to maintain interest. Generally, children are taught in homogeneous groups (113) because of practical limitations of case load and because the social context can be used to motivate and to represent the social reality implicit in the concern for language. Occasionally, indirect as well as direct work can be demonstrated. That is, nurses, parents, and teachers can help by giving instruction and by monitoring speech in the usual social contexts and during activities not considered primarily linguistic and therapeutic (130).

Much of the actual work in speech therapy—selection of specific goals and procedures, for example—is the result of trial and error. As with most patterns of instruction, methods are not tied to a precise rationale. An exception has been the work of Rigrodsky (104, 105), who developed a procedure for retarded children based on Mowrer's *autistic theory*, which was described in Chapter 5. Rigrodsky found that positive identification and secondary reinforcement could be used to construct specific procedures, which he applied in forty daily lessons. The main comparisons were build around an alternative therapeutic regimen applied to two levels of retardation. The important conclusion was one of no significant difference between techniques. This is not the same as saying procedures were ineffective, however; it may be that the crucial factor of subjects' perceptions of procedures was similar in both cases. If this were the case—that is, if the therapeutic figure were most important, regardless of the procedures—the commonalities of procedures would outweigh their differences. Lassers and Low conducted a comprehensive study contrasting procedures labelled "conventional" with novel procedures they identified as "communication-centered" (73). Articulation improved significantly, indicating that development of a new rationale produced better therapy. This is a second exception to the general pattern of clinical instruction based on *ad hoc* procedures.

The preceding paragraph, while discussing the rationales of therapy, inevitably touched on effectiveness of therapeutic procedures. In a sense this issue has plagued the problem of speech therapy from the beginning and has accounted for the pessimism once so universally expressed. Given the standards applied to non-retarded children with speech problems, criteria built around return for the investment of time, and eventual level of performance, the case for helping retarded children is slim. Given the more generous standard of development from personal base-line data and using personal rate of growth as the optimal speed, the case can be made more defensible. Under this separate but appropriate set of considerations, therapy for retarded children is both advisable and profitable (*111*). The value of speech therapy holds for all degrees of retardation. Three studies using populations with approximately the same IQ range, 40-75, have been conducted by Strazzulla (*127*), Mecham (*85*), and Schlanger (*114*); all found improved articulation, which in the case of Mecham's inquiry was evident after only two months. Forty more seriously retarded persons given therapy made progress in communication, with positive outcomes for themselves and for those charged with their care (*126*). Wilkins undertook speech development with a man whose low ability was compounded by comparatively advanced age (*136*). Despite the man's mental age of three and a half years, he progressed. Appropriately, Wilkins pointed out that the vicious cycle of limited language and limited intellect had contributed to the man's disability. A comparable case reported by Schlanger corroborates this finding (*112*). Other studies from places as far apart as New Zealand (*124*) and Florida (*138*) confirm the positive changes in language which can be produced in even the seriously retarded.

It is not enough, however, to evaluate attempts to develop speech by purely linguistic criteria. A well-documented event is the development of happier, alert and better motivated children, even when linguistic growth is small. The literature is replete with instances of positive changes in retarded persons exposed to small-group and individual instruction. The explanation seems to lie in the ameliorative effect which interest and concern produce. Another factor is the potential for personal rather than linguistic attainment which can be tapped in even the seriously retarded. The paradigm of personal attention suggests that work—be it linguistic or occupational— has a therapeutic dimension much as play does; this is especially the case when work is molded by a supportive person who initiates a structure within which the retarded are expected to perform or learn. Too often the matter of personal and emotional change has been assumed to depend on discharge of feelings. Tradition and reality suggest that positive change can come about through structured, reality-tinged pressure to grow. Confusion of authority with authoritarianism, directive therapy with negative results, and love with permissiveness has plagued the case of the retarded too long. It seems to this author that structure and support for retarded children can be quite positive in outlook and productive in outcome.

In closing this brief discussion of speech therapy, it is wise to reiterate an observation made earlier: using a personal base-line for estimating growth, rather than the norm of full linguistic performance, there

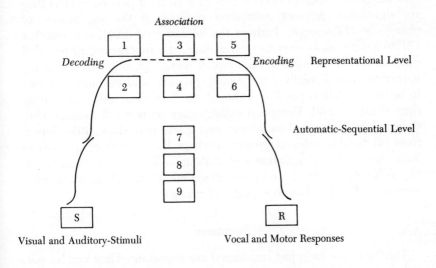

Figure 9·1

The Illinois Test of Psycholinguistic Abilities

is every reason to see speech work as a valuable form of human development.

Psycholinguistic Skills. A second form of language development is the description and subsequent training of verbal behaviors in the form described by Kirk and McCarthy (68). These investigators have developed a set of testable behaviors based on Osgood's work. The tests, nine altogether, are incorporated into a battery called the *Illinois Test of Psycholinguistic Ability*. Each test represents a level and a process in the linguistic cognitive act and may best be understood by examining the figure by Kirk and McCarthy (68). Briefly, the *ITPA* has three dimensions: (1) *channels of communication,* output and input; (2) *levels of organization,* automatic, sequential, and representational; and (3) *psycholinguistic processes,* decoding, encoding, and association.

A series of studies have shown that the *ITPA* performance level is amenable to change through training and drill (51, 120, 121). Not all the changes are stable (134), but for at least brief periods of time they are significant. A most interesting question is the significance of changes in *ITPA* scores. Perhaps the fundamental question is whether *ITPA* changes mean that low psycholinguistic functioning of retarded children can be changed in the sense of being radically shifted toward normality. This is really a traditional question, and the answer seems to be that growth is possible, although the increment will vary sharply from child to child. Untapped ceilings may be reached in some children, while optimally functioning youngsters may show little change from predictable rates of growth. Perhaps the best observation is to hope that clinical description and analysis, followed by clinical teaching, will be extended to more children. Only then will we know what amount of amelioration to expect and predict.

Summary

The issues we have just considered are important. They involve partial and tentative answers to the question of whether we can raise abilities in children by means of certain kinds of interpersonal interaction and by the use of certain kinds of tasks of a roughly instructional nature. There are several ways to approach the matter, the least cogent of which is to ask whether IQ's can be changed. There is no doubt that IQ's do change and that the shift can be large or small. Many changes are attributable to the predictable error of measurement.

The more fundamental question is whether the effectiveness of children can be shifted significantly and in such a fashion that it persists beyond the end of the procedure in use. Kirk's data suggest that progress is possible and that the changes resulting are meaningful. The children changed as a result of a rich pre-school experience. Data from the Clarkes, who worked from negative premises, are equally encouraging. Bad homes do affect children, and a different setting seems to produce more effective behavior at a higher level of functioning.

None of the studies in fact suggest that *all* retarded youngsters can make substantial changes, nor do they suggest that in any case the data justify the expectation that development will rise to the level of non-retarded youngsters.

There is another form of training that may be mentioned. It is the practice of giving religious training to retarded children. Sometimes the influence of religion is present implicitly when, for example, educational programs are started under religious auspices (*7, 44, 117*). In such cases there may be a theoretical postulate indicating that education is incomplete unless conducted in an atmosphere of religious influence apart from formal instruction. In other cases religion may be introduced as a specific topic only as services conducted on prescribed days. Religious education centers on sublime concepts. Their acquisition is a stimulating topic for research.

In conclusion, the better evidence suggests that directed experiences can help the retarded. If the expectations are not radical and if a program is carefully developed, progress and growth can be anticipated in selected cases.

PSYCHOTHERAPIES

Human abilities do not function in a vacuum. In all of us, competence and effectiveness are functions of the total person. From time to time most people experience frustrations and alternate periods of satisfaction. In those circumstances our performance, which is the operational definition of intelligence, fluctuates.

There is much truth in the saying that nothing succeeds like success. Conversely, nothing lowers effectiveness and the value of trying like repeated failures. It is entirely possible that most effective people are effective in spite of some personal problems and because of others. The point is that our use of creative and intellectual powers may be quite contingent on other components of the total personality.

Those of us who are adequate have one advantage the retarded individual does not have. We are able to muster our success when we run into the failure experiences which are a part of living. Some sort of balance is possible because we have the native ability to behave adequately. We can draw on our balance of successes to help us face the failures.

The retarded are not so fortunate; with them, it is doubtful that the credits and debits of experience ever match. The positive affect that grows out of success experiences is rooted in the ability to perform successfully, and this ability to achieve success is a way of defining intellectual ability—i. e., one can do certain things correctly.

In many retarded individuals the limited ability to succeed is limited further by the negative affect that accompanies past experiences of failure. In many cases the over-all picture is of a limited capacity whose ceiling is not reached for reasons of personality. In other cases, limited ability may not be fully used because the child has been trained, not towards independence, but rather towards dependence. Experiences in a pre-school setting might well be said to place covert demands on children, moving them in the direction of independence. The resolution of the negative feelings that accompany low performance is not so easily accomplished as a by-product of doing other things. The resolution of personal problems and the development of a good self-image is a far more deliberate process.

Forms of Psychotherapy

Psychotherapy has many forms. There is the act of talking things over with an accepting listener. There is the deliberate interaction of two people working at the resolution of problems and the development of insight. Occasionally, several people interact under the direction of a group leader. The result is that psychotherapy is a process, involving two people or more, which attempts to solve personal problems largely by talking about them and developing insight.

A vital addition to this formulation is the rationale which guides the therapist. Behavior changes in therapy and counseling reflect movement from one point to another. There must be a master-plan to guide the formulation of objectives for each case. The alternative would be to see each problem as so nearly unique that much time would be spent simply trying to develop a plan to direct growth.

The various formulations cover (1) the nature of behavior, (2) the ways to effect change, and (3) the goals of treatment. The various "schools" adhere to widely differing points of view on these issues.

The Nature of Behavior. To some people, human thought and action are replete with symbolism. Dynamically oriented counselors follow one of the many generic forms of Sigmund Freud's work. The behavior of the client is analyzed in a gigantic structure of thought which uses the Greek myths as its model. This is a highly non-empirical school of thought and violates many of the principles of empirical science. It is, nonetheless, effective.

Others view the nature of behavior as meaningful to the client and guide him towards greater insight as the key to resolving his problems. A point of view generally in this idiom is the non-directive counseling of Rogers, which does not attempt to force behavior into an all-encompassing schema. Even so, it is not without metaphysics and ideology.

There is what has been called the eclectic school. Realizing that clinicians with irreconcilable views of human nature still produce good results, some people have chosen to use whatever techniques seem effective, largely ignoring the theoretical considerations.

Locus. Traditionally, psychotherapy has been conducted on an individual basis. A trend of the last several years has been extension of counseling to groups of retarded persons. This innovation does not seem to have a rationale which sets it apart from individual work; the issue of rationale tends to be set aside in favor of discussing procedural problems (125). Since they can be serious, the matter is not trivial. On the other hand, many of the accounts have a negative tone and suggest that group counseling is a laborious process. On the one hand, the clinician wishes to convey acceptance, a phenomenon not incompatible with control in individual work. On the other hand, as anyone who has dealt with the young will recall, groups of youngsters, retarded and non-retarded, simply require structure. Emergence of spontaneous group structure can be anticipated, but the intervening threat to life and limb should not be ignored. In view of the realistic counseling needs of retarded persons, we need to encourage group process. We need not, however, overestimate its effectiveness or its freedom from procedural problems.

Ways to Effect Change. The vital component in all the therapies is that the client talks. In some cases he seems to talk to himself—the counselor intervening minimally; in other cases the expression of the client is the basis for building a relationship which is then analyzed as a model of interpersonal relations. In the group experience, people exchange and defend ideas reciprocally.

The Goals of Treatment. Some schools of therapy plan to rebuild the personality. They are therefore slow and ambitious; psychoanalysis is the best example. Others take a presented problem and help solve it. A good example is the act of preparation for return to community living (64). This is short-term, intensive therapy.

The Commonalities. It would seem that all sorts of counselors with all sorts of techniques produce results. Some people seem to be therapeutic, and those who seek their help usually anticipate success, a fact which is most important.

Certain elements seem to occur in the various therapies, and it is these commonalities that make the use of counseling at all defensible with the retarded (*141, 144*).

1. *Catharsis.* The majority of retarded people can express their feelings or can learn to put them into words. A note of caution is in order: expression is not necessarily therapeutic, *per se.* The romantic view of human nature from Rousseau to the present day has generally held that self-expression is always good; this can be a dangerous point of view.

2. *Transfer.* An interesting phenomenon is that people in counseling tend to project their inner dispositions onto the person who is in the role of counselor. The result is that the enlightened therapist reacts to the client's feelings with an appreciation of their broader significance.

3. *Learning.* From the standpoint of the empiricist, the therapeutic milieu is amenable to analysis as a learning process. The client can therefore be helped to learn new ways of interacting with people; he can, for example, learn acceptable modes of expressing feeling and learn how to inhibit responses that are inappropriate.

4. *Acceptance.* In the case of the retarded individual living in the home and moving through the community, it is only rational to expect a certain number of rejection experiences. The counseling situation operating under any of the rationales can demonstrate acceptance and offer reassurance. While it would be too much to expect one situation of acceptance to compensate for many rejections and rebuffs, we can presume that any degree of acceptance is better than none. Glassman has shown that less-than-average ability is no barrier to this experience (*47*).

Problems in Psychotherapy for the Retarded

All psychotherapies are means to an end. The end is thus the crucial factor, although it is not the obvious one. The consideration of goals for a general series of individual or group sessions presents some problems. The following examples will illustrate.

1. *Retardation as a contraindicant.* Traditionally, mentally retarded persons have been considered unsuitable for therapy because they lack the ego-resources necessary for growth. This position seems, superficially, similar to that once held by speech pa-

thologists, who have now modified their views considerably. Similar optimism does not seem to have emerged from experience with disturbed retarded persons. Albini and Dinitz found no tangible positive outcomes in their treatment of moderate and mildly retarded boys; they found a couple of trends, at best, in their data (*1*).

2. *Adjustment to the special class or to the whole school.* There is general disagreement on whether special classes should be integrated with the regular school or segregated. Should the teacher try to build an expectation of participating with all the children? An alternative might be to capitalize on the sense of identity in a group of special-class youngsters.

3. *Perception of the self.* Should we try to build concepts of self-assurance and competence; or should we try to produce "good" handicapped individuals, people who realize their limitations and plan to be the hewers-of-wood and drawers-of-water in this world?

4. *Community living and institutional living.* (a) With those retarded individuals who live in residential centers, there is a practical problem of adjusting children to the norms of behavior peculiar to that setting. To be a "good" retarded individual in a residential setting requires that a person come to derive more satisfaction from his immediate milieu and see the "outside"—the community —as less urgent and rewarding. (b) A more serious problem centered within the family is the direction which counseling should take when a child must eventually face residential living. In the home the retarded child learns to find satisfaction in the family circle. Thus, problems arise when institutional living is necessary; a child will not have an easy time moving from home and community life to residential living. The consequences are profound. The reverse of this situation has been seen since about 1945, when institutions attempted to place high-grade individuals—even in one case a "normal"—in the community and found that they had taught their patients too well to live in institutions. As Sarason has put the issue, there seems to be a choice of goals—either the welfare of the child or the smooth running of the institution (*109*). This point is also discussed by Thorne (*129*).

Evidence. The nature of psychotherapy makes the evaluation process difficult (*1*). One immediate difficulty is that subjective evidence has to be relied on much of the time. In 1949 Axline reported some data on changes in children exposed to play therapy (3). The S's were fifteen young children of low psychometric intelligence. Defining play as "freedom or room to act," she found that in children who later presented a better psychometric appearance there was evidence of rejection in the family backgrounds. Play therapy helped them considerably.

An earlier study of three children by Chidester has given anecdotal evidence of differential therapies for them (17). Two cases were complicated by neurotic and psychotic considerations which yielded to some extent during therapy.

Heiser has reported the successful treatment of children at the Vineland Training School (52). Selecting fourteen children, mostly nonfamilials, he reported that twelve made significant changes for the good. Heiser's over-all conclusion was that psychotherapy has a positive value in the care of the mentally retarded, if used appropriately.

An interesting account of the nature of group therapy with the retarded has been given by Michal-Smith (88). His subjects were in groups of ten and were between eighteen and twenty-seven years of age. There were thirty sessions lasting two hours.

The goals were to meet the following needs: "(1) stimulation and socialization, (2) ego-development, (3) improvement of the self-concept, (4) integration of fantasy life with orientations to reality" (88, p. 91).

The procedures were group motor activities and oral-language training. The process seems to have been successful with "more adequate emotional and social adjustments" resulting (88, p. 96).

Cotzin has graphically reported his experiment in group psychotherapy at the Southbury Training School in Connecticut (22). He held ten seventy-five-minute sessions with nine boys and reported that after an inauspicious beginning his subjects made progress. Their growth persisted after cessation of the series of meetings.

It is appropriate to point out that psychotherapy is more than an ameliorative process. It is, in behavioral terms, an opportunity for extended sampling of behavior. In an earlier chapter, the need to employ elaborate rather than simple diagnostic procedures was advanced. From a variety of diagnostic situations, one can derive multiple formulations of behavior. The counseling process provides one more situation, with the addition of a great deal of time for sustained evaluation. The counseling process can help us make accurate differential diagnoses within the nexus of abnormal behavior. An interesting observation which may be added is the interim observation by Schacter, Meyer, and Loomis that retarded children made slightly more progress than schizophrenic children after one year of psychotherapy

(*110*). Further, treatment made diagnosticians more comfortable with their diagnostic and classificatory statements. Psychotherapy has its own ends, but confirmation of diagnostic hypotheses is a valuable by-product.

Summary

It has been shown that psychotherapy for the retarded can produce a positive change in the level and manner of behavior. The data used to substantiate this position are not as satisfactory as one would like. There seems to be an inescapable subjectivity in evaluating the counseling process that leaves the investigator better satisfied than the reader. This in no way refutes the value of psychotherapy, but it does suggest the need for care in formulating reports of therapeutic progress.

A word of caution is offered: the positive results have been positive in that they raised the S's from some degree of inadequacy to a lesser degree. They did not raise the seriously inadequate to normality.

SURGICAL THERAPIES

The surgical therapies are those procedures which are essentially observable and which intervene in the functioning of the body. They require that a physician make structural changes of some kind, with the intent of making an inefficient constitution work more effectively. The desired outcome is a higher level of physical and psychological functioning.

From the following discussion it will become apparent that the use of physical intervention of a gross manipulative nature can take many forms. The diversity of forms is matched by the diversity of results. In some cases complete success seems possible; in others no change occurs. This is a further example of the need for specificity in defining conditions before considering the possibility of improvement.

The techniques to be discussed are (1) those actions which relate to the blood and its circulation, (2) surgery on and within the skull, and (3) assorted therapeutic surgical procedures.

Treatment of Blood-Related Problems

Rh incompatibility has been discussed elsewhere. In those infants whose mothers are unfortunately rh-negative, serious disorders follow delivery. Generally speaking, erythroblastosis fetalis poses a very serious threat to the welfare of the child, including the possible threat of mental retardation of some degree. In recent years attention has been called to the value of exchange transfusions which ensure that the blood supply does not precipitate other serious problems. This is a valuable treatment and prevents the serious limitation of intellectual capacity that has generally been observed (49). If the disorder is left untreated, jaundice and other very serious conditions develop, posing serious threats to the child.

In 1954 Day and Haines reported their experience with exchange transfusion in children who were subject to erythroblastosis fetalis (24). Their findings are quite significant and optimistic. These investigators matched sixty-eight cases with sixty-eight control cases. The particular issue was the extent to which IQ in the treated cases corresponded to IQ in the controls, who were unaffected older siblings. The expectation would be that in the absence of treatment the experimental subjects would be mentally retarded to some degree. The findings for the sixty-eight controls are that the mean IQ was 106, a normal mean, while the mean IQ of the experimental group was 112. The difference is not functionally significant, and it may be concluded that the treatment was successful in preventing the development of mental retardation in the experimental subjects.

Another approach to treatment has been based on the recognition that the blood circulation in the brain of some mentally retarded individuals has been limited. The possibility of improving the blood supply and therefore the nourishment of individual cells was considered by Beck, McKhann, and Belnap (6). They attempted to augment the blood supply in 125 cases of mental retardation. The S's were cases of organic brain damage. The investigators concluded that their procedure was helpful in some cases.

A more interesting analysis of the same principle was reported by Jervis and his associates (61). Their procedure was to connect the external carotid and internal jugular by creating an opening of about four millimeters. Their sample consisted of twenty-five cases. Ten S's were post-encephalitic problems, seven were cases of mental retardation traceable to birth injury, and several were epileptics. Interestingly, the data consist of IQ's and EEG readings. IQ's did not improve, and the EEG's showed negative effects in a few cases. The technique did not seem to be particularly appropriate as a means of making mentally retarded individuals more effective.

Surgery and the Skull

When a child's disorders are traceable to birth injury, we often think of damage to the skull and corresponding cerebral damage as the prime focus. We reason that the head of an infant is fragile and particularly susceptible owing to the immaturity of the child. Interestingly, there is reason to believe that despite the fragility of a new baby he is capable of absorbing damage to the skull that would, in proportion, be quite fatal to an adult (36).

We are led to two considerations: first, brain injury and survival are not incompatible; and second, such is the tolerance of the infant that in some cases further insult in the therapeutic form of surgery may be tolerated.

A condition which can have serious consequences for an infant is the tendency for the sutures of the skull to close too soon. It will be remembered that a baby has fontanelles, palpable openings between the bones of the skull. In rare cases there may be premature— and hence abnormal—fusion of the bones, limiting brain growth and producing deformities of the head. Since about 50 per cent of the brain's growth after birth comes in the first year or so, the result can be imagined when the boundaries of growth are set prematurely.

Only in infancy can surgical intervention be useful. The result of failure to intervene surgically is called *craniostenosis*. The causes are obscure but may be due to disorders in the germ plasm. French and Suechting have reported cases of craniostenosis in siblings which suggest a familial incidence (38).

In 1959 Vera Cruz reported the successful treatment of a case of craniostenosis:

> Complete dissection of the coronal suture and partial dissection of the temperosquamous sutures were done, and a bilateral longitudinal dissection was made along the sagittal sinus, one inch lateral from the midline and extending posteriorly to the lamboid sutures. Polyethylene sheets, used to cover the bone edges, were sutured to the bones. The post-operative course was uneventful . . . (132, p. 13).

It is significant that Vera Cruz' case grew normally thereafter. A larger series of over 100 cases has been treated by McLaurin and Matson (83). Thirty-six children under six months of age were particularly reported. In nineteen cases the site for surgery was the sagittal suture, while the second most prevalent site was the coronal suture. Treatment was largely effective, and early diagnosis was the basis for the success. One of the children studied by French and Suechting (38) was diagnosed six weeks after birth. Her progress after surgery was good and reflects the role of preventive practices in avoiding mental retardation.

In most cases of mental retardation associated with damage to a child's head, or with congenital disorders, the site of the problem lies within the skull. Treatment therefore becomes a much more complex process, and the surgical complications would appear to be greater. Nevertheless, it has proved possible to intervene by means of surgical techniques in recent years, with results that are profitable. Such has been the state of the art that entire books on the problems of surgery have appeared (60). The results that have been demonstrated in the face of remarkable technical problems are striking.

Conditions such as subdural hematomata occurring at birth seem to produce cerebral atrophy if left untreated. Spitz has pointed out that prompt attention may result in normal or near-normal development (123). In the years 1954 to 1959 he reported that his group had treated children, 80 per cent of whom showed substantially normal development subsequently.

A condition which symptomizes a disturbance in the circulation of cerebro-spinal fluid is called *hydrocephalus*. As with many human ills, the intellectual core of treatment for hydrocephalus was established long before technology had produced a practical tool. Meindl's analysis of surgical therapies between 1825 and 1835 has demonstrated that the principles of treatment were grasped (86). The pathology was not fully understood, however. An 1826 report by Clutterbuck in which inflammation is held to be the cause is cited by Meindl as an example. He has also recounted two successful examples of tapping the ventricles by Dr. Conquest in 1829. The practice was not free from criticism and was largely abandoned. However, as Meindl has put it, today we do things done in the last century, but at a more sophisticated level.

In recent years Ingraham and Matson have reported surgical techniques applicable to the several forms the disease takes. Their particular contribution has been the technique of diverting fluid from the brain to the excretory system by removing one kidney. In the technique of ventriculo-ureterostomy, a plastic tube inserted in the paraspinal region carries the fluid from the ventricular system to the ureter.

In 1953 Matson reported data on fifty cases who had been operated on for hydrocephalus (84). The technique used was the arachnoid-ureterostomy. Thirty of the subjects were alive at that time. Twenty-four were normal or close to normal. In 1954 there were fifty-eight cases of ureto-arachnoid shunts of whom forty-one were without symptoms (60).

Spitz has suggested an alternative technique (123). Rather than evacuating the fluid to the external environment, he suggests a ventriculo-vascular shunt. The technique consists of using a valve to shunt excessive fluid into the vascular system. The crucial device invented by Holter is set at about 50mm H_2O pressure. The value of the technique has been demonstrated by Spitz on the basis of 400 cases and corroborated by MacNab (80). Spitz has commented, "In summary, we at the Children's Hospital of Philadelphia, in common with many of our pediatric colleagues, are encouraged by the many excellent results we see following operations in hydrocephalus" (123, p. 1235). Ultimately, we may see drugs used to control the amount of cerebro-spinal fluid, rendering surgical intervention unnecessary.

A more radical treatment for severe multiple-handicapped cases of mental retardation, those cases in which there is also motor paralysis and severe epilepsy, has been reported by Morello and his associates (89). In those cases an entire cerebral hemisphere has been removed. In giving details of the indications for this radical procedure, the investigators emphasize the severe physical anomalies in the brain—hemiatrophy, etc.—and other gross distortions of the cerebral tissue.

It would not be reasonable to expect a radical change to normality in such cases, but in considering one typical case the writers reported the impression of the ward personnel that the patient was more sociable and seemed a little brighter after the operation.

Assorted Techniques

One other surgical procedure may be mentioned. Over the years various states have passed legislation intended to prevent the further procreation of the mentally retarded by sterilization. The peak of such legislation came in the first two decades or so of this century and coincided with the period when mental retardation was believed by most workers to be almost exclusively a hereditary condition.

The purpose of surgery, simple in males, more complicated in females, is to make the retarded incapable of producing children. It had its vogue when institutions were custodial in their practices rather than oriented towards habilitation.

One purpose of the custodial procedures was to segregate the retarded from the rest of the community. At least one reason for the segregation was the attempt to prevent the birth of more mentally retarded individuals. It was only a matter of time before someone decided that (1) sterilization was cheaper than segregation and (2) it would render impossible what segregation did not—namely, the procreation of children by one or more retardates (42).

When one considers the inadequacy of past provisions for the mentally retarded, it seems remarkable that people would consider sterilization a positive contribution to social hygiene. Further, if the purpose were to eliminate the transmission of genetic errors, one would have to sterilize virtually the entire population. Any given normal individual may have doubtful characteristics lurking in his background that may show up in the next generation if not in his own. Examination of a proposed legal statute from Canada indicates that the goal of preventing "mental disability or deficiency" by surgical assault holds considerable fascination for the credulous (116). The perceptions of sterilized persons indicate that there is more to the matter than that, however. Sabagh and Edgerton interviewed fifty sterilized persons who had been discharged from Pacific State Hospital (108). Of forty who expressed an opinion, two-thirds disapproved the surgery they had experienced. About one in five approved and, as the investigators put it, "welcomed" it. A majority of the persons interviewed considered sterilization a degrading experience. Since they were capable of living in the community, we might profitably inquire into the role this barbaric practice plays in advancing or retarding successful personal adjustment.

While no surgical therapy can restore the intellectual integrity of cerebral-palsied people who are mentally retarded, there seems reason to believe that some of the physical symptoms may be alleviated. From Japan, Narabayashi and associates have reported the surgical treatment of eighty cases. Of their sample 62.5 per cent showed beneficial results. Their technique is the injection of procaine (.4 to .8cc) into the pallidum. Athetoids seem to respond best, and in many cases speech has been improved considerably (92). From the Soviet Union, Eidinova and Pravdina-Vinarskaya have advocated the administration of galanthamine as a foundation for physical and other therapies (31). They believe the agent, which is an alkaline, facilitates neural transmission, and also *destroys*, to use their term, pathological symptoms of neural operation. Western comment has generally been skeptical, and criticism has focused on the reality of reported gains.

Summary

In considering the surgical therapies, we have considered methods which attempt to deal with the blood and its circulation and procedures that deal directly with the prime substance of the nervous system, the brain.

The results turn out to be as varied as the scope of the therapies. Some conditions are intransigent, and some therapies are ineffective. In other cases the basic pathology is successfully by-passed, and the technique is a way of compensating for serious structural damage.

The total situation re-emphasizes the need to relate problem and therapeutic technique selectively. No universal method has been discussed but a number of narrow techniques which are promising have been described.

THE CHEMOTHERAPIES

A most interesting medical advance in recent years has been the introduction of chemical forms of therapy (50). These are preparations which modify the action of the nervous system without producing any structural alteration in the body. Apart from the simplicity of the treatment, the avoidance of surgical problems for example, there is the advantage that the patient can maintain his therapeutic course under minimal supervision. Merely taking a pill at prescribed intervals is the usual regimen for some of the newer drugs.

The particular therapies which we will consider are (1) the control of body chemistry, (2) the role of the tranquilizing agents, and (3) the issue of drugs to increase intellect directly.

There are several precedents for the use of the newer tranquilizing drugs, not the least of which has been the use of preparations to alter the state of cretinous youngsters, children who have a seriously underactive thyroid. As an example of what the use of hormone therapy can accomplish, consider the findings of Gesell, Amatruda, and Culotta (45). They reported the data shown in Table 9·2 in 1936.

TABLE 9·2

GAINS AS A RESULT OF THERAPY IN CRETINISM

Subject	1	2	3	4	5	6
Final Mental Status	Delayed	Normal	Normal	Normal	Normal	Normal
Gain in Development Quotient	15	65	20	40	30	25
Final Development Quotient	45	80	60	90	75	75

In one case, the first one, treatment did not begin in infancy but at age forty-four. As a result, no improvement was observed. More recently, a French study reported an increment in intelligence after treatment (93). Sixty young children were treated for infantile myxoedema at a hospital in Nancy, and one-third of them were subsequently reported functioning at an adequate intellectual level. Not all responded fully, but growth to a greater—but still less than desirable—mental level was produced in many. Still another example is the report of attempts to alter the status of pituitary dwarfs (59). Using human pituitary hormone obtained at autopsy, Hutchings and his associates treated an eleven-year-old girl whose height was forty-one and a half inches, instead of the expected fifty-two inches. Bone age was four and a half years at chronological age eight and three-fourths years. The effect of the treatment was to triple some rates of development.

The use of endocrine preparations has been reported by Goldstein (48). He reported improvement in the status of mongoloid youngsters treated differently for endocrine dysfunction by the use of sicca-cell preparations. A critique of this approach may be found in Cowie (23).

Another form of therapy, applicable to the mentally retarded, is the use of preparations not so much to cure the condition as to upgrade the somatic level of functioning. One example is the total personality problem found in boys who are cases of gonadal immaturity. In such cases the goal is not to raise intelligence through more effective endocrine function but rather to produce personality changes that will allow the boys to use their abilities better. The technique is to use chorionic gonadotropin (9). After treatment, according to Berman, Albert-Gasorek, and Reiss, their sample of thirty-two boys showed a mean gain of seven IQ points, which, functionally, is not especially significant. On the other hand, the boys were more responsive to attempts to teach them. Also, handwriting and passivity, for example, changed for the good.

A comparable therapy has been proposed for mongoloids by Turkel (131). His purpose is not to cure the condition but to develop the body to its most effective level. Turkel feels that whatever potentials for growth exist may then be elicited by parents and teachers in their attempts to socialize and educate the child. The treatment consists of administering what Turkel describes as his "U" series of drugs for at least twenty-four to thirty months. Independent evaluation by Bumbalo, Morelewicz, and Behrens, however, found the treatment ineffective (14).

Thyroid treatment for mongolism has been advocated over the years. Koch, Sharp and Graliker administered sodium lyothyronine to seventy-three mongoloid children (69). Their evaluation after a six-year period was that neither height nor skeletal age had been significantly advanced. More positive results of a non-intellectual nature have appeared from other attempts to alter some somatic traits of mongoloid children. Ray et al. were able to increase height to their satisfaction through administration of steroids (102). From Japan, Tanino has reported developmental gains in forty-eight mongoloid children (128). Multiple vitamins were administered as individualized regimens for periods of time from one to three years. Tanino explicitly declined to conclude that the rate of intellectual growth had increased. When somatic improvement is reported, it is wise to recall that many retarded children are ill-cared-for and that long-standing physical neglect may respond to good care fairly easily.

The Ataraxic Drugs

The last several years have seen remarkable strides in the treatment of psychiatric problems. Progress has been initiated by the finding that *rauwolfia serpentina* and its derivatives can produce significant changes in the emotional state of people. Understandably, people have attempted to apply the drug and collateral medications to a variety of problems (50). Mental retardation has been among the conditions investigated with special emphasis on the tranquilizer drugs.

In considering the action of the tranquilizing drugs, some account of their mechanisms is in order. According to Kugelmass, chlorpromazine and smaller doses of reserpine depress the functions of the hypothalamus (71). The result is that metabolism, blood pressure, temperature, and the sleeping-working cycle are affected. Reserpine in significant amounts depresses the hypothalamic functions but arouses the activating system. The result is that the patient is in a state of "wakeful sedation."

It should be pointed out that the result in people of normal or subnormal intelligence is not to effect a fundamental change but rather to suppress behavioral symptoms. In 1955, for example, Penman and Dredge applied physiological and psychometric measures to eighty schizophrenics on reserpine (98). They demonstrated physiological changes after ninety days of therapy, but there were no changes in the profiles derived from the *Minnesota Multiphasic Personality Inventory*. This is analogous to putting a plaster on a corn: no radical change is intended, but the patient can get along much better than before. When one sees what relief appears in people with distressing symptoms there seems to be reason to reconsider the utility of the psychotherapies discussed earlier. In the author's opinion, the effectiveness of the ataraxic drugs casts a serious pall over the need to further develop rationales of psychotherapy. This is a flat assertion; but any therapy stands or falls by the criterion of effectiveness, rather than by the subtlety of the intellectual edifice which it supports.

Tranquilizers and Mental Retardation

An investigation by Zimmerman and Burgmeister has suggested that reserpine has a place in the treatment of mentally retarded youngsters (147). Those with serious behavior problems seem to respond. The nature of the changes does not seem to have been consistent. The only over-all finding seems to have been that intelligence-test results were not materially altered. There were isolated cases of positive changes in test scores. The conclusion offered by Zimmerman and Burgmeister is that reserpine produces highly individualized responses which are largely dependent on the personality of the particular child.

Kirk and Bauer reported that their sample of sixty retardates experienced "inner turmoil" attributable to the release effect of the drug. They noted a weakening of inner defense mechanisms also (65).

According to Noce, Williams, and Rapaport, reserpine can be used profitably in high-grade retardates (95). Using thirteen of their most intractable patients, they reported considerable success after three months of therapy. One patient, for example, changed from a vegetative existence to a responsive if limited interaction. A not insignificant finding is that the attendants who had cared for these patients had experienced considerable relief and their morale was heightened.

The use of chlorpromazine has been reported by Rettig and by Robb (103, 106). Rettig's study used twenty-seven mentally retarded individuals of varied ages. All of these people exhibited hyperactivity and destructiveness which other therapies—psychotherapies, electroshock, etc.—had not affected. Nineteen of the twenty-seven patients responded well, and only two showed no response.

Robb's study also applied chlorpromazine. In this case there were forty-two unstable defectives using the drug for periods up to four years. Thirty-six of these S's showed some improvement, and only six were unchanged by the therapy.

Another useful drug is thorazine. Esen and Durling administered the drug to fourteen hyperactive boys for two months (34). Ten boys improved, and IQ's increased on the average of ten points, while that of a control group of boys increased by seven points. The difference is not great, but there were changes in behavior, such as the lessening of hyperactivity and destructiveness. Four other tranquilizers which have been used effectively with retarded persons are promazine (115), thioridazine (4), chlorpromazine, and trifluperazine (58). Of course there are always persons who do not respond to tranquilizers; Galambos gave diazepam to forty-two adults who had not responded to other ataraxics for periods from three to twenty-four months. Thirty-three were greatly improved and subsequently participated in occupational and recreational therapy (41). It is possible to conclude that chemical agents have a contribution to make to the treatment of behavioral problems in retarded children.

In summary we may turn to Kugelmass, who amassed evidence on the differential effects of the many drugs on the varied disorders seen in retarded children (71). Figure 9·2 shows Kugelmass' judgment of the relative effectiveness of the various chemotherapeutic agents.

The figure may be interpreted by reading the line scales to indicate the percentage improvement of symptoms. The groups of children studied for each symptom ranged in size from ten to fifty (71, p. 327).

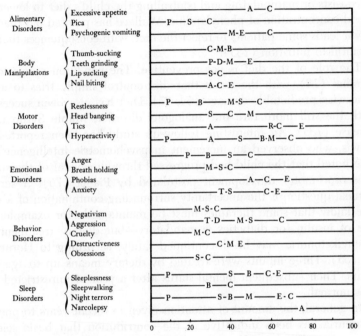

Comparative effectiveness of psychochemotherapeutic agents in amentia symptomatology of children. Code A = amphetamine; B = Benadryl (diphenhydramine hydrochloride), C = chlorpromazine; D = Dilantin (diphenyl-hydantoin sodium); E = Equanil (meprobamate); M = Miltown (meprobamate); P = phenobarbital; R = Ritalin (methylphenidylacetate hydrochloride); S = Serpasil (reserpine); T = Tolserol (mephenesin).

Figure 9·2
Comparative Effects of Chemotherapeutic Agents

The Treatment of Phenylpyruvic Oligophrenia

It is always interesting to see how the care of the sick crosses national boundaries: such is the nature of science, and such is the nature of knowledge. Phenylpyruvic oligophrenia typifies scientific procedures at their most productive. Discovered by the Norwegian, Folling, in the 1930's, this disease is now screened for routinely in many hospitals. Accounts of successful treatment have been reported in many parts of the world. Investigations and therapies have come from the United States, the United Kingdom, Sweden, Switzerland, Belgium, and Ireland (*18, 19, 54, 72, 91, 133, 139, 140*). In each case the size of the sample of children is small. This is because the condition is not common. According to Larson there are about 2.5 cases per 100,000 of the population (*72*).

The results of the treatment seem to depend on when it is begun. It consists of manipulating and controlling the child's diet to lower the blood concentration of phenylaniline. Wallace has pointed out that the flavor leads some patients to reject the diet, with consequences that are harmful to nutrition (*133*).

The role of the diet is not preventive. The condition seems to be familial (*18*), with the result that diet control simply tries to avoid otherwise predictable damage (*54, 87*). Diet has also been successful with the still more rare but analogous disorder, Maple Syrup urine disease (*135*). An interesting follow-up study has been reported by Lewis, who observed an increment in psychometric intelligence and also noted that the child had progressed through several of the stages of sensori-motor development postulated by Piaget (*76*). A serious clinical question is the uncertainty surrounding continuation of a diet. We know that some therapies must be maintained—for example, the use of insulin for diabetics is mandatory—but dietary treatment for phenylketonuria may be discontinued safely, according to Horner *et al.* (*55*). Three infants were treated by dietary means up to age four years. Their subsequent mental status after a year of unrestricted diet was normal.

In general, the amount of attention given in recent years to phenylketonuria has been indicative of the contribution that basic science can make to human welfare. It would be misleading to think that treatment is always successful, and it would be equally unwise to think that the disease is common.

Glutamic Acid and Mental Retardation

As the study of phenylpyruvic amentia in many ways typifies science at its best, so the complex surrounding glutamic acid may well illustrate the less desirable aspects of science.

At the beginning of the chapter attention was called to "magic bullets" in the search for cures of mental retardation. In all probability glutamic acid may typify a fourth consideration—namely, the search for a "brain food" intended to nurture that particular organ of the body.

The controversy which has surrounded glutamic acid will probably not be completely unraveled. This is because the experiments which reported results did so for reasons other than the value of the drug. Several investigators have called attention to experimental errors in the published accounts of research procedures (15, 33, 118).

The findings of Quinn and Durling, published in 1950, were that glutamic-acid therapy over a twelve month period was effective (100). After six months of therapy they found an IQ increment of 3.9 points on the average. Such a variation is entirely predictable and cannot be said to reflect clearly either a serious gain or an increase in functional intelligence.

A comparatively little-known but crucial study of glutamic acid was reported by Ellson, Fuller, and Urmston also in 1950 (33). The value of this study lies not in using more subjects or fewer subjects but rather in its attention to problems in methodology. One crucial point was the great care taken to withhold information from psychometrists and other personnel as to which of two groups was receiving the experimental treatment. The alternative procedure inevitably vitiates the independence of the observers in a study and contaminates their perceptions of performance. The essentials of the experiment were the administration of the drug to groups of retardates, matched by age and Binet IQ. The experimental $\overline{M}$ IQ was 49.05, and the control $\overline{M}$ IQ was 49.00. The eventual conclusions related differences in post-treatment changes in IQ and were that the increments were not significantly different.

Other investigators (15, 77, 81, 140, 146) report no significant rise in intelligence behavior from glutamic-acid therapy. Zimmerman's and Burgmeister's data on 464 subjects over a period of several years showed a mean IQ change of 5.64 points. It is significant that in a paper published concurrently they chose to call attention to the behavioral traits which changed: ". . . the most reliable results are in the realm of behavioral changes following glutamic acid therapy and that IQ point change is only an incidental or secondary factor, no doubt arising from removal or assuagement of emotional barriers" (145, p. 657).

This reference to other factors in the realm of personality is important. In too many cases the assumption has been wrongly made that IQ is a suitable dependent variable. By and large, even if IQ were a crucial factor, it would seem that scales loaded with items of cultural learning are scarcely relevant for treatment periods of a few months. On the other hand, there is a confounding problem when a cultural-achievement measure of intelligence is used. It is not possible to separate readily the effect of the passage of time (maturation) from the experimental treatment.

The resolution of this problem might have been speeded by using either power tests with modest cultural content or, preferably, *careful* observation data of levels of functioning in the S's using first-class observation techniques (29). The writer has long viewed sympathetically but cautiously statements about children "looking" brighter after experimentation failed to produce objective evidence of change.

In conclusion, there seems to be reason to believe that the results of glutamic-acid feeding are not generally significant. In some individual cases (15, 146) striking results obtain, but they are not changes in intellect, *which glutamic was held to produce;* rather they were effects more suitably classed with those of the previous section—namely, the effects of the ataraxic drugs on personality.

There is an entire literature which has developed around the agent *deanol*. Reports of its effectiveness have come from several parts of the world, and they indicate that positive changes in academic and intellectual status may occur (16, 57). Louttit has suggested that mood rather than intellect may be altered, however (78). Dayan examined the issue by administering deanol and a placebo to thirty-two children divided into two matched groups (25). The experimental regimen consisted of three 100-milligram tablets per diem for ten days and then one per diem for a total of five months. No significant changes were found in WISC IQ, school behavior, rending ability, and EEG readings. At the time of writing there seems to be an increase in the number of studies of deanol. It is safe to say this issue is comparable to the glutamic-acid controversy in a disturbing number of ways; the promise of deanol seems similar to that claimed for glutamic acid, and the design problems seem quite similar. In assessing the literature on the topic it would be wise to consult the study by Ellson, Fuller, and Urmston (33). Their experiment stands as a criterion for evaluating the evidence offered to support claims on the effectiveness of chemical treatments for retardation.

SUMMARY

In this chapter we have considered the attempts to raise the intellectual level of the mentally retarded. The techniques used in these attempts have been classified as (1) functional therapies, (2) psychotherapies, (3) surgical therapies, and (4) chemotherapies.

The conclusion to be drawn from these data is that change is possible in the status of retarded individuals, provided that there are no expectations of broad therapy. Rather, in selected cases selected therapies produce results. There seems to be reason to believe that the ataraxic drugs can render an individual more amenable to training; but there is little evidence for believing that we have yet developed, or will ever develop, a therapy that will radically alter the status of retardates from intellectual inadequacy to normality.

BIBLIOGRAPHY

1. Albini, J. L., and Dinitz, S., "Psychotherapy with Disturbed and Defective Children: An Evaluation of Changes in Behavior and Attitudes," *Amer. J. Ment. Def.*, 1965, *69*, 560-567.

2. Aserlind, L., "An Investigation of Maternal Factors Related to the Acquisition of Verbal Skills of Infants in a Culturally Disadvantaged Population," unpublished Ph.D. dissertation, University of Wisconsin, 1964.

3. Axline, V., "Mental Deficiency: Symptom or Disease?" *J. Consult. Psych.*, 1949, *13*, 313-327.

4. Badham, J. W., *et al.*, "A Trial of Thioridazine in Mental Deficiency," *Brit. J. Psychiat.*, 1963, *109*, 408-410.

5. Bangs, J. L., "A Clinical Analysis of the Articulatory Defects of the Feebleminded," *J. Speech Dis.*, 1942, *7*, 343-356.

6. Beck, C. S., McKhann, C., and Belnap, W., "Revascularization of the Brain," *Am. J. Ment. Def.*, 1950, *55*, 218-219.

7. Behrmann, E., "The Organization of a Department of Special Education in the Archdiocese of St. Louis," unpublished Ph.D. dissertation, St. Louis University, 1952.

8. Bell, D. M., "Methods of Teaching Speech and Language to the Severely Mentally Retarded Child," unpublished Ph.D. dissertation, University of Denver, 1958.

9. Berman, H. H., Albert-Gasorek, K. E., and Reiss, M., "Gonadal Immaturity as an Etiological Factor in Some Forms of Mental Deficiency, and Its Therapy," *Dis. Nerv. Syst. Mon. Suppl.*, 1959, *20*, 3-7.

10. Bibey, L., "A Rationale of Speech Therapy for Mentally Deficient Children," *Train. Schl. Bull.*, 1951, *47*, 236-239.

11. Birnbrauer, J. S., and Lawler, J., "Token Reinforcement for Learning," *Ment. Retard.*, 1964, *2*, 275-279.

12. Blanchard, I., "Speech Pattern and Etiology in Mental Retardation," *Amer. J. Ment. Def.*, 1964, *68*, 612-617.

13. Bostock, J., and Shackleton, N., "The Use of 2-Dimethylaminoethynol (Deanol) in Remedial Education," *Slowlearn. Child.*, 1961, *8*, 101-107.

14. Bumbalo, T. S., Morelewicz, H. V., and Behrens, D. L. "Treatment of Down's Syndrome with the U Series of Drugs," *J. Amer. Med. Assoc.*, 1964, *187*, 361.

15. Chambers, G. S., and Zabarenko, R. N., "Effects of Glutamic Acid and Social Stimulation in Mental Deficiency," *J. Abnorm. Soc. Psych.*, 1956, *53*, 315-320.

16. Charles, H., "The Use of a Selected Drug in the Reading Process," paper presented to the Council on Exceptional Children, 1965.

17. Chidester, L., "Therapeutic Results with Mentally Retarded Children," *Am. J. Orthopsychiat.*, 1934, *4*, 464-472.

18. Christen, J.-P., "Etude de Deux Cas d'Idiotie Phenylpyruvique traités par un Régime Pauvre en Phénylaniline," *Helvet. Paed. Acta.*, 1959, *14*, 271-281.

19. Clader, D. E., "Accelerated Intellectual Growth and Personality Developments as Seen in Phenylketonuric Subjects during Medical Treatment," *Am. J. Ment. Def.*, 1957, *62*, 538-542.

20. Clarke, A. D. B., and Clarke, A. M., "Cognitive Changes in the Feebleminded," *Brit. J. Psych.* 1954, *45*, 173-179.

21. _____, and Reiman, S., "Cognitive and Social Changes in the Feebleminded—Three Further Studies," *Brit. J. Psych.*, 1958, *49*, 144-157.

22. Cotzin, M., "Group Psychotherapy with Mentally Defective Problem Boys," *Am. J. Ment. Def.*, 1948, *53*, 268-283.

23. Cowie, V. A., "Niehans' Theory," *Dev. Med. Child Neurol.*, 1963, *5*, 220-230.

24. Day, R., and Haines, M. S., "Intelligence Quotients of Children Recovered from Erythroblastosis Fetalis Since the Introduction of Exchange Transfusion," *Pediat.*, 1954, *13*, 333-338.

25. Dayan, M., "Effect of Deaner on School Learning and Behavior of the Educable Mentally Retarded," unpublished Ph.D. dissertation, University of Florida, 1962.

26. _____, "Toilet Training Retarded Children in a State Residential Institution," *Ment. Retard.*, 1964, *2*, 116-117.

27. Dean, S. A., "A Review of Speech and Language Problems of Educable Mentally Retarded Children with Suggestions for a Classroom Speech Improvement Program," unpublished M.S. thesis, Southern Connecticut State College, 1960.

28. Despert, J. L., and Pierce, H. D., "The Relation of Emotional Adjustment to Intellectual Function," *Genet. Psych. Mon.*, 1946, *34*, 3-56.

29. Dews, P. D., *et al.*, "Techniques for the Study of Behavioral Effects of Drugs," *Ann. N. Y. Acad. Sc.*, 1956, *65*, 247-356.

30. Doll, E. A., "Is Mental Deficiency Curable?" *Am. J. Ment. Def.*, 1947, *51*, 420-428.

31. Eidinova, M. B., and Pravdina-Vinarskaya, Ye. N., *Cerebral Palsy in Children and Its Treatment*, Macmillan, 1963.

32. Ellis, N. R., "Toilet Training the Severely Defective Patient: An S-R Reinforcement Analysis," *Amer. J. Ment. Def.*, 1963, *68*, 98-103.

33. Ellson, D. G., Fuller, P. R., and Urmston, R., "The Influence of Glutamic Acid on Test Performance," *Science*, 1950, *112*, 248-250.

34. Esen, F. M., and Durling, D., "Thorazine in the Treatment of Mentally Retarded Children," *Arch. Pediat.*, 1956, *73*, 168-173.

35. Evans, M. F., "Problems in Cerebral Palsy," *J. Sp. Dis.*, 1947, *12*, 87-103.

36. Fabian, A. A., "Prognosis in Head Injuries in Children," *J. Nerv. Ment. Dis.*, 1956, *123*, 428-431.

37. Francey, R. E., Psychological Test Changes in Mentally Retarded Children During Training," *Canad. J. Pub. Hlth.*, 1960, *51*, 69-74.

38. French, L. A., and Suechting, R. L., "Familial Incidence of Craniostenosis," *Am. J. Dis. Child.*, 1955, *89*, 486-488.

39. Frisina, D. R., "Psychological Study of the Mentally Retarded Deaf Child," unpublished Ph.D. dissertation, Northwestern University, 1955.

40. Fulton, R. T., and Graham, J. T., "Puretone Reliability with the Mentally Retarded," *Amer. J. Ment. Def.*, 1964, *69*, 265-268.

41. Galambos, M., "Long-term Clinical Trial with Diazapam on Adult Mentally Retarded Persons," *Dis. Nerv. Syst.*, 1965, *26*, 305-309.

42. Gamble, C. J., "The Prevention of Mental Deficiency by Sterilization," *Am. J. Ment. Def.*, 1951, *56*, 192-197.

43. Gens, G. W., "Correlation of Neurological Findings, Psychological Analyses, and Speech Disorders among Institutionalized Epileptics," *Train. Schl. Bull.*, 1950, *47*, 3-18.

44. George, J. A., "Issues in the Development of a Special Education Program," unpublished M. A. thesis, St. Louis University, 1962.

45. Gesell, A., Amatruda, C. S., and Culotta, C. S., "Effect of Thyroid Therapy on Mental and Physical Growth of Cretinous Infants," *Am. J. Dis. Ch.*, 1936, *52*, 1117-1138.

46. Girardeau, F., and Spradlin, J., "Token Rewards in a Cottage Program," *Ment. Retard.*, 1964, *2*, 345-352.

47. Glassman, L. A., "Is Dull Normal Intelligence a Contraindication for Psychotherapy?" in Stacey, C. C., and DeMartino, M., *Counseling and Psychotherapy with the Mentally Retarded*, Free Press of Glencoe, 1957.

48. Goldstein, H., "Sicca-Cell Therapy in Children," *Arch. Pediat.*, 1956, *73*, 234-239.

49. Gerver, J. M., and Day, R., "Intelligence Quotients of Children Who Have Recovered from Erythroblastosis Fetalis," *J. Pediat.*, 1950, *36*, 342-348.

50. Gordon, H. L., *The New Chemotherapy in Mental Illness*, Philosophical Library, 1958.

51. Hart, N. W. M., "The Differential Diagnosis of the Psycholinguistic Abilities of the Cerebral Palsied Child and Effective Remedial Procedures," *Spec. Schls. Bull.*, (Austral.) 1963, 3-20, cited by McCleod, J., in "The Search for Measurable Intellectual Causes of Reading Disability," *Slowlearn. Child.*, (Austral.) 1964, *11*, 80-94.

52. Heiser, K., "Psychotherapy in a Residential School for Mentally Retarded Children," *Train. Sch. Bull.*, 1954, *50*, 211-218.

53. Hill, A. S., "Does Special Education Result in Improved Intelligence for the Slow Learners?" *J. Excep. Ch.*, 1948, *14*, 207-214.

54. Horner, F. A., and Streamer, C. W., "Phenylketonuria Treated from Earliest Infancy," *A.M.A. J. Dis. Child.*, 1958, 97, 345-347.

55. Horner, F. A., *et al.*, "Termination of Dietary Treatment of Phenylketonuria," *N. Engl. J. Med.*, 1962, *266*, 79-81.

56. Hotchkiss, F. C., "A Suggested Therapy Program to Improve the Communicative Ability of the Mongoloid Child Based on a Review of the Literature," unpublished Master's thesis, Southern Connecticut State College, 1960.

57. Huddlestone, W., *et al.*, "Deanol as an Aid in Overcoming Reading Retardation," *Clin. Med.*, 1961, *8*, 7.

58. Hunter, H., and Stephenson, G. M., "Chlorpromazine and Trifluperazine in the Severely Subnormal Child," *Brit. J. Psychiat.*, 1963, *109*, 411-417.

59. Hutchings, J. J., *et al.*, "Metabolic Changes Produced by Human Growth Hormone (li) in a Pituitary Dwarf," *J. Clin. Endocr. and Metab.*, 1959, *19*, 759-769.

60. Ingraham, F. D., and Matson, D. M., *Neurosurgery of Infancy and Childhood*, Charles C. Thomas, 1954.

61. Jervis, G. H., *et al.*, "Revascularization of the Brain in Mental Defectives," *Neurol.*, 1953, *3*, 871-878.

62. Jordan, T. E., "Crucial Dimensions of Mother/Retarded Child Interaction," paper presented to the American Association on Mental Deficiency, Baltimore, 1960.

63. ———, "Early Developmental Adversity and Classroom Learning: A Prospective Inquiry," *Amer. J. Ment. Def.*, 1964, *69*, 360-371.

64. Kauffman, M. E., "Group Psychotherapy in Preparation for the Return of Mental Defectives from Institution to Community," *Ment. Retard.* 1963, *1*, 276-280.

65. Kirk, D. C., and Bauer, A. M., "Effects of Reserpine (Serpasil) on Emotionally Maladjusted High Grade Mental Retardation," *Am. J Ment. Def.*, 1956, *60*, 779-784.

66. Kirk, S. A., and Johnson, G. O., *Educating the Retarded Child*, Houghton Mifflin, 1951.

67. Kirk, S. A., *Early Education of the Mentally Retarded*, University of Illinois Press, 1958.

68. _____, and McCarthy, J. J., "The Illinois Test of Psycholinguistic Abilities—An Approach to Differential Diagnosis," *Amer. J. Ment. Def.*, 1961, 66, 399-412.

69. Koch, R., Sharp., J., and Graliker, B., "The Effects of Cytomel on Young Children with Down's Syndrome (Mongolism): A Double-Blind Longitudinal Study," *J. Pediat.*, 1965, 66, 776-778.

70. Kratter, F. E., "The Physiognomic, Psychometric, Behavioral and Neurological Aspects of Phenylketonuria," *J, Ment. Sci.*, 1959, 105, 421-427.

71. Kugelmass, I. N., "Psychochemotherapy of Mental Deficiency in Children," *Internat. Rec. Med.*, 1956, 169, 323-338.

72. Larson, L. A., "An Estimate of the Frequency of Phenylketonuria in Southern Sweden," *Fol. Hered. et. Path.*, 1954, 4, 40-46.

73. Lassers, L., and Low, G., "A Study of the Relative Effectiveness of Different Approaches of Speech Therapy for Mentally Retarded Children," *Final Report*, U. S. Office of Education, Cooperative Research Program, 1960.

74. Lee, E. S., "Negro Intelligence and Selective Migration," *Am. Soc. Rev.*, 1951, 16, 227-233.

75. Lencione, R. M., "A Study of the Speech Sound Ability and Intelligibility Status of a Group of Educable Cerebral Palsied Children," unpublished Ph.D. dissertation, Northwestern University, 1953.

76. Lewis, E., "The Development of Concepts in a Girl after Dietary Treatment for Phenylketonuria," *Brit. J. Med. Psych.*, 1959, 32, 282-287.

77. Lombard, J., Gilbert J., and Donofrio, A., "The Effects of Glutamic Acid upon the Intelligence, Social Maturity, and Adjustment of a Group of Mentally Retarded Children," *Am. J. Ment. Def.*, 1955, 60, 122-132.

78. Louttit, R., "Chemical Facilitation of Intelligence," *Amer. J. Ment. Def.*, 1965, 69, 495-501.

79. Lyle, J. G., "The Effect of An Institution Environment Upon the Verbal Development of Imbecile Children: III. The Brooklands Residential Family Unit," *J. Ment. Def. Res.*, 1960, 4, 14-23.

80. MacNab, G., "Hydrocephalus," *J. Am. Med. Assn.*, 1959, 170, 1337.

81. McCulloch, T. L., "The Effect of Glutamic Acid Feeding on Cognitive Abilities of Institutional Mental Defectives," *Am. J. Ment. Def.*, 1950, 55, 117-122.

82. McKinney, J. P., and Keele, T., "Effects of Increased Mothering on the Behavior of Severely Retarded Boys," *Amer. J. Ment. Def.,* 1963, *67,* 556-562.

83. McLaurin, R. L., and Matson, D. D., "Importance of Early Surgical Treatment of Craniosynostosis," *Pediat.,* 1952, *10,* 637-652.

84. Matson, D. D., "Hydrocephalus Treated by Arachnoid-Ureterostomy," *Pediat.,* 1953, *12,* 326-334.

85. Mecham, M. J., "The Development and Application of Procedures for Measuring Speech Improvement in Mentally Defective Children," *Amer. J. Ment. Def.,* 1955, *60,* 301-306.

86. Meindl, J. L., "Early Medical Notes on Mental Retardation," unpublished paper, 1962.

87. Mertz, E. J., "Psychometabolic Changes in Phenylketonuria Treated with Low Phenylaniline Diet," *A. M. A. Arch. Intern. Med.,* 1958, *101,* 1094-1105.

88. Michal-Smith, H., *The Mentally Retarded Patient,* Lippincott, 1956.

89. Morello, A., O'Neill, F. J., and Hoen, T. I., "Treatment by Hemispherectomy of Nine Cases of Spastic Hemiplegia, Severe Mental Retardation, and Intractable Epilepsy," *Psychiat. Quart.,* 1959, *33,* 44-54.

90. Mueller, M., and Smith, J. O., "The Stability of Language Age Modifications over Time," *Amer. J. Ment. Def.,* 1964, *68,* 537-539.

91. Murphy, D., "Phenylketonuria Treated from Early Infancy," *Irish J. Med. Sc.,* 1959, *405,* 425-427.

92. Narabayashi, H., *et al.,* "Procaine Oil-Wax Pallidotomy for Double Athetosis and Spastic States in Infantile Cerebral Palsy," *Neurol.,* 1960, *10,* 61-69.

93. Neimann, W., Pierson, M., and Berthier, X., 'Le Prognostic Mental du Myxoedeme Infantile," *Arch. Franc. Péd.,* 1962, *20,* 147-159.

94. Nicod, M., "L'Action du Niamid Sur Le Comportment Intellectuel de l'Enfant," *Ann. Paed. (Basel) Suppl.* 1963, *201,* 31-43.

95. Noce, R. H., Williams, D. B., and Rapaport, W., "Reserpine (Serpasil) in the Management of the Mentally Ill and Mentally Retarded," *J. Am. Med. Ass.,* 1955, *158,* 11-15.

96. Oliver, J. N., "The Effect of Physical Conditioning Exercises and Activities on the Mental Characteristics of Educationally Sub-Normal Boys," *Brit. J. Ed. Psych.,* 1958, *28,* 155-165.

97. Page, J. D., "The Effect of Nursery School Attendance upon Subsequent IQ," *J. Psych.,* 1940, *10,* 221-230.

98. Penman, A. S., and Dredge, T. E., "Effect of Reserpine and Open-Ward Privileges on Chronic Schizophrenics," *Arch. Neurol. Psychiat.,* 1956, *76,* 42-49.

99. Plutkin, W. H., "Situational Speech Therapy for Retarded Cerebral Palsied Children," *J. Sp. Hear. Dis.*, 1959, *24*, 16-20.

100. Quinn, K. U., and Durling, D., "Twelve Months' Study of Glutamic Acid Therapy in Different Clinical Types in an Institution for the Mentally Deficient," *Am. J. Ment. Def.*, 1950, *54*, 312-332.

101. Räihä, C. E., and Kauppinen, M., "An Attempt to Decrease Perinatal Mortality and the Rate of Premature Births," *Develop. Med. Child Neurol.*, 1963, *5*, 225-232.

102. Ray, C. G., *et al.*, "Studies of Anabolic Steroids: II, The Effect of Oxandrolone on Height, Skeletal Maturation in Mongoloid Children," *Amer. J. Dis. Child*, 1963, *106*, 375-380.

103. Rettig, J. H., "Chlorpromazine for the Control of Psychomotor Excitement in the Mentally Deficient," *J. Nerv. Ment. Dis.*, 1955, *122*, 190-194.

104. Rigrodsky, S., "Application of Mowrer's Autistic Theory to the Speech Habilitation of Mentally Retarded Pupils," unpublished Ph.D. dissertation, Purdue University, 1959.

105. _____, and Steer, M. D., "Mowrer's Theory Applied to Speech Habilitation of the Mentally Retarded," *J. Sp. Dis.*, 1961, *26*, 237-243.

106. Robb, H. P., "Use of Chlorpromazine in a Mental Deficiency Institution," *J. Ment. Sc.*, 1959, *105*, 1029-1031.

107. Rushton, C. S., and Stockwin, C. E., "Changes in Terman-Merrill IQ's of Educationally Subnormal Boys," *Brit. J. Educ. Psychol.*, 1963, *33*, 132-142.

108. Sabagh, G., and Edgerton, R. B., "Sterilized Mental Defectives Look at Eugenic Sterilization," *Eugen. Quart.*, 1962, *9*, 213-222.

109. Sarason, S. B., "Individual Psychotherapy with Mentally Defective Individuals," *Am. J. Ment. Def.*, 1952, *56*, 803-805.

110. Schacter, F. F., Meyer, L. R., and Loomis, E. A., "Childhood Schizophrenia and Mental Retardation: Differential Diagnosis Before and After One Year of Psychotherapy," *Amer. J. Orthopsychiat.*, 1962, *32*, 584-595.

111. Schneider, B., and Vallon, J., "The Results of a Speech Therapy Program for Mentally Retarded Children," *Amer. J. Ment. Def.*, 1955, *59*, 417-424.

112. Schlanger, B. B. "A Longitudinal Study of Speech and Language Development of Brain Damaged Retarded Children," *J. Sp. H. Dis.*, 1959, *24*, 354-360.

113. _____, "Mentally Retarded Children," *J. Speech Hear. Dis.*, 1958, *23*, 298-301.

114. _____, "Speech Therapy Results With Mentally Retarded Children in Special Classes," *Train. Sch. Bull.*, 1953, *50*, 179-186.

115. Schulman, J. L., and Clarinda, S. M., "The Effect of Promazine on the Activity Level of Retarded Children," *Pediat.*, 1964, *33*, 271-275.

116. "The Sexual Sterilization Bill," introduced into the Alberta provincial legislature, 1957.

117. Shapiro, H., "Jewish Religious Education for Retarded Children," *Ment. Retard.*, 1964, *2*, 213-217.

118. Sharp, H. C., "Glutamic Acid Feeding," *Excep. Child.*, 1952, *18*, 230-232.

119. Siegel, G., "Prevailing Concepts in Speech Research with Mentally Retarded Children," *Asha.*, 1964, *6*, 192-194.

120. Smith, J. O., *Effects of a Group Language Development Program upon the Psycholinguistic Abilities of Educable Mental Retardates*, Peabody College Special Education Research Monograph Series, 1962, No. 1.

121. Smith, J. O., "Group Language Development for Educable Mental Retardates," *Excep. Child.*, 1962, *29*, 95-101.

122. Smith, M. E., "A Study of Some Factors Influencing the Development of the Sentence in Preschool Children," *J. Genet. Psychol.*, 1935, *46*, 182-212.

123. Spitz, E. B., "Neurosurgery in the Prevention of Exogenous Mental Retardation," *Pediat. Clin. N. Am.*, 1959, *6*, 1215-1238.

124. Spragge, C. M., "Speech Therapy for the Mentally Handicapped Child," *Speech Path. Therap.*, 1962, *5*, 79-86.

125. Sternlicht, M., "Establishing an Initial Relationship in Group Psychotherapy with Delinquent Retarded Male Adolescents," *Amer. J. Ment. Def.*, 1964 *69*, 39-41.

126. Stoddard, H. M., "The Relation of Parental Attitudes and Achievements of Severely Mentally Retarded Children," *Am. J. Ment. Def.*, 1959, *63*, 575-598.

127. Strazzulla, M., "Speech Problems of the Mongoloid Child," *Quart. Rev. Pediat.*, 1953, *8*, 268-273.

128. Tanino, Y., "A Long-Term Administration of Multiple Vitamins to Mongoloid Children and Observation of the Resultant Improvement," *Ann. Paed. Japon.*, 1961, *7*, 56-73.

129. Thorne, F. C., "Counseling and Psychotherapy with Mental Defectives," *Am. J. Ment. Def.*, 1948, *52*, 263-271.

130. Tufts, L. C., and Holliday, A. R., "Effectiveness of Trained Parents as Speech Therapists," *J. Speech Hear. Dis.*, 1959, *24*, 395-401.

131. Turkel, H., Personal communication, 1960.

132. Vera Cruz, P. G., 'Craniostenosis," *Clin. Proc. Child. Hosp. Washington, D. C.*, 1959, *15*, 11-18.

133. Wallace, H. W., "Phenylpyruvic Oligophrenia," *Bull. Tufts, N. Engl. Med. Cent.*, 1959, *5*, 16-27.

134. Weld, R. G., "An Investigation of the Long-Term Effects of Language Training on the Mentally Retarded," unpublished master's thesis, University of Wisconsin, 1963.

135. Westall, R. G., "Dietary Treatment of a Child with Maple Syrup Urine Disease (Branched-Chain Ketoaciduria)," *Arch. Dis. Child.*, 1963, *38*, 485-491.

136. Wilkins, J. L., "Problems Involved in Trying to Teach an Imbecile to Speak," *Sp. Path. Therap.*, 1960, *3*, 13-17.

137. Wilson, L., "A Survey of Speech Defects among Mentally Retarded Pupils in the Public Schools of Des Moines, Iowa," unpublished master's thesis, State University of Iowa, 1945.

138. Wood, B., "The Effects of Specialized Speech Training on Selected Feebleminded Subjects at the Florida Farm Colony," unpublished master's thesis, University of Florida, 1952.

139. Woolf, L. I., *et al.*, "Treatment of Phenylketonuria with a Diet Low in Phenylaniline," *Brit. Med. J.*, 1955, 57-64.

140. Woolf, L. I., and Vulliamy, D. G., "Phenylketonuria with a Study of the Effect upon It of Glutamic Acid," *Arch. Dis. Child.*, 1951, *26*, 487-494.

141. Wiest, G., "Psychotherapy with the Mentally Retarded," *Am. J. Ment. Def.*, 1955, *59*, 640-644.

142. Yannet, H., "The Progress of Medical Research in the Field of Mental Deficiency," *Am. J. Ment. Def.*, 1953, *57*, 447-452.

143. Yasse, L., "Observation Clinique d'une Oligophrenie Phenylpyruvique Familiale," *Acta Paed. Belg.*, 1959, *13*, 86-102.

144. Yepsen, L., "Counseling the Mentally Retarded," *Am. J. Ment. Def.*, 1952, *57*, 205-213.

145. Zimmerman, G. T., and Burgmeister, B. B., "Analysis of Behavior Patterns Following Glutamic Acid Therapy," *Arch. Neurol. Psychiat.*, 1959, *81*, 649-657.

146. ———, "A Controlled Experiment of Glutamic Acid Therapy," *Arch. Neurol. Psychiat.*, 1959, *81*, 639-648.

147. ———, "Preliminary Report upon the Effect of Reserpine on Epilepsy and Behavior Problems in Children," *Ann. N.Y. Acad. Science*, 1955, *61*, 215-221.

Chapter 10

EDUCATION

It has been stated in Chapter 2 that mental retardation is basically a problem of human lives, the lives of the retarded individuals and the lives of members of the immediate family. Generally speaking, society's attempts to help the retarded give a different picture: primarily that mental retardation is an educational issue. That this work chooses to stress the individual impact of mental retardation in no way detracts from the educational significance of the problem. There are several reasons why the consideration of mental retardation as primarily an educational issue is so widespread. First, there is the reality that children's inadequacies show up strikingly during the developmental tasks, largely educational, of the middle childhood years. The second reason is that the school is the social agency which most frequently and consistently encounters mentally retarded individuals. A third reason is that the opportunities for increasing growth and development in children seem greater in an educational context than in most others (45, 46).

It remains then to analyze the issue and to discuss the problems of educating retarded individuals. There are several ways to approach the undertaking. It may be justly said that the education of retarded children is a subject for entire books. This is quite true, and an examination of such texts reveals the significance of the problems (*48, 37*). Consideration of the matter within the scope of one chapter must necessarily be limited. A second approach is to ask what *needs* to be said in a consideration of educational problems.

Usually, educational issues are at an *applied* level and reflect the obvious significance of instructional problems. It is virtually impossible to find a consideration of the education of the retarded at a *conceptual* level; on the other hand, there are many papers which consider the matter at a *theoretical* level. In this context the word *theoretical* describes matters of policy and goals, and the word *conceptual* indicates a consideration of applied problems in such terms as to permit and encourage more fruitful analysis.

In this chapter matters of conceptual significance will be introduced in addition to applied and theoretical considerations. It is the author's contention that our awareness of *theoretical* and *applied* problems is adequate (*85*) but that we have no adequate *conceptual* treatment of educational issues in mental retardation.

As an aside it may be observed that special education is still an offshoot of regular education. It is staffed by personnel identified with professional education rather than with other disciplines. An analysis of special- and elementary-education practices of 200 teachers conducted by Goldman revealed different applications of essentially identical approaches (*26*). Intentions of the two groups of teachers differed, of course; but Goldman concluded his analysis by stressing "greater emphasis" on some aspects of development, rather than fundamental differences. Special education shares with regular education the same poverty of conceptual schemata and a dearth of rigorous models to analyze its processes. In this chapter attention is called to some conceptual problems; for intensive treatments of the applied and theoretical issues, the reader may consider the several excellent works already available (*37, 49, 75, 90, 103*). We shall, however, indicate the major applied and theoretical problems in order to put the conceptual problems on a realistic basis. One which may be treated expeditiously at this point is the size of present enrollments in special classes.

ENROLLMENTS

Serious study of enrollments should be conducted with at least brief attention to the problem of compiling figures. The sources of difficulty are several. The first problem is in the public sector of education. Constitutionally, education in the United States is not a national issue. It is a function delegated to state action with attendant consequences for financial support; no compulsion to coordinate practices, to share innovations, or to discuss mutual problems exists. For this discussion we may add that gathering statistics and establishing criteria to guide that step is also quite clearly restricted to the states. Within each state a further problem exists, since there are unique patterns of state services, even apart from the public schools. There are, for example, state institutions which offer schooling but do not do so under the state department of education; quite extensive programs exist under state agencies for public health, mental hygiene, and public welfare. Even since the 1957 revolution in education with its doctrine of federal strategy paralleling but not replacing state responsibility, gathering statistics at the national level has remained difficult.

The second problem lies in the private sector. In each state there exist private schools run "for fun and profit" by entrepreneurs, while others are supported by local associations affiliated with the National Association for Retarded Children. These facilities are a substantial but ill-defined portion of the services available to children. Parallel to these services are the programs maintained by religious groups. Their enrollments are only partially known, a situation surely leading to first appreciation of the problems faced in gathering statistics, and, second, caution in attributing to statistics a finality not intended by persons developing them. Table 10·1 shows representative 1965 statistics describing various populations.

TABLE 10·1

REPRESENTATIVE ENROLLMENT FIGURES ON RETARDED
SCHOOLCHILDREN

	National	State	Private Catholic	Other
Day facilities	393,430[a]	12,735[b] 34,159[e]	3,715[d]	
Residential	————	10,935[c*]	3,313[d]	38,640[a]

*This figure represents the use of the term *state school* and has no automatic connotation of ages 6-16.

The data in this table were abstracted from the following sources available in 1965.

[a] U.S. Department of Health, Education, and Welfare (61).
[b] Office of the State Superintendent of Instruction, Springfield, Ill. (69).
[c] State Department of Mental Health, Springfield, Ill. (93).
[d] National Catholic Educational Association (10).
[e] New York Times, (78).

It will be seen from the entries in Table 10·1 that a great deal of development has occurred in recent years, culminating in the present enrollments. By far the greatest enrollment lies in the services provided by public schools. Services offered by Catholic schools are not as well developed, for various financial reasons; but they exist, and they provide invaluable service when taken in conjunction with Protestant and Jewish programs throughout the country.

THEORETICAL PROBLEMS I

Perhaps the major theoretical issue in any consideration of education whether for the gifted or for the retarded is the problem of what the outcomes should be. There is a means-and-ends issue in every type of education, with the ends too frequently playing a minor role. Viewed dispassionately, such controversial terms as *segregation* and *integration* or *manual curricula* and *academic curricula* have meaning only when considered in light of their different purposes. Thus, classroom procedures for the retarded do not stand or fall alone but acquire basic justification when considered as ways of reaching objectives.

It is justifiable to raise the question "What is education?" The last decade has seen many programs for trainable retarded children develop where none had previously existed. The children had always been there, parents had always paid school taxes, but "education" as a social institution had not considered the seriously retarded youngster. The word *education* meant something academic and was interpreted to exclude children whose rate of intellectual growth was below a quotient of .50.

The basic answer to the question "What is education?"—at least in the 1960's—has not really changed. Rather, we have seen an extension of services to all youngsters, with the acceptance of a seriously limited capacity for academic work as the lower limit of eligibility (27). In many instances the argument is advanced that one cannot define a child as ineducable until he has manifestly failed to profit from instruction. This line of reasoning, however open to question, has generally been supported by the ethic of the society which argues that everyone should have his chance at a modicum of schooling.

At a slightly less hazy level there is the pressing question of setting up goals of instruction. A more pedestrian way of considering this issue is to ask what we want the child to get out of schooling, be he educable or trainable. It is by answering this question that we obtain a criterion to measure programs by, one which enables us to decide whether, in fact, schooling is successful.

Consider for a moment how goals of education for the intellectually inadequate may be derived. There is the *a priori* consideration, for example: It may be cogently argued that every human being has a mind and that training, in the widest sense, is the way to develop that mind. Parochial-school programs for the retarded accept this idea. This position does not seek justification in terms of community benefit or political heritage but in terms of the inherent attributes of any human being.

A widely held point of view derives the goals of the educational enterprise largely on a deductive basis from the political-ethical values of the society. From this point of view, the mentally inadequate are no less members of the community. If the collective citizenry are to be educated, so is every individual, even if he has limited ability to learn.

A further position is paradoxically weaker and stronger than the other two arguments. Weak on logic, it is strong on conviction and has recently accounted for most programming for trainables. This argument accepts a *quid pro quo:* if the parent pays taxes to support the commonwealth, he has a corresponding claim to services. The weaknesses lie in the relativity of claims and in setting aside any demands based on an inherent, if limited, ability to learn. The strength lies in the political embarrassment the argument can produce and in the zeal it has created in the minds of its supporters.

In this discussion we accept the common goals regardless of the special nature of their deviation. This is not to say that all three bases of formulating goals are equally appealing. The author accepts certain *a priori* considerations as the basis for determining the goals of education for all, be they retarded or gifted. Attention is called to this matter, since discussions of values and goals in education are often attenuated by accepting all ethical systems as equally cogent.

Another factor leading to attenuation of discussions of objectives is a widespread aversion to honest differences of opinion. A given in educational circles is the idea that discussion must end with resolution of differences on basic issues. In fact, conciliation may be at the price of principle, since there exist basic and important differences about education and special education in particular. Intellectual tolerance does not hinge on agreement about answers but on acceptance of the questions as important. From that premise irreconcilable answers can flow; tolerance lies in accommodation to other people's responses to the questions of *why* we should organize classes, *how* we know if they are useful or useless, and *when* they have made their optimal contribution to children's welfare.

An application of these ideas probably lies ahead of us, since method in special education seems about to take a historic step. Briefly, we may expect to see divergent approaches to instruction as some, but not all, programs move from the impasse created by the decline of general methods of instruction sixty years ago to a really viable alternative. Something, probably best described as clinical method, will emerge, not based on the paradigm of elementary education, but on the unique processes of teaching the retarded.

We may now consider instructional goals once more, paying attention to the level at which they are to be phrased. Since they are criteria to guide evaluation, goals should be concrete. As Stevens has pointed out, they are often far from that (85). Perhaps the most expeditious approach would be to define the goals for the education of the retarded *operationally*. This means that whatever term or concept is formulated is accompanied by a coordinating definition in the form of a concrete operation. Thus, to be honest is to pay one's taxes and to observe a long list of caveats. Whether a retarded adolescent is in fact honest means does he cheat, or does he pay his debts, for example.

A remaining issue is the scope of goals for the retarded youngster's education. Shall they be immediate and life-centered, which is to say that they concern *his* life; or shall they be cosmic and inspirational, which means that they really refer more to the teacher and indicate the teacher's commitment to all manner of value systems and ideals? General education often holds to the latter. The Educational Policies Commission has raised a number of wholly laudable considerations, but they have no necessary operational counterpart in the classroom for retarded youngsters, except as we deduce a set of axioms for immediate consideration (18, 21).

Alternative sets of goals have been offered by many school systems (1, 2, 3, 13). The following commonalities emerge in the many contemporary statements of educational goals for the retarded.

1. *The Schools and the Society.* There is wide acceptance of the idea that the curriculum of the schools has ends which relate to society. In some instances, formulations of goals may make societal considerations virtually the only goals. In previous generations societal issues were considered relevant only as they indicated trades and skills for the non-academic pupil. The mentally retarded pupil is currently regarded as a person who should be educated to play a role in the society. This may be a modest role, but we no longer consider schooling a mechanism to segregate the intellectually inadequate from the community.

2. *The Mentally Retarded and the Tool Subjects.* The vast majority of the mentally retarded can learn. What they should learn is no longer limited to purely manual skills and sense training. It is the rare program that does not try to develop some of the simple academic tools. Reading and number skills can be taught if suitable attention is paid

to readiness. The achievement may not be high, and it may be that we underestimate what can be acquired in the special classroom (11, 42).

3. *The Mentally Retarded and Economic and Social Independence.* There has been increasing acceptance in recent years of the fact that society spends money on the retarded whether it realizes it or not. In view of this fact, the question arises whether money spent on institutional care and on such indirect services as public welfare and aid to dependent children might be profitably spent in attempts to make at least some of the retarded less dependent and more economically self-sufficient. Most statements of goals now list basic economic skills and social competence as desirable. Such has been the acceptance of this idea that curriculum materials have emerged which make vocational consideration the matrix within which to teach the basic skills (75).

4. *Mental Retardation and Health.* The need to improve the physical hygiene of the mentally retarded youngster is apparent. Many such youngsters live in poorer sections of cities and reflect in their own lives the family standards which they have been used to. In this regard it is interesting to note the extent to which teachers' acceptance of responsibility for hygiene may surpass even the theoretical statements of intent. Many teachers of the retarded take a responsibility for the grooming of their adolescents, which reflects their personal dedication.

In recent years mental hygiene has been recognized as important for the retarded. It is no exaggeration to say that neuroses often accompany mental retardation. The personal problems of the retarded are often grounded in the reality problems precipitated by their limitations. Chapter 9 contains a discussion of the role of psychotherapy in helping the retarded solve their problems and acquire insight.

THEORETICAL PROBLEMS II

Having considered the goals of education at a conceptual level, we may now consider them at an operational level. We shall do so by considering various dimensions of the problem: first, the ability of the learner; second, the age of the child; and third, the area of instruction. Implicit in this schema is a child-centered point of view. Whatever the goals of the curriculum, they should be arranged around the child rather than the material to be acquired. The act of learning is itself best understood as a change in behavior rather than a disposition of the knowledge.

The Ability of the Learner

The intellectual ability of retarded youngsters, like that of the overall population, is distributed along a continuum. The alternative would be to consider retarded children's abilities as arranged in discrete groups. By definition, the retarded are usually below IQ 70 and go down as far as psychometric constructs permit. There are no sharp changes and the levels of difference are not immediately and closely discernible. As one considers children in the IQ 50+ range and then drops to lower IQ's, the transitions are subtle and not clear-cut.

Unfortunately, psycho-educational terms in vogue are not equally subtle. In a remarkable oversimplification of the matter, people often use the terms *educable* and *trainable* and feel that two quite different groups are involved. As another example of the hazards in using IQ concepts too often, IQ 50 is used to separate children as educable or trainable. The errors are two: first, the assumption that an IQ has immediate and clear instructional correlates; and second, the assumption that educability and trainability as operational constructs or ideas are quite different. In fact, IQ is related to classroom performance approximately, and the terms *educable* and *trainable* are broad and quite complementary. The result is that educational goals cannot be formulated in distinctive ways for the "totally trainable" or the "totally educable" since such classes of performance rarely exist in the children. The children show intra-individual differences of a wide sort.

What one can say is that there are some skills that higher-level children and *some* lower-level youngsters can acquire and that there are other goals that may be reached by indirect learning in brighter retardates but which must be approached directly in those at the lower end of the continuum. The goals, so considered, are not appropriate to discrete groups of children but exist at varying levels of probability for all retarded youngsters, if not for *all* youngsters.

A relevant inquiry by Rychlak and Wade consisted of sending a questionnaire to members of the American Association on Mental Deficiency (79). The respondents showed consistency in assigning meaning to the term *educable* but were inconsistent in their use of *trainable*. The investigators felt that connotations distinguishing one term from the other were largely "socio-cultural" (79, p. 74) and were exemplified by exceptions of higher performance on behavior dimensions such as self-control.

The Age of the Child

As one may set up development tasks for normal youngsters, so an approximation of those tasks may be made for the retarded. The correlation of specific goals and specific children cannot be formulated except in light of a given case.

This much seems certain: the pre-school period in the life of a retarded child will not bring him to the same state of development as other youngsters. Successful passage of the first five years will consist of learning the skills of the first three years for some children and, for more severe cases, of learning the skills of the first two years. The specific skills are the matters of toilet training, self-feeding, walking, talking, and play.

The next five years present the non-handicapped child with developmental tasks that are largely instructional. The retarded youngsters of various degrees will spend part or all of this period developing good speech, acquiring some degree of independence, sharpening up sensory acuities, and developing motor skills. The slower children will require all this period; high-grade or border-line retarded children will require a period up to age eight to develop these skills. By age eight they may be ready for introduction to the tool subjects. The remaining two years can be profitably spent on the introduction of simple educational material and the development of good and appropriate self-concepts.

Perhaps the years ten to sixteen show the greatest differences. The slowest children will be in need of continued speech help, and their interest and attention will be short-lived. Such young people usually require programming beyond the usual school-leaving age, and legislation usually permits programs to be run up to age twenty-one. If an attempt at academic learning is to be made with the more seriously retarded, it has its greatest chance during the period up to age sixteen. Beyond that age most retardates have little interest in schooling.

Less severely retarded young people in the years ten to sixteen may acquire increasing facility with the elements of reading, the tool subjects, and the social studies. Occupational considerations and vocational planning are serious issues for the adolescent retardate. In many ways the mildly retarded adolescent resembles brighter youngsters. Discovery of the other sex, the personal problems of adolescence with limited ability to cope with them, and adjustments to physical changes emerge as serious issues. All of these present developmental tasks which are a function of the young retarded individual's steady progress toward adulthood, if not maturity.

Areas of Instruction

To reiterate a basic consideration, the differences in programming for the various degrees of retardation are best comprehended as matters of (a) direct or indirect learning and (b) levels of probability that a given area of instruction is relevant. Thus the brighter retardate will pick up more learning *incidentally* while the slower child must be taught the same matters *deliberately;* the relevance of an area of instruction such as occupational information is probably greater for the brighter than the slower.

1. *Language.* This is an important area for the retarded. Examples of concrete-operational objectives are (a) developing good articulation; (b) developing skill at reading simple material; (c) learning to listen carefully; (d) learning to write one's name; (e) learning to read and fill out an application form; (f) learning to recognize simple signs such as *stop, danger, no left turn, exit,* etc.; (g) learning to express thoughts and ideas.

These are varied items at different levels. They illustrate some of the concrete objectives that can be aimed for at various levels of instruction with various groups of children.

2. *Number.* The retarded need various concepts of a spatial-numerical sort. Some of the specific items are (a) acquiring concepts of size; (b) acquiring concepts of shape; (c) learning ordinal numbers; (d) acquiring concepts of addition, etc.; (e) developing skill at measurement; (f) learning to count one's weekly wages; (g) learning to make a simple budget; (h) learning to make change.

3. *Interaction.* The following items refer to interpersonal interaction: (a) learning to play with others; (b) learning to share; (c) learning to communicate; (d) acquiring norms of behavior; (e) learning to inhibit inappropriate behavior; (f) acquiring courtesy and respect for others; (g) learning to cooperate.

4. *Health and Safety.* The following indicate the range of specific skills that may be relevant: (a) learning to cross roads carefully; (b) learning to travel by bus; (c) learning to identify sources of danger; (d) learning to swim; (e) learning elementary nutrition; (f) learning how to buy food wisely; (c) learning to bathe a baby.

5. *Social and Societal Living.* All children need to learn how to live effectively and pleasantly vis-à-vis their normal associates. They need to learn (a) to respect property rights; (b) to be honest; (c) to help one another; (d) how to vote; (e) to play games; (f) occupational skills; (g) to travel by bus.

All of these items have been arranged to illustrate the range of abstraction and performance that retardates can learn to some degree, some more than others. Depending upon age and degree of intelligence, these items will be more or less relevant and may be acquired directly or indirectly.

APPLIED CONSIDERATIONS

Selection of Pupils

The education of children is basically the responsibility of their parents; however, because of the realities of life in an industrial age, it is necessary to adopt some less informal method of instruction than home teaching to obtain the best instruction for each youngster. The answer to the problem has been the development of schools and the social complex of education. The technique of instruction is generally that one teacher instructs several children who are variously identified as groups and the aggregates of groups. These we call classes.

Once we concede that the most expeditious instruction is for one adult to teach several youngsters, the problem arises of how one determines the membership in a group. Even today, with more knowledge than ever, we generally admit children to school by the singularly insensitive standard of chronological age. Society has absorbed this principle; and most parents feel that a child, their child, will start to school at the age of six and will promptly start to learn.

The reality that teachers face is quite different. Some of the youngsters will have been ready to learn for some time; others, particularly those considered in this chapter, may not be ready for a few years. Clearly, some principle of organization is necessary to put the ready with the ready.

The implication of this statement is clearly that we will also put the unready together. The problem remains, however, of deciding what characteristics in children can be related to learning aptitude. Obviously, birthdate is only faintly connected with this aptitude; to study the children's life ages will not do.

The concept of mental age is probably better than many other indices of development. Its utility has been somewhat overstated, but it has its merits (66). Perhaps the value lies in the fact that a mental age (MA) is an absolute measure of intellectual height. It tells us how tall a child stands intellectually at a given time. On this basis it may be profitable to put children of comparable mental ages together. There is a stipulation, however, that they be of roughly the same life age (CA).

According to this system, children who are between five and eight years of age, with mental ages as low as three or four and as high as six or seven, may be grouped together in a primary unit.

A slightly higher unit may contain children between eight and thirteen years of age whose mental ages are about six to ten. A secondary group usually has youngsters to age sixteen. In many cases they leave school at sixteen, and permissive regulations which allow for schooling to eighteen or older may go unheeded.

Two things should be kept in mind in considering these groupings. First, these are not prescriptive groupings. Only when there are large populations to draw on can one establish consistent limits. Even then, effective special-education programs make decisions on the basis of individual case studies. An equally cogent consideration is that the CA and MA limits given are approximations. Such ranges might be found in some classes for educables. Children with less potential for growth might fit these CA limits, but they would have proportionately lower levels of mental maturity (MA).

Up to this point the term IQ has not entered the picture. The reason is that it is less relevant. By way of explanation, recall the comment about the MA as an *absolute* measure of intellectual height. The MA may not be precise, since it is subject to the errors of measurement, but it is a good approximation.

The IQ is a purely relative index and affords no basis for comparisons between children unless they have the same chronological age. Its relativity is to factors *within* any given child, and it indicates the *velocity* of growth but not the height. At the level of computation one derives an IQ by putting MA over CA (MA/CA) for each child. Thus, the concept is discrete and applies to a given child. In a few instances a radically different approach, the deviation IQ, may be used. Any current text on measurement will discuss this issue more fully and more appropriately.

The selection of children for special-class membership is best performed by using several considerations in addition to the measurement of intellect. Social development is relevant and is fairly easy to assess using the *Vineland Scale of Social Maturity* (29). Social maturity is often ahead of intellectual maturity. There are, of course, several ways in which the various forms of maturity may relate to each other.

Were it possible, measures of motivation would help in the selection of special class candidates. There is usually a lower level of achievement motivation in the retarded which is not accounted for by their level of intellect (42). Additional complications are that motivation is not easy to measure, nor are our techniques very sensitive at this point. We may reasonably expect greater precision in measuring motivation as time goes by.

Of the many issues that enter into the selection of children for special programs, we may consider the presence of other handicaps. Intellect, social development, and motivation are uniquely combined in any given child. Convulsive disorders and their impact have implications too. At the risk of anticipating an issue to be approached soon, it may be pointed out that the placement of a retarded child with convulsions has implications for the teacher and for the other children, as well as the afflicted child.

A matter requiring attention is that selection should include consideration of a manifest defect. In other words, a poor performance in important areas of living must be evident. By itself it may mean little. Thus, a poor reader may or may not be retarded; probably not. But, however low his IQ-test score, a school child should be manifestly a low achiever also.

Since the achievement lag in poor students increases as they grow older, few absolute statements about achievement deficit may be made. To prevent the entire issue from evaporating in a haze of relative statements, it might be well to do the following. (1) Avoid decisions about all but the clearly retarded until age eight. (2) Require a minimum achievement lag of two years at age nine or ten. (3) Stipulate that eligibility for special classes be determined by psychometrists but also by educational specialists who can efficiently measure educational performance.

Jolles has suggested a three-step process which has worked effectively in Illinois and which has involved careful procedures by a number of specialists (40). The steps consist of analyzing classroom data to detect pupils whose performances are below expectation, administering group and individual scales of intelligence, and then using direct teacher nomination as a third step.

It is apparent that the selection of children for special classes cannot be accomplished by administrative fiat or by legislative prescription. What is needed is the formulation of general principles of placement covering chronological age, mental age, achievement lag, and multiple disabilities.

The application of these principles must be flexible and should take into account the nature of the children to be considered. A sensitive respect for the individuality of children is the guide to placing retarded children in the best setting.

The Course of Study

In considering the course of study we come close to issues whose detailed presentation requires many chapters rather than one. There are several references to which the reader may be profitably directed in order to correlate this issue-centered presentation with the complex realities of day-by-day, hour-by-hour, classroom practice. The following references listed in the bibliography will prove valuable; they are also representative works. The reader is advised to consult the following references: (1, 2, 3, 4, 50, 80).

We may now consider the heart of the problem of education—the daily program in the classroom. Apart from the direction imposed by the limits of ability in the children and by their age, there are variations in curricular emphasis within each level of programming.

There is, first of all, the classroom in which the emphasis is on crafts, to the detriment of other items in the curriculum. Some people refer to this as the "basket-weaving" or "pot-holder" emphasis. In this sort of program the teacher concentrates on work which has a rewarding value for the children and which is appealing to visitors. In many ways this is a descendant of the manual-arts approach of fifty years ago that was based on a fallacious theory of compensation. This doctrine originally held that those incapable of abstract work—head work— were capable of handwork. The fact is, of course, that no such compensation occurs.

A second type of classroom is governed by the notion that vocational adjustment is largely dependent on social adjustment, which is further defined as etiquette. In this classroom the children may spend an inordinate amount of time on manners and on activities such as dancing. In this case the children are happy and enjoy themselves but may learn little.

Still another option is to say that no real deviation from the orthodox school curriculum is necessary. The same emphasis on language and abstract issues is maintained, and the pupil struggles with the regular subjects. This has been too much the norm and is exactly what transpires when school systems provide few facilities for special education.

Perhaps the best balance would be to see that the activities of the classroom are continuous with the activities of other habilitation agencies. Under this orientation the objective is effective living. The implications for daily activities are numerous. First, the goals are different: the pupil should be acquiring skills and knowledge that have an instrumental value. Secondly, the degree of application is no less intense, but the goals are pursued more flexibly. For example, more but shorter periods in the day are devoted to skill subjects such as reading. Finally, the teacher's role shifts from that of transmitting information to that of manipulating the learning situation to produce learning of (a) instrumental skills such as sight reading, (b) concepts of role and self-respect, and (c) items of knowledge that normal children pick up alone, such as name, address, and elementary hygiene.

The day's program, then, differs in purpose, in emphasis, but not in degree of application. This statement is perhaps overly optimistic when one considers the oral language training of another group of children, the auditorally handicapped. There are few areas of instruction where the degree of concentration is as great as with the deaf and hard-of-hearing. A sense of urgency is given by the knowledge that as the years pass the child with hearing disorders becomes more in need of language. The hearing disorder is of a different kind but it would be an exercise in biases to say that it is worse than another disorder. At the point of programming, the retarded child often does not have as purposefully structured a program as the youngster with hearing losses.

Early Childhood Programming

The activities of the pre-school program seem to be fairly well agreed upon (5, 30, 36, 39, 45, 53, 91, 101, 108). They may be grouped as follows.

1. *Language Development.* The child engages in activities that develop receptive and expressive language skills. Listening to simple stories, hearing records, and engaging in auditory discrimination exercises such as identifying sounds, following direction, and playing rhythm games are all appropriate activities. All of these activities develop receptive language skills. The utility of receptive skills is that they provide a basis for developing expressive language skills.

Expressive language activity depends on the need to express. Following auditory stimulation, some attention to articulatory disorders is appropriate. Formal articulation drills are not profitable without an appropriate mental level, experience level, or the requisite background of stimulation. Activities such as sharing experiences, learning games, communicating requests, and reciting simple poems and nursery rhymes are appropriate.

Placing language first is important. To a very great extent, language is both the vehicle and the content of instruction. The result is that the child's later achievement is contingent on previous language training, apart from the implicit problem of ability. Generally speaking, early language training also produces other desirable effects such as increased sociability and better adjustment.

2. *Divergent Thinking.* It is important that children use whatever ability they possess. To that end story-telling and other controlled phantasy material is important. Much creative imagination can be developed by art work; children's finger painting can be a stimulation to developing imagination. The other activities that stimulate thinking, such as cutting designs and using more advanced materials, will be appropriate as the children seem ready for them.

Both Tisdall (96) and Rouse (77) have introduced relevant ideas into experiences for retarded children, indicating that standard measures of cognitive divergence and brainstorming are helpful concepts. Presumably, early experience helps shape cognitive style, together with the constitutional factors (amino-acids) alluded to in Chapter 8. Educational experiences undoubtedly had contributed to Tisdall's finding of greater divergence on verbal measures for retarded children given special class training (96). Rouse's work dealt with brainstorming, the act of producing strategies for problem-solving while suspending evaluation (77). She found that her attempts to produce ideational fluency through specific activities produced scores on two tests of divergent thinking which were higher than those in a matched control group of retarded children. There is every reason to think that programmed activities for divergent thinking can be introduced into the early experience of children.

3. *Motor Activity.* All young children need to dance and play. In many young retarded children motor skills are restricted, and activities such as hopping and skipping may be quite demanding. The precise motor skills, holding a pen, grasping scissors, folding paper, and the rest, may also be quite hard for very young children. In some children multiple handicaps may make motor activity the salient feature of the program (108).

4. *Social and Personal Development.* The pre-school retarded child may be quite like other youngsters at age two or three. Social development is likely to consist of some isolated activity, some parallel activity, and, hopefully, some sociable activity. The social development of young retarded children is helped by all manner of group experiences centered around language activities and motor activities.

The child achieves personal development as he participates in daily classroom routines, such as hanging up clothes, interacts with the teacher, plays with other children, and enjoys some concrete experiences of success. Not the least important factor in the child's personal development may be the teacher's implicit attitude towards independence, an issue to be considered a little later.

5. *Experimental Background.* It has been pointed out that one way to distinguish between the levels of maturity in retarded youngsters is to note the probability that an item of behavior can be acquired and the probability of its being acquired incidentally or deliberately.

Normal pre-school youngsters "pick up" many items of experience incidentally, but it does not follow that the young retarded child exposed to an experience will also profit from it. The experience background in young retardates must be taught directly, meaning that the whole universe of a young child's experience is appropriate activity for the young retarded. Currently, McCarthy and Friedlander are pursuing this idea in their attempts to program sensory experience for infants at the Wisconsin residential facility in Madison (57). Analogous work has been described by Blatt, who has extended the work of Omar K. Moore to include pre-school familial retardates (6).

Such activities as keeping pets, naming common objects, seeing such things as pictures from magazines, visiting other classrooms, and taking field trips around the community are also valuable experiences. Such simple sensory skills as distinguishing and naming colors, sorting shapes, matching objects and sorting families of items are also useful. Memory games may also be played with the same materials.

6. *Work Habits.* Within the limits set by ability, mentally retarded children can learn to follow directions, to persist rather than succumb to immediate failure, to evaluate performance, to work rather than daydream, and to pay attention when being addressed.

7. *Recreation Skills.* People are often surprised to learn that some children do not know how to play. In many young retarded children there may be no awareness of what to do with toys. A more advanced pre-schooler may move purposefully and intently into manipulative and phantasy play with the same objects.

A relatively passive form of recreation for the young retarded is watching TV. Unfortunately, while TV keeps the retarded child occupied, it does not have to compete for his attention as it does with normal youngsters. Retarded youngsters need to spend their recreational time in some active pursuits, and in some cases these need to be taught directly.

8. *Parent Help.* The pre-school program should help the parent and the child. This help may take the form of parent-counseling and parent help. Most parents lack information, and the attempt to transmit information to them may be most practical. Apart from any dynamic considerations, such obvious problems as the academic future of a child and the desirability of residential placement require attention (*84*). At a more immediate level, questions such as toilet training, discipline, and family tensions may provide a full agenda.

9. *Developmental Diagnosis.* In Chapter 6 attention was called to the problems of diagnosis. Whatever problems exist implicitly when one tries to differentiate the many disorders in children are aggravated when children are small. Among other complications problems in speech may render communication very difficult. A pre-school experience can make a major contribution by creating an opportunity for detailed, sustained observation. The result is that what may not be clear in a diagnostic setting may emerge over a period of time.

Middle-Childhood Programming

The kinds of activities undertaken by pre-school retarded children tend to have the same general charcter for all but the most severely limited. There is a great deal of similarity in the activities for most with obvious modifications for the various degrees and rates of maturation in the children.

As the children enter the middle childhood years, some differentiation in daily activity is discernible. This is based on the extent to which children seem to have the potential to move towards some degree of independent living.

This raises the problem of how far down the distribution of ability one can go and still expect progress. Riese found that a girl with an IQ of 41 was able to develop some academic skills beginning late in the middle childhood years (74). Goldstein has suggested that the relevant data for deciding whether progress is possible can be found in the areas of motor ability, social behavior, sensory skills, and perceptual processes (27). In this view, based on ninety-four cases, a Kuhlmann IQ of 25 is probably the lower limit of eligibility.

The Seriously Retarded. Those children who are least capable of the effort to develop academic skills but who are not totally helpless may be considered first, since their program is fairly consistent with the earlier programming. Apart from the comments which follow, the reader is directed to the accounts of programming and procedures given by Hudson (34) and by Hall, Francey, and Girvin (31).

Daily activities are much the same as in earlier years and are those activities which produce a tractable child, a happy child. These activities encourage language growth through listening to records, singing, sharing, reciting poems, and the other activities that stimulate the urge to communicate.

A program for school-age children who are moderately retarded usually attempts to teach some recreational skills. The day's activities may include some play with bicycles and swings and balls, the purpose being to instruct some children in the ways that one can play with these pieces of equipment.

Play activities of a less gross motor form include drawing in pencil, chalk, and paint. Block building and the use of what are sold as "educational toys" are also valuable daily activities.

For the most part, health and personal habits are taught informally in the incidents of eating, drinking, and toileting. The informality is in the method of approach rather than in the teacher's mind. One of the hardest tasks in teaching is to impart an air of spontaneity to what has been planned and considered quite deliberately.

Lessons in social development are partially by-products of other well-planned activities in the day's program. For example, a rhythm-band experience is ostensibly in the area of music, but it can help children achieve some skill in relating to social groups and in working and cooperating with others. Teaching the children to inhibit bursts of

anger and to conform to adults' wishes is also best handled incidentally
(25). The alternative would be to try to lecture on the subject, and this
has the obvious weakness of trying to approach didactically what can
only be acquired experientially.

Occasionally, individual children may be ready for some instruction
of a modestly academic sort. For example, a number concept may be
introduced through the day's activities. The specific content is not
arithmetic—subtraction and addition—but concepts of size and relativity—big and little, bigger and smaller, near and far, a few, a lot, and
so forth. In each case the concepts are presented concretely as the children play games with small objects that can be counted and grasped
easily.

Reading is a visual discriminatory task to be viewed in a context of the
language arts and the child's background of experience. Not all reading
is impossible during the middle childhood years. The child who can
learn a minimum can recognize some simple words and signs that mean
danger. LaValli and Runge pointed out that most common signs are not
hard to understand, that many of them are within the grasp of retarded
children (52). The distinctive shape of most signs is an additional clue
for their meaning.

A program for the non-academic child can usually incorporate some
daily activity of a deliberately cognitive sort. Concepts such as likeness
and difference are useful if not too difficult. Games of visual memory are
also useful, their purpose being to maximize existing ability rather than
to develop new ability. Comparable activities in what used to be called
"sense training" can also be used, experiences that develop hearing,
recognizing, and remembering.

Excellent summaries of program development have been offered by
Hafemeister, Johnson, McCaw, and Wirtz (30, 38, 58, 105). In each case
the activities are largely functions of daily living and have an instrumental value of a fairly obvious sort. In a similar vein Rosenzweig has
discussed program organization built around the need for self-care, relating to other children, or group experiences (76).

Whatever the activities, they should be defensible in light of such
questions as:

1. Can the child do more things for himself?

2. Is he happier than he was?

3. Is he easier to live with?

4. Is his speech better?

5. Is he more coordinated than he was?

Regarding the entire problem of how one evaluates a program for the non-academic, but not helpless, child in the middle years, two observations are in order. First, evaluation must be geared to slow progress. We do not ask the questions listed above every day. Second, the evaluation must be solely in terms of previously set goals. The goals come first, and the questions are asked to measure progress towards those goals.

Ginglend has given some useful ways to evaluate progress in trainable children by asking questions about mental health, language, and social development (24). Weiner has developed an eighty-item checklist for children having a mental age below six years (99).

In considering what can be accomplished when children are seriously limited, Neuhaus has pointed to several areas of growth in children below MA two years and six months (68). All were between seven and ten years of age and below IQ 30.

The Mildly Retarded. Important distinctions between the seriously retarded and the mildly retarded are that (1) there are more of the mildly retarded and (2) the mildly retarded are capable of moving toward some degree of independent living. The vehicle for the growth of this large group is a curriculum which has some of the skills needed for partial or fully independent living in an industrial society.

The curriculum has obvious instrumental values. It is not the same as the curriculum for the non-academic, nor is it the regular curriculum. It is rather a different curriculum intended to equip the child with those skills needed to make a living and to become an effective human being.

Garrison has suggested that four areas of activity may be appropriate: (1) physical and mental health, (2) homebuilding, (3) societal relations, and (4) occupational information (23).

The state of Illinois has approached the problem by identifying ten "life functions": citizenship, communicating, home and family, leisure time, management of materials and money, occupational adequacy, physical and mental health, safety, social adjustment, and travel (2).

Other sources of theoretical statements, for example the U. S. Office of Education's 1960 paper on education and the mentally retarded, gives much the same analysis (103).

A further analysis has yielded seven "areas of knowledge." These areas are arithmetic, fine arts, language arts, physical education, practical arts, science, and social relationships. These areas of knowledge are largely agreed upon and are found in curriculum guides (4, 13).

In considering these points it is apparent that several of the terms are applicable to the education of normal children. The difference is that the areas of knowlege are drawn upon in a specialized way. For example, consideration of the language-arts area of knowledge for normal children sets up some ambitious goals (92). In the case of the retarded the intent is to produce (1) less advanced readers, (2) less generalized skill in the language arts, and (3) competence in the more instrumental use of language. The instrumental use of language suggests a specialized vocabulary (8, 28) and a more utilitarian context to supply meaning (75), a consideration indicated by the work of Dunn (17).

Methods of Instruction

It is generally agreed that education is a conservative enterprise, to which change comes slowly. With a fair degree of frequency, innovations appear, but their freshness is often more a matter of technological change than one of unprecedented tactics. Historically, instructional method achieved systematic form with the Madras technique in the early nineteenth century. Unlike an early innovation, the *Ratio Studiorum* of the sixteenth century, the Madras technique was readily adaptable to large-scale instruction. Based on a multiplier concept, a monitor was instructed in sufficient detail to impart knowledge to his fellow pupils. The method was cheap and it provided a limited degree of instruction for a large number of children. By the end of the nineteenth century, the Herbartian system had evolved and spread around the world. Its demise close to the end of the nineteenth century came more at the hands of its friends and their excesses than from its opponents or its inherent limitations. With the decline of this last great attempt at generalized theory of instruction there came a hiatus in pedagogy which has persisted to this day, interrupted by spasms of activity known to us as the "child study" and "object-teaching" movements; instruction remained untroubled by anything less frail than John Dewey's commentaries. In recent years, TV teaching and programmed learning have appeared, but only the latter has received much attention. Programmed learning is expensive, and it seems unlikely that it will be widely used in special education, a comparatively expensive enterprise in any circumstances.

Recent work at the Universities of Illinois and Wisconsin on psycholinguistics has provided the basis for a radical innovation in the theory and practice of special education. The hiatus in systematic pedagogy noted in an earlier paragraph may well be ended if the psycholinguistic movement extends from special to elementary education. In Chapter 6, "Psychodiagnostics," there was an account of the *Illinois Test of Psycholinguistic Abilities*. That instrument allows educators to describe specific strengths and weaknesses and to build the tactics of instruction on clinical description of children's performance, rather than on the strategies of presentation. The latter accepts as given the following points (1) consistency of cognitive style in children, and (2) homogeneity of modality style. From these two premises, method has emerged as tactical procedures directed at groups. The psycholinguistic movement in instruction largely rejects both points and bases tactics on the inhomogeneity of learning style and on the priority of individual learning traits over modes of presentation. By extrapolation, the elementary-education paradigm for special education may give way to the clinical model. Of course the clinical model has antecedents—for example, remedial reading and the parallel strategies of teaching language to aphasic children. However, the extension of specificity of planning based on psycholinguistic studies suggests to the author that the language portions of special curricula—content as well as the medium—may be susceptible to far greater amelioration than we have seen so far. In fact, better tactics based on sounder analysis of learning traits may well provide a compatibility of theory and practice missing since the demise of Herbartianism.

Teachers

The shortage of teachers remains one of the obstacles to expansion of special-education programs. In a fairly typical statement of need, the Western Interstate Conference on Higher Education reported in 1960 that the western states needed 8,660 teachers for the retarded children, but had only 3,132 employed (94). The number employed was highest in the case of educable children (38.2 per cent) and lowest for trainables (22.8 per cent), in relation to need. Exactly where the teachers are to come from is not clear to people who have studied the matter carefully. An analysis reported by Meyers found that teaching retarded children is not usually the ambition of students who have decided to teach (65). It seems from Meyers' account that we shall continue to find experienced teachers the prime source of instructors for retarded children. Such a pool does not necessarily consist of persons trained to teach retarded children, and willingness rather than technical competence continues to be an important consideration in recruitment.

In reflecting on the considerations mentioned so far, it is easy to arrive at a picture of personnel working in conditions of scarcity. Their morale might be high, if based on their perceived value, or low, if based on the nature of the clientele they serve. The latter consideration is a logical absurdity in a professional sense but a common reality. It is due to the frequent employment of persons whose inadequacy is attested to by incomplete certification.

Condell and Tonn administered the *Minnesota Teacher Attitude Inventory (MTAI)* to fifty-seven people in groups of approximately equal size (12). Their study indicated the highest scores were obtained by experienced elementary teachers in special classes; they were followed by experienced teachers in regular classes; and the lowest scores came from college students taking their first course in special education. Despite the hazards of concluding anything from the *MTAI*, significant differences were found, indicating that special teachers have favorable attitudes toward their jobs. Spencer's study of morale was conducted on a population of Illinois teachers who had been asked, and in other cases had volunteered, to teach retarded children (82). Analysis of 162 questionnaires revealed that volunteer teachers were less dissatisfied with physical working conditions than persons who had been asked to tend a special class. More favorable attitudes were associated with undergraduate special training and with being a woman. Sources of dissatisfaction were other teachers, parents, working conditions, and teacher training.

The last source of dissatisfaction mentioned by teachers, professional training, is a topic of considerable importance. Several issues may be indicated in this rather treacherous area—treacherous because it is open to oversimplification and to facile, if inept, observations.

A basic issue is the nature of training. Arguments for a unique pattern of undergraduate training can be advanced, and they have merit when good facilities allow special training to be grafted onto a basically sound elementary-training program. Within such a program, articulation of the professional components becomes a problem. For example, retarded children are sufficiently different that extended experiences with them are desirable. The result is a very crowded four years, or preferably, a fifth year of intern-teaching.

The fifth-year approach suggests graduate training; in many instances this has been implicitly the pattern because special-class training has been taken by licensed, experienced teachers. Its virtues are the maturity and experience of the trainees; its drawbacks have been the incidental and fragmentary nature of the actual training. Not the least problem with both graduate and undergraduate courses has been the scarcity of good teachers of teachers.

In a publication which is generally cited when discussing the issue of training, Mackie, Williams and Dunn reported that teachers felt student teaching was the vital experience, and they expressed aversion to what they considered "theory" (62). The teachers considered (1) recognition of individual differences within the special classroom, (2) development of acceptable behavior, and (3) judicious selection of reading materials the three most vital professional skills in a list of ninety-four factors they considered *important*. Six other factors centered around testing and administration they rated *less important*.

Problems in Instruction

1. *Beginning Academic Work.* A serious problem is deciding when the educable child is ready for a formal learning situation. The important elements here are the mental maturity of the child and the adequacy of his experiential background. In most children who eventually show some academic achievement, the time usually occurs no sooner than age eight. Prior to that time an extensive readiness program is suggested by most authorities (49). Failure to observe this delay usually produces a poor attitude to later learning and little actual achievement at the time.

2. *The Medium of Learning.* In view of the limits to the young educable's grasp of abstractions, it is generally suggested that learning be presented at a concrete level. For example, number is taught using objects for counting, and skills such as multiplication are postponed.

3. *The Organization of Learning.* An important issue is the way in which the elements of the curriculum are arranged and presented to the learner. Ingram has pointed out the utility of the unit method, a system which organizes some, but not all, of the work around a theme or a coordinated series of experiences (37). The more recent Illinois publications have advocated the integration of materials under a variety of topics (2). This does not mean that arithmetic skills, for example, are never taught in a pure arithmetic lesson, but it does suggest that learning can be advanced by ingenious organization of the course of study.

4. *Special Characteristics.* In considering mental retardation and education, it is usually the practice to schematize the issues by the degree of retardation and the age of the child. In some cases of mental retardation it is necessary to add another component; this is the case when the child's intellectual inadequacies are due to brain damage. The particular patterns of disability are due to damage to an originally sound nervous system.

The resultant picture has been well described by Strauss, Strauss and Kephart and by Strauss and Lehtinen (88, 89, 90). The brain-damaged child manifests disorders in many ways. Processes affected include any or all of the following: perception, reasoning, language, and behavior. As Wortis has pointed out, there are several possible combinations of disorders that may appear (107).

At the point of education the brain-injured child may show many symptoms that interfere with learning. Instruction usually involves some seeing. The brain-injured may not be able to resolve the figure-ground relation of objects on a printed page. An additional problem may be the tendency to persist in a verbal response when such activity may no longer be appropriate. A high degree of distractability may impinge on the learning process in the form of a failure to concentrate and to resist distractions in the learning environment. Sometimes the brain-injured can show a lack of inhibition that makes emotional outbursts frequent. Such difficulties can greatly affect the teacher and the other pupils and disrupt the process of instruction.

Another complication commonly encountered is the presence of multiple handicaps. Orthopedic disorders, emotional disorders, sensory disorders, and communicative disorders make instruction much more difficult and place endless demands on teachers (32, 33, 51, 97).

5. *Types of Programming.* Two problems may be mentioned here. First, there is a general shortage of schools for the retarded; and second, among the existing schools there are many types and many qualities. In some cases schooling consists of regular schooling or no schooling. There are times when a residential setting is appropriate, and it has its problems (84).

In large junior high schools which employ homogeneous sectioning of pupils, the last section by ability may well be a class for educables in everything but the essential element of programming (14). An equally aggravated situation in the technical high school arises when a scientifically minded fifteen-year-old has to compete for the attention of his teacher with uninterested, inept, and unambitious boys simply awaiting their sixteenth birthday. Fox and Parrotte have offered some suggestions for the post-sixteen group in a residential setting (22).

The Adolescent Years

As the last comment indicated, there are some special issues when the retarded reach adolescence. In the case of the educables the entire educational enterprise approaches its climax. The use of vocationally oriented subject-matter, the attempt to teach some academic skills, all hinge on whether the adolescent intends to use them.

Some issues may depend on whether we are discussing boys or girls. Specific issues for girls are the problems of homemaking and selection of appropriate occupations. Lovell has suggested that the consideration of the occupation issue might begin in the primary grades (55). To the extent that values and attitudes are formed early, this is a sound observation. In the case of boys considerable guidance may be needed to prevent behavior disturbances. It is not easy for the teacher to command the respect of lower-class boys. In many ways such boys may be potential juvenile delinquents. The good teacher in that case is the one who can command the respect of boys by acting as tough as they may feel a man should be and yet keep in mind the goals of the curriculum. There are such men, and one known to the author has run his own probation-placement-counseling service. The value of such a man to his community is inestimable.

Hungerford, DeProspo, and Rosenzweig have suggested that a curriculum might have five goals; giving the young person information needed to understand various occupations, providing suitable training and guidance, help in finding a job, and help in adjusting to the social order (35).

The utilitarian value of such an approach is obvious. Hegge has suggested that education, work, and guidance are crucial elements in the program for adolescents. He has also called attention to the advantage of preventing unnecessary failure experiences (33). A comparable problem is the need to consider the emotional problems of this period (7).

Perhaps the most comprehensive statement on the curriculum for adolescents in recent years has come from Kolstoe and Frey (50). Their ideas, based on experience and research over a period of years, suggest that the adolescent years provide a period of time sufficient for curricular experiences directed toward effective job placement. Kolstoe and Frey assert that four years of training in academic, social and vocational training can produce a high probability of effective post-school living. They believe that young people should go through three stages of experience. The first stage is prevocational training incorporating experience in a sheltered workshop and acquisition of vocational information. The second stage is job tryout or the process of exploring vocational adjustment. Last comes a period of vocational placement with supervision. At all times the programming is validated by appraisal in light of the life circumstances within which the youngsters function.

The Attainment of Curricular Goals. A practical matter is the extent to which the adolescent retardate approaching the end of his schooling has reached the goals of the curriculum. A different phrasing of the problem would ask if the expense and planning have been worthwhile. In order to answer the question it is necessary to recall an earlier statement to the effect that the goals must be carefully considered before any evaluation becomes meaningful.

The first section of the chapter outlined the range of objectives. Largely, they are academic with the deliberate addition of some non-academic issues such as personal adjustment and mental health.

The success of regular or special classes for retardates has been considered in representative studies by Jordan and de Charms (42), Cassidy and Stanton (11), and Tisdall (96). Two issues may be analyzed by these studies: academic achievement and personality outcomes in retardates exposed to special or regular classes.

1. *Academic achievement.* The Cassidy and Stanton data using the Stanford-Achievement Test reported differences at < .01 level of probability in favor of higher achievement in retardates educated in *regular* classes. The Jordan and de Charms data using a matched group of special- and regular-class retardates yield a difference in reading achievement at < .001 level of probability in favor of retardates educated in *regular* classes.

2. *Personality outcomes.* The Cassidy and Stanton study indicates altered personality outcomes for the retardates who have been exposed to the curriculum of the special class. The data are based on the California Test of Personality. The Jordan and de Charms data substantiate this finding, being based on "fear-of-failure" imagery in projective thematic material. Tisdall's data give partial support; he found significantly different scores on three verbal tests of divergent thinking, but not on non-verbal tests.

A review of the literature on the outcomes of special class instruction has been made by Sparks and Blackman (81). It reported studies by Blatt, Jordan, and others, and presented a less certain picture of the social and academic outcomes. However, as those authors pointed out in their brief but valuable paper, there continues to be a lack of evidence indicating superior achievement in children assigned to special classes.

Stein, Susser, and Lunzer examined the number of literacy skills of forty-nine Lancashire men and women between ages twenty and twenty-four (83). Those below IQ 70 who had attended special classes were significantly more literate but not more numerate. While not directed to evaluation of special classes, we may note an observation on language attainment reported by Ohlsen (70). He found an insignificant difference in ability to use abstract words between retarded youngsters in regular and special classes.

Warren has reported the level of attainment reached by trainable children after five years of schooling (98). Only eight at most out of 177 had independent reading skills. Warren felt that the case for academics in special classes for trainables was not strong.

In the case of trainable children, Wigger has reported on evaluation of a large program of classes which dealt with different issues (102). He concluded that special education was helpful, and that parents found the program valuable to both themselves and their children. In Wigger's analysis, the mental health of trainable children was a valuable clue to the effects training had on them.

It seems in conclusion that the goals of the special curricula are largely achieved. Since academic skills are not the only goal pursued, academic achievement is below potential. On the other hand, the mental-hygiene goals seem achieved and the special curricula produce high achievement in this area. Again, it must be pointed out that an evaluation depends on predetermined goals. This evaluation suggests that the commonly ascribed goals are reached and that the special classes seem to fulfill those responsibilities they are charged with.

The Non-Academic Pupil. The problems of the trainable adolescents are probably less acute, if only because these adolescents are not being moved in the direction of a great deal of community participation. One of the problems in the education of these young people is the issue of when they cease to be eligible for special-class membership. Happily, in some places two lines of development are appearing. One is the extension of eligibility for special classes to age twenty-one. The other is the development of sheltered workshops to occupy the time of these dependent human beings who would otherwise probably sit at home and vegetate.

In closing this section, we can attend to a few miscellaneous observations about special education. First is the matter of organization. The general model of operation which is used in planning programs and training teachers is urban rather than rural. Homogeneous grouping for special classes presumes fairly large school populations; only urban areas can generally accomplish this feat to a practical degree. Another aspect of organization is the failure to develop cooperative programs in areas where population is sparse. Even in rural areas planning, and indeed regulations, presume some concentration of children. Such presumptions do not stand close scrutiny outside metropolitan areas. Even there, the best programming needs to be cooperative, as in the county-wide organizations found in Baltimore and St. Louis. Finally, we should note that curriculum change in special education does not exist in a vacuum. At the time of writing, modern mathematics and foreign languages exemplify change in content of instruction. Largely unanswered is the host of questions probing the significance modern curriculum content holds for special classes. Equally pregnant is the emerging stress on new instructional media. The Elementary and Secondary Education Act of 1965 has undoubtedly shaken the fabric of presumptions underlying instruction. The implications for special education are likely to be equally great.

CONCEPTUAL ISSUES

At the beginning of this chapter it was indicated that an attempt would be made to consider the education of the retarded at a conceptual level. The *conceptual* approach is a consideration of applied problems in such terms as to permit and encourage more fruitful analysis. An example of the rare application of conceptual considerations to mental retardation is Farber's second monograph on family integration. In this paper, Farber applies the theory of games to families with retarded children (19).

The Educative Process

All teachers have some informal model of the educative process in mind, although the model may be very simple or even inadequate. By and large, the adequacy of such models is determined by the extent to which they lead to better instruction. The following are typical models.

1. *The "Bucket" Model.* One of the widely held notions about the process of instruction is that there is a quantum of information to be acquired by the student. The basic consideration is that the teacher has a great deal of information; his job is to take his "bucketful" of information and fill up the "bucket" of the learner. Instruction becomes a matter of transferring knowledge, and the teacher is the locus of the process because his "bucket" is fuller.

2. *The "Garden" Model.* Among those who educate the young there is a notion in the romantic tradition of education which goes back 200 years, that a classroom is like a garden. Diligently cultivate the garden, and the flowers grow; provide the right setting, and the children will then grow in learning.

3. *The "Love" Model.* A similar consideration is that love leads to education. Love the children, lavish affection on them, and they will love you in return. Loving you, they will perform their tasks in order to please you. Unfortunately, not all of us are, in fact, lovable.

It is clear that these models of instruction are inadequate. It is not clear what the alternative is. In many ways we have not advanced beyond Herbart, and certainly his methods are more widely used throughout the world than any others. It is equally clear that the cognitive-substantive organization which he used is not useful except at the procedural level; at that level it has considerable utility. A more extensive treatment of Herbart may be found in such works as Mayer's history of education (63).

At this point there seems to be no contemporary model of the educative process. Some prescriptions on how to construct one might be as follows.

1. *Learning is a function of many elements.* The learner does not learn *in vacuo*. The retarded child learns in a classroom; he learns when interacting with the teacher and the other children. He learns as a consequence of situational factors. A model should specify the variables which affect learning.

2. *The unit of education is the learner.* Viewed phenomenally, the learner is the locus of education. Also, even when he is a member of a group, his acquisition of learning or formation of concepts is still internal to him and therefore an individual process.

3. *Learning is a behavioral change.* Learning means a demonstrable change in the state of the learner. A model of the educative process should be grounded in the various disciplines that study human phenomena empirically.

4. *A model of the educative process should be consonant with other social processes.* The social sciences are largely behavioral in idiom. A model of the educative process should be phrased so that its continuity with other social disciplines will be clear.

5. *Teaching does not equal learning.* Unfortunately, that which children learn may not always correlate with teacher activity. Also, the learner may learn when the teacher is not teaching. Consequently, the total situation must recognize that teaching and learning are related but not entirely complementary matters.

6. *A model should have a predictive value.* Any system of thought is validated by the adequacy of predictions made from it (43).

7. *A model should be comprehensive.* The model should be applicable to all pupils and to all subjects.

The elements in the situation are items in the *teaching/learning process*. The various elements may be described as (1) those variables whose locus is the learner, (2) those variables whose locus is the teacher, and (3) those variables which arise from the behavioral dialogue of teacher and child, their *interaction*.

1. *Learner Variables.* Learner variables include the intelligence of

the child, his age, sex, ethnic group, level of motivation, previous experience, and what McDonald has called the "cognitive-attitudinal-value system" (60).

As an example of the uncertainties that need to be resolved, consider the retarded child and his retardation. How do we handle the reality of his disability as a learning issue? Largely we indicate what he cannot do. But the results of this procedure are too indefinite. What is needed is a deductive schema to relate disabilities in general to the learner. In fact, the habilitation disciplines need a taxonomy of disability. The author has struggled with the attempt to build a taxonomy but does not have the vital deductive problem, or *equivalence* problem, of disorder and instruction settled. Stevens has worked on this problem with results that are more sanguine (85).

Another uncertainty is that surrounding the learner and his personality. Education currently recognizes that the learner's personality as well as his intellect play a role in his education. Unfortunately, "personality" can be very hazy also.

On a purely speculative basis, the material in Figure 10·1 is offered. The dimensions are those of extraversion-introversion and a second continuum of polar degrees of affect. Four quadrants emerge, and each represents a possible typology. Clearly, two dimensions of personality are slim, but at this point it seems difficult to manage much more than that. A third dimension of intellect would add depth to the schema. In analyzing bright college students, Lynn has used "neuroticism" as a relevant dimension of behavior (56).

The suggestion is made that retarded children as learners in a classroom may be considered, using this schema, as (1) how they in fact behave and (2) what they should be as a result of education.

The four possibilities are (1) a hostile, extroverted learner; (2) an extroverted, loving learner; (3) an affectionate but withdrawn learner; and (4) a hostile and withdrawn learner. Certainly this is a range of types we may encounter.

On the other hand, the desired learner, the kind of person we would like to see the retarded youngster become, is best described in the upper-right-hand quadrant. This is the extroverted-affectionate type, who is the stereotype for the middle-class youngster of normal intelligence. It would not hurt to incorporate into our thinking the improbability that this will occur. Generally speaking, retarded youngsters do not grow that way, and our expectations may be elucidated by considering Figure 10·1 further.

General education usually sets its mental-hygiene goals in the upper-right quadrant. It postulates a mid-point on the imaginary dimension of

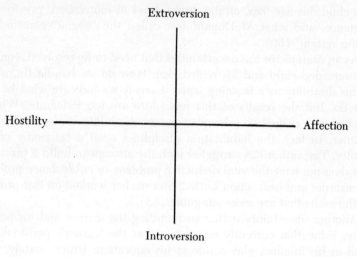

Figure 10·1

Dimensions of Personality

intellect. In reality, other sorts of configurations may be necessary for life situations. This certainly holds true for the retarded. Since by definition they are not at the same point on a continuum of intellect, we might question the wisdom of expecting the learner to become the same sort of person, or indeed the advisability of it.

The realistic goal for the retarded learner might suggest a little less extroversion and a little more hostility as acceptable elements. This is a value choice, of course, but it is important to consider carefully how the retarded learner shapes up and in what quadrant we can realistically expect him to end. The uncertainties are partially the failure to evaluate our concept of the learner critically. They also stem from the uncertainty of the crucial dimensions of behavior in a school child. This last point will be considered a little later.

2. *Teacher Variables.* In a happier time the role of the teacher was simple—to transmit knowledge. Today that role has acquired extra responsibilities, and the teacher is expected to be a psychiatrist, a social worker, a parent substitute, a social scientist. To that unenviable list we apologetically append one more and offer the role *investigator.* The problem to be investigated is the question "How do retarded children learn?"

This is in many ways a rhetorical question, since pondering the question will suffice, and no comprehensive answer is necessary at the moment. What is necessary is that the teacher become a questioning person attempting to relate substantive knowledge to instruction. The crucial steps are those of forming conclusions based on evidence and relating them to the specific teaching/learning situation. The only rule is that the teacher must question and develop new questions. All procedures are open to scrutiny, and the teacher of the retarded is very much a person relying on precedent rather than evidence. Under such circumstances the teacher needs to contribute to knowledge, as well as to consume it.

Most teachers of the retarded work alone. The result is that they have a large area of decision-making, of professional autonomy. A vital consideration in a conceptual analysis is that the teacher be justified in the exercise of professional autonomy.

This autonomy consists in the right to make crucial decisions about the teaching/learning process. The phrase itself has been coined by the eminent scholar Lieberman (54). It is based on the teacher's degree of expertise. The relevant questions here are (1) what are the bases of sound decision-making by teachers, and (2) what decisions fall under the province of the teacher's autonomy.

As for the first question, there are three bases of decision-making for the teachers of the retarded. First, formal training in the education of the young. Special education is a branch of the profession of education. Secondly, a great deal of knowledge is required about the nature of mental retardation, specifically an awareness that the condition is more than an instructional problem. Finally, skill is required in understanding the nature and conditions of learning and teaching based on an analysis of the behavior called learning.

The answer to the second question is that a teacher of the retarded is the person chosen to implement policy statements often made by non-teachers, for example school boards. Note, this is not the same as saying the teacher's job is to reach the goals of the curriculum set by the school board. It seems best to analyze the issue operationally by saying the teacher has to change theoretical statements about the learning enterprise into applied statements. To the extent that the teacher meets the three requirements described above, she should be a free agent in the determination of classroom procedures.

Other Considerations

In closing this chapter on education it is appropriate to direct the readers to some quasi-educational procedures which also merit attention. *Home training* is the name given to the program of activities which parents can initiate informally long before children are ready for school. Essentially, sensory training and discrimination can begin in the pre-school period. Discipline and moral training can do a great deal to advance the welfare of children and to provide a basis for subsequent formal instruction. *Occupational therapy* is the practice of developing good routines in craft and allied activities. Virtues claimed for this valuable enterprise are stabilization of emotions and increased cooperation (16). Some of the activities of this kind of regimen overlap those of art activities conducted in school programs (59). *Recreation* has become an organized experience for handicapped children in recent years. The value of camping and outdoor life for physically handicapped children is well known, both by impressions and by means of data-centered evaluation. It seems reasonable to believe, although without evidence, that recreation and outdoor living experiences have great value for retarded children. The opportunities for development of skills of independent living are enormous. Also, the opportunity exists to conduct explicit functions such as speech and physical therapy in an atmosphere of comparative relaxation. Oliver's work, alluded to in Chapter 9, indicates that a positive set towards tasks seems to develop when children are exposed to a program of physical conditioning. Not the least benefit is to parents of retarded children whose responsibilities are eased for a brief but blessed period of time.

SUMMARY

The education of the retarded child is a field with several characteristics. First, it tends to be a specialized case of elementary education for the most part, with differences appearing more in degree than in technique. Second, to a considerable extent the field is a practice-centered activity with neglect of conceptual analyses which permit other fields to appraise their practices from time to time. We have seen in this chapter that there are a number of conceptual issues whose clarification can be most profitable. The model of the educational practices which we hold can be made explicit, and we have examined several formulations of variables in the process of information. Attention has been called to the increasing role of occupational therapy and recreation as quasi-educational experiences for retarded children.

BIBLIOGRAPHY

1. *A Curriculum Guide for Teachers of Pupils Educable but Mentally Retarded,* Kansas City, Mo., Public Schools, Bulletin 109, 1961.
2. *A Curriculum Guide for Teachers of Trainable Mentally Handicapped Children,* State Department of Education, Springfield, Ill., 1955.

3. *A Curriculum Guide for Teachers of the Educable Mentally Handi-capped*, State Department of Education, Springfield, Ill., 1958.

4. *An Adjusted Curriculum for the Mentally Retarded*, Alton Community Unit School District 11, Alton, Ill., 1954.

5. Bindman, A. J., and Klebanoff, L. B., "A Nursery Center Program for Preschool Mentally Retarded Children," *Am. J. Ment. Def.*, 1959, 64, 561-573.

6. Blatt, B., "Effects of Responsive Environments on the Intellectual and Social Competence of Educable Mentally Retarded Children: Theoretical Considerations (1)," paper presented to the American Educational Research Association, 1962.

7. Brown, F. W., "A Psycho-Therapeutically Oriented Co-educational Program for Mentally Retarded Adolescents in a Comprehensive High School," *Ment. Hyg.*, 1955, 39, 246-270.

8. Borreca, F., Burger, R., Goldstein, I., and Simches, R., "A Functional Core Vocabulary for Slow Learners," *Am. J. Ment. Def.*, 1953, 58, 273-300.

9. Caine, L., and Levine, S., "A Study of the Effects of Community and Institutional School Classes for Trainable Mentally Retarded Children," Cooperative Research Program, U. S. Office of Education, 1961.

10. *Catholic Special Education: Concepts and Statistics*, National Catholic Education Association, 1965.

11. Cassidy, V. M., and Stanton, J. E., *An Investigation of Factors Involved in the Educational Placement of Mentally Retarded Children*, Ohio State University, 1959.

12. Condell, J. F., and Tonn, M. H., "A Comparison of MTAI Scores," *Ment. Retard.*, 1965, 3, 23-24.

13. *Curriculum Guide: The Slow Learning Child*, St. Louis Public Schools, December, 1954.

14. Dawe, A. M., "Trends Toward the Extension of Special Services for the Educable Mentally Handicapped at the Junior High School Level," *Am. J. Ment. Def.*, 1957, 61, 692-697.

15. deCharms, R., *Personal communication*, 1960.

16. Dewing, D., "Use of Occupational Therapy in the Socialization of Severely Retarded Children," *Am. J. Ment. Def.*, 1952, 57, 43-49.

17. Dunn, L. M., "A Comparison of the Reading Processes of Mentally Retarded and Normal Boys of the Same Mental Age," *Mon. Soc. Res. Ch. Dev.*, 1956, No. 58.

18. *The Purposes of Education in American Democracy*, Educational Policies Commission, N. E. A., 1938.

19. Farber, B., "Family Organization and Crisis: Maintenance of Integration in Families with a Severely Mentally Retarded Child," *Mon. Soc. Res. Ch. Dev.*, 1960, No. 75.

20. Farson, M. R., "A Program for Low Ability Children in the Regular Grade," *Am. J. Ment. Def.*, 1945, *50*, 107-114.

21. Featherstone, W. B., *Teaching the Slow Learner*, Columbia University Press, 1941.

22. Fox, W.W., Parrotte, I., "Continuation Schooling for Boys and Girls over Sixteen Years of Age in the Institutional Environment," *Am. J. Ment. Def.*, 1947, *52*, 148-152.

23. Garrison, I. K., "A Developmental School Program for Educable Mentally Handicapped," *Am. J. Ment. Def.*, 1953, *57*, 554-564.

24. Ginglend, D. R., "Some Observations on Evaluating the Progress of Severely Retarded or 'Trainable' Children in a School Program," *Am. J. Men. Def.*, 1957, *62*, 35-38.

25. Goldberg, I. I., "Current Status of Education and Training in the United States for Trainable Mentally Retarded Children," *Excep. Ch.*, 1957, *24*, 146-154.

26. Goldman, W. J., "Identification of Teaching Practices Peculiar to Special Classes of Educable Retarded Children in Selected Massachusetts Schools," *Amer. J. Ment. Def.*, 1957, *63*, 775-777.

27. Goldstein, H., "Lower Limits of Eligibility for Classes for Trainable Children," *Excep. Ch.*, 1956, *22*, 226-227.

28. Goldstein, I., and Mann, H., "An Occupational Vocabulary for Retarded Adolescents," *Am. J. Ment. Def.*, 1949, *54*, 38-72.

29. Gottsegen, M. G., "The Use of the Vineland Social Maturity Scale in the Planning of an Educational Program for Non-Institutionalized Low-Grade Mentally Deficient Children," *Genet. Psych. Mon.*, 1957, *55*, 85-137.

30. Hafemeister, N. R., "Development of a Curriculum for the Trainable Child," *Am. J. Ment. Def.*, 1951, *55*, 495-501.

31. Hall, J. G., Francey, E. and Girvin, L., "A Program for the Ineducable-Trainable Child," *Canad. J. Pub. Hlth.*, 1956, *47*, 338-394.

32. Halpin, V., "Basic Issues Concerning the Education of Children with Cerebral Defects," *Am. J. Ment. Def.*, 1958, *63*, 31-37.

33. Hegge, T. F., "Education for Mentally Retarded Pupils of Senior High School Age," *Am. J. Ment. Def.*, 1949, *54*, 190-191.

34. Hudson, M., "An Exploration of Classroom Procedures for Teaching Trainable Mentally Retarded Children," *C. E. C. Res. Mon.*, 1960, No. 2.

35. Hungerford, R. H., DeProspo, C. J., and Rosenzweig, L. E., "Education of the Mentally Handicapped in Childhood and Adolescence," *Am. J. Ment. Def.*, 1952, *57*, 214-228.

36. Ikeda, H., "Adapting the Nursery School for the Mentally Retarded Child," *Excep. Ch.*, 1955, *21*, 171-173.

37. Ingram, C., *Education of the Slow-Learning Child*, Ronald Press, 1960.

38. Johnson, G. O., *Severely Retarded Children: Report*, New York State Interdepartmental Health Resources Board, Albany, 1957.

39. _____, *Training Program for Severely Mentally Retarded Children*, New York State Interdepartmental Health Resources Board, Albany, 1958.

40. Jolles, I., "Discovering the Educable Mentally Handicapped: A Public School Screening Technique," *Am. J. Ment. Def.*, 1955, 59, 610-616.

41. Jones, E. E., and Thibaut, J. W., "Interaction Goals as Bases of Interference in Interpersonal Perception," in Tagiuri, R., and Petrullo, L., *Person Perception and Interpersonal Behavior*, Stanford University Press, 1958.

42. Jordan, T. E., and deCharms, R., "The Achievement Motive in Normal and Mentally Retarded Children," *Am. J. Ment. Def.*, 1959, 64, 457-466.

43. Kantor, J. R., "Preface to Inter-Behavioral Psychology," *Psych. Rec.*, 1942, 5, 172-93.

44. Kephart, N. C., *The Slow Learner in the Classroom*, Charles E. Merrill Books, Inc., 1960.

45. Kirk, S. A., *Early Education of the Mentally Retarded*, University of Illinois Press, 1958.

46. _____, "Experiments in the Early Training of the Mentally Retarded," *Am. J. Ment. Def.*, 1952, 56, 692-700.

47. _____, "A Project for Pre-School Mentally Handicapped Children," *Am. J. Ment. Def.*, 1950, 54, 305-310.

48. _____, *Teaching Reading to Slow-Learning Children*, Houghton Mifflin, 1940.

49. _____, and Johnson, G., *Educating the Retarded Child*, Houghton Mifflin, 1951.

50. Kolstoe, O. P., and Frey, R., *Work-Study Programs at the Secondary Level for the Mentally Subnormal*, Southern Illinois University Press, 1965.

51. Langan, W., "The Education of the Blind Mental Defective," *Am. J. Ment. Def.*, 1948, 52, 272-277.

52. LaValli, A., and Runge, L., "Teaching Slow Learners to Read Common Signs," *Excep. Ch.*, 1952, 18, 38-40.

53. Leberfeld, D. T., and Nertz, N., "A Home Training Program in Language and Speech for Mentally Retarded Children," *Am. J. Ment. Def.*, 1955, 59, 413-416.

54. Lieberman, M., *Education as a Profession*, Prentice-Hall, 1956.

55. Lovell, C., "Education-Occupational Program for Special Class Girls," *Am. J. Ment. Def.*, 1947, *51*, 452-455.

56. Lynn, R., "Two Personality Characteristics Related to Academic Achievement," *Brit. J. Educ. Psych.*, 1959, *29*, 213-216.

57. McCarthy, J. J., Personal communication, 1965.

58. McCaw, W. R., "A Curriculum for the Severely Mentally Retarded," *Am. J. Ment. Def.*, 1958, *62*, 616-621.

59. McDermott, W. H., "Art Therapy for the Severely Handicapped," *Am. J. Ment. Def.*, 1954, *59*, 231-234.

60. McDonald, F. J., *Educational Psychology*, Wadsworth, 1959.

61. Mackie, R. P., and Hunter, P. P., "Special Education Enrollments and Number of Teachers," Bureau of Educational Research and Development, U. S. Department of Health, Education, and Welfare, 1965.

62. Mackie, R. P., Williams, H., and Dunn, L. M., "Teachers of Children who are Mentally Retarded," U. S. Office of Education, 1957.

63. Mayer, F., *A History of Educational Thought*, Charles E. Merrill Books, Inc., 1960.

64. Menzel, M. Z., "Psychotherapeutic Techniques Among the Mentally Deficient: Occupational Therapy" *Am. J. Ment. Def.*, 1952, *56*, 796-802.

65. Meyers, C. E., "Realities in Teacher Recruitment," *Ment. Retard.*, 1964, *2*, 42-46.

66. Morphett, M., and Washburne, C., "When Should Children Begin to Read?" *Elem. Sch. J.*, 1931, *31*, 496-503.

67. Myklebust, H. R., "Training Aphasic Children," *Volta Rev.*, 1955, *57*, 149-157.

68. Neuhaus, E. C., "An Experimental Class for the Severely Retarded Child," *Am. J. Ment. Def.*, 1958, *63*, 419-421.

69. *Newsletter*, Illinois Council for Exceptional Children, May, 1965.

70. Ohlsen, R. L., "The Effects of Concretion and Abstraction on Vocabulary Performance of Mentally Retarded Average and Bright Children," unpublished Ph.D. dissertation, University of Kansas, 1963.

71. *One Hundred Twenty-Five Low Cost—No Cost Projects for Home, School and Hospital*, Dixon State School, Dixon, Ill. 1964.

72. Piaget, J., *Language and Thought of the Child*, Harcourt, Brace, 1926.

73. *A Program of Instruction for Elementary School Children with Retarded Mental Development*, Kansas City, Mo., Public Schools, Bulletin 107, Vol. I and II, 1959.

74. Riese, H., "Academic Work with an Eleven-Year-Old Girl with an IQ of 41," *Am. J. Ment. Def.*, 1956, *60*, 545-551.

75. *Rochester Occupational Reading Series,* Syracuse University Press.

76. Rosenzweig, L., "Report of a School Program for Trainable Mentally Retarded Children," *Am. J. Ment. Def.,* 1954, 59, 181-205.

77. Rouse, S. T., "Effects of a Training Program on the Productive Thinking of Educable Mental Retardates," *Amer. J. Ment. Def.,* 1965, *69,* 666-673.

78. Rusk, H. A., "Rehabilitation in '64—II," *New York Times,* Sunday, January 10, 1965.

79. Rychlak, J. F., and Wade, I., "American Usage of the Terms 'Educable' vs. 'Trainable' Mental Retardates," *J. Ment. Subnorm.,* 1963, 9, 70-75.

80. *The Slow Learning Program in the Elementary and Secondary Schools,* Cincinnati, Ohio, Public Schools, Bulletin 119, 1964.

81. Sparks, H. C. and Blackman, L. S., "What is Special about Special Education Revisited: The Mentally Retarded," *Excep. Child.,* 1965, *31,* 242-247.

82. Spencer, E. F., "Morale Factors Among Teachers of the Mentally Retarded," unpublished Ph.D. dissertation, University of Illinois, 1962.

83. Stein, Z., Susser, M., and Lunzer, E. A., "Reading, Reckoning, and Special Schooling Among the Mentally Handicapped," *Lancet,* 1960, 305-307.

84. Stern, E. M., "If Your Child Needs a Special School," *Parents Magazine,* 1958, *33,* 40-41.

85. Stevens, G. D., "An Analysis of the Objectives for the Education of Children with Retarded Mental Development," *Am. J. Ment. Def.,* 1958, *63,* 225-235.

86. _____, Personal communication, 1961.

87. _____, and Birch, J. W., "A Proposal for Clarification of the Terminology Used to Describe Brain-Injured Children," *Excep. Ch.,* 1959, *23,* 346-349.

88. Strauss, A. A., "The Education of the Brain-Injured Child," *Am. J. Ment. Def.,* 1952, *56,* 712-718.

89. _____, and Kephart, N. C., *Psychopathology and Education of the Brain-Injured Child,* Vol. II, Grune and Stratton, 1955.

90. Strauss, A., and Lehtinen, L., *Psychopathology and Education of the Brain-Injured Child,* Grune and Stratton, 1948.

91. Strazzulla, M., "Nursery School Training for Retarded Children," *Am. J. Ment. Def.,* 1956, *61,* 141-151.

92. Strickland, R., *The Language Arts in the Elementary School,* D. C. Heath, 1957.

93. *Supplement to Administrator's Manual,* State Department of Mental Health, Springfield, Ill., 1965.

94. "Teachers of Exceptional Children for the West," *WICHE*, Boulder, Colo., 1960.

95. Thibaut, J. W., and Kelley, H. H., *The Social Psychology of Groups*, John Wiley & Sons, 1959.

96. Tisdall, W., "The Efficacy of a Special Class Program Upon the Productive Thinking Abilities of Educable Mentally Retarded Children," unpublished Ph.D. dissertation, University of Illinois, 1962.

97. Tretakoff, M. L., and Farrell, M. J., "Developing a Curriculum for the Blind Retarded," *Am. J. Ment. Def.*, 1958, *62*, 610-615.

98. Warren, S. A., "Academic Achievement of Trainable Pupils with Five or More Years of Schooling," *Train. Sch. Bull.*, 1963, *60*, 75-88.

99. Weiner, B. B., "A Classroom Achievement Inventory for Young Mentally Retarded Boys," *Am. J. Ment. Def.*, 1949, *53*, 460-465.

100. _____, "A Report on the Final Academic Achievement of Thirty-Seven Mentally Handicapped Boys Who Had Been Enrolled in a Prolonged Pre-Academic Program," *Am. J. Ment. Def.*, 1954, *59*, 210-219.

101. _____, "The School Curriculum of the Prolonged Pre-Academic Program at the Wayne County Training School," *Am. J. Ment. Def.*, 1947, *51*, 674-679.

102. Wigger, O. L., "An Assessment of Effects of a Large County Wide, Public School Program of Special Training Classes on Trainable Retarded Children," unpublished Ph.D. dissertation, University of Southern California, 1963.

103. Williams, H. M., *The Retarded Child Goes to School*, U. S. Department of Health, Education and Welfare, 1960.

104. _____, and Wallin, J. E. W., "Education of the Severely Retarded Child," U. S. Department of Health, Education, and Welfare, 1959.

105. Wirtz, M., "The Development of Current Thinking about Facilities for the Severely Mentally Retarded," *Am. J. Ment. Def.*, 1956, *60*, 492-507.

106. Wolk, S. M., "A Survey of the Literature on Curriculum Practices for the Mentally Retarded," *Am. J. Ment. Def.*, 1958, *62*, 826-839.

107. Wortis, J. R., "A Note on the Concept of the Brain-Injured Child," *Am. J. Ment. Def.*, 1956, *61*, 204-206.

108. Yum, L. C., "The Nursery School for the Multiple Handicapped Cerebral Palsied Child," *Excep. Ch.*, 1956, *22*, 7-9.

Chapter 11

INDEPENDENT LIVING

There was a time when retardation was intimately associated with institutions; the presumption was that intellect played an initial role in adjustment and that diagnosis of retardation was grounds for commitment to residential living with no hope of a more independent and pleasant existence. The attitude was not merely held by the public, it was also held, in fact if not in theory, by residential agencies which programmed for custodial care to the virtual exclusion of alternatives.

Happily, that time is past, and we see the residential agency as only part of the milieux within which retardation can be formulated, other parts being the family and the community. This innovation has been seized upon by residential agencies, and today they generally see commitment to custodial care as a last resort. Their concern is to keep as many retarded children as possible functioning in the natural context

405

of home and community (49). The question arises, naturally, about the feasibility of this attitude and about the extent to which it is a rational course to pursue.

In this chapter we shall consider issues which arise when community living for the retarded is given serious attention. Two matters claim our attention; first there is the problem of how well retarded persons function as members of the community; the second centers on the steps we can take to optimize the probability that retarded persons can function effectively in the community.

One of the problems with mental retardation is that it is an unstable property of human beings. It is a pattern of behavior which is subject to various degrees of modification in all but the tiny fraction of severe cases. This is simply illustrated by recalling the way in which educable retarded adolescents fade from view when they leave school. Even in those instances where programming has been incomplete, educable adolescents disappear into the ranks of the semi-skilled and unskilled and are hard to distinguish from other people in the same social strata. As Saenger has documented (p. 121), even the seriously retarded have the ability to maintain many of the processes of urban living, although in a marginal way, with a modest degree of independence. When we look at the life styles of persons earlier adjudged retarded, we often find instances of striking effectiveness, and more commonly, a pattern of comparative effectiveness. Evidence has come from Scotland in the work of Ferguson and Kerr (19), who looked at the lives of 203 retarded persons, three-fourths of whom (N=159) were between IQ 60 and 79. At about twenty-five years of age, nearly a third were married (this proportion was slightly below the average), while about half or slightly fewer (N=71) had a police record of some kind. Many of them came from quite poor homes in Glasgow, and the investigators expressed "amazement" that so many of these young men and women had been successful in holding jobs under adverse conditions.

In 1962 Mrs. Ruby Jo Reeves Kennedy reported information on the retarded persons she had previously studied in 1948 (28). Fourteen years after her original study she found them living comparatively effective lives, and she was able to project her study into a second generation by studying their children. Family size was essentially the same as that of non-retarded controls, two or three children on the average. Offspring of the experimental (retarded) persons were not significantly lower in intelligence on the average, although more of the offspring of controls had IQ's above 90, and children of controls had made better academic progress. Like Peterson and Smith (42), Mrs. Kennedy found community participation in the form of voting quite reduced, but she found no difference in criminal records. More experimental subjects worked at higher occupational levels, and the proportion was higher in 1962 than in 1948. No differences emerged in job mobility and tenure, and only in speed of learning were the experimental subjects rated lower by employers. In only eight of forty-nine tests of economic adjustment were the experimental subjects statistically different from the controls. These materials are generally congruent with Dinger's 1961 investigation of 333 former special class pupils (15). Eighty-three per cent of them were employed at unskilled and semiskilled jobs which required little academic skill. Few of them were law violators, and they generally possessed desirable personal characteristics.

Altogether, Mrs. Kennedy examined seventy-three indices of social adjustment in the following five areas: family size and status, IQ's and academic progress, economic adjustment, antisocial behavior, social participation. Fifty-nine of seventy-three social factors revealed statistically insignificant differences. Mrs. Kennedy concluded that the retarded persons she investigated had made acceptable adjustment in economic, social, and personal aspects of life.

In 1965 Baller, Charles, and Miller presented a similar status report on retarded persons whose lives Baller had previously studied in 1936 (1). At mean age fifty-six years the low-ability subjects represented about 61 per cent of Baller's original group. The prime sources of sampling variation were mortality, institutionalization, and mobility. Sixty-five per cent of the males and 70 per cent of the females were engaged in "complete self-support," to use the investigators' term. The incidence of divorce was well above the national average, and the subjects were generally law-abiding, although arrests for being drunk and disorderly were not unknown. Stability generally characterized their work histories, and occupations consisted of unskilled jobs for about one-half of the males and relatively high-status jobs for a small proportion of the males. Looking to the future, the investigators wondered what effect increasing automation would have on the work careers of their subjects.

Briefly, then, there is reason to think that retarded persons are capable of relatively adequate adjustment in spite of their intellectual limitations. The success or failure they achieve depends on the attitudes, skills, and concepts they have acquired over the years (29). Those factors determine how intellectual resources are marshalled for the task of meeting the challenges which life presents.

INTELLIGENCE AND WORK

The Psychology of Occupations

Super has pointed out that virtually every human being has something in his background that can be considered a handicap (51). He has indicated that religion, minority status of any sort, and political beliefs can produce limitations that make people ineffective workers.

Work success is also subject to whims and vagaries. History gives a long account of multiple claims to inventions by people in different countries at the same time. In one society a discovery leads to fame and fortune—work success— and in another society the same degree of intelligence and the same artifact or skill are not followed by vocational success.

There are two things illustrated by this observation. The first is the serendipity that characterizes the lives of some people. The second is the less-than-paramount role that intelligence plays in determining the effectiveness of workers. This last point may be pursued a little further.

Without regard to intelligence, consider the vocational careers of most young people who leave school at the minimum age. Usually they do not come from the strata of society that value schooling most highly. Also, since they spend a short period of time at a number of occupations, their work careers tend to be highly unstable. O'Connor has reported comparative failure rates of normal and defective laborers at a building site (38). After one year, only 29 per cent of the normals were still on the job. Occasionally, success follows a series of jobs, and the worker credits it to the richness of his background. If he is merely adequate at a given task, another piece is added to a mosaic of unmatched jobs.

Since many retarded youngsters come from a cultural level that is largely semi-skilled or unskilled, we may say that their work histories would be less than ideal in any circumstances. Were they of normal intelligence, their work careers would be checkered. Their socially determined work uncertainty is compounded by the interaction of low general ability. We should not hope to reshape the social order, but we may try to counteract the other disabilities found in young handicapped persons.

These possibly remediable defects include work habits and character. In the analysis of work success and failure by Collman and Newlyn, 52 per cent of the placement failures were due to problems other than intellect (11). A large number of the girls studied by Shotwell had essentially social-emotional problems, although they had a mean IQ of 67 (48). Shotwell further points out that it was possible to "reclaim" about half of them by means of appropriate training. Employers are willing to concede that non-intellectual factors influence their perceptions of workers. In his study of laundry managers, Beckham found that personal qualities were important: "Congeniality on the job, desire to please, ability to get along with others, willingness to obey directions, and resourcefulness" (3). These were the qualities that managers felt influenced their perceptions of workers.

We may say the following things about work and effectiveness.

1. People of normal intelligence may have unstable work careers.

2. Any level of intelligence—high, medium, or low—may be accompanied by an undistinguished work history.

3. Work success may be due to chance factors beyond the individual's control—e.g., political beliefs and minority status.

4. Non-intellectual factors such as those described by Beckham influence the employer's perception of the worker's effectiveness.

In summary, we may say that jobs of an obviously intellectual order will always be beyond the capabilities of retarded young people. On the other hand, many of them come from a background which usually produces semi-skilled workers. In such cases non-intellectual factors may be paramount. To prepare such young people to enter the work force would seem to be a rational undertaking.

Productivity and Mental Retardation

Motivation. A paper by the author and de Charms on the achievement motive has demonstrated two things which are relevant to this discussion. The first is that level of *n* achievement in mentally retarded adolescent males is not a function of their level of intelligence. Competition with a standard of excellence may be found at low levels of intelligence. Indeed, while doing the research which unearthed these findings the writers were deeply moved by the sight of a young person valiantly struggling to do a good job (but not *perseverating*) in the face of a sheer lack of ability. A second observation, also relevant, was that the mentally retarded S's were lower in achievement motivation. This last finding was analyzed against a background of social experiences. Putting these two observations together, we can say that the mentally retarded may show less desire to compete with a standard of excellence. Clearly, such a desire is basic to effective production. A vital consideration is that the habilitation of the young retarded person stresses the arousal of a desire to do well. The occurrence of this de-sire seems to be related to the extent to which the young person is expected to show a degree of self-care at an early age. Self-care may be seen in such activities as dressing and feeding oneself.

A note of caution is in order. There seems to be no formula to pro-duce the desired effect. Too much stress on independence, too soon, can produce a degree of reinforcing negative affect that leads to de-pendence rather than independence. Clearly, more research on the dynamics of early training of the young retardate is vital to clarify this and similar ambiguities.

Performance.   Many of the basic papers on the employability of the mentally handicapped worker have come from the United Kingdom (7, 24, 38, 45). These papers are distinguished by the realistic and in-genious nature of the work they describe.

Tizard and O'Connor have examined the temperament of retarded workers with a view to relating it to job performance (52). In their judgment the retarded worker cannot be excluded from a job on the grounds that he lacks persistence. In some respects, he shines. Many industrial tasks are repetitive and are monotonous to people of normal intelligence. The mentally retarded may therefore be better suited to some jobs than their more fortunate brethren. There seems to be no greater variability in performance in mentally retarded workers, and while the evidence is scanty, they are not known to be more accident-prone. The prevention of accidents is partially a management respon-sibility. The President's Committee on the Employment of the Physi-cally Handicapped has viewed careful placement of the worker as one of the ways to ensure his effectiveness (41). Evidence on the compara-tive susceptibility of retarded workers to accidents seems to be unavail-able.

In a summary of the judgment of 200 personnel directors, Michal-Smith reported four prescriptions for the employment of the retarded on jobs which were manual and repetitive: (1) the worker should not tire, (2) he should avoid danger, (3) he should follow orders, and (4) he should show caution (35).

Beard has pointed out three problems which affect the performance of the retarded worker: (1) he is a slow learner, (2) he develops a modest amount of transfer, and (3) he lacks judgment and insight (2). This does not mean that he cannot learn; rather it indicates the slow response to training and the need to emphasize careful guidance of the individual during training. In the case of jobs involving equip-ment, careful supervision may be appropriate after training when the worker is on the job.

An interesting problem is that of deciding just how retarded a worker can be and still be productive. A most interesting piece of experimentation on this problem has been reported by Clarke and Hermelin (7). Six males between CA 20 and 30, having a mean Stanford-Binet IQ of 33, were used. They were, to use the expression of the investigators, "typical imbeciles." At the time of reporting, the six had been producing cardboard-box folders for two and a half years. They had produced 30,000 to 40,000 each week. Such was their satisfaction that they even gained access to the workshop over a weekend and proceeded to produce a morning's output as a way of avoiding boredom.

Clarke and Hermelin conclude that even for these severely retarded individuals gainful work is possible. They may be distinguished from workers of a higher IQ on this sort of task not so much by the eventual level of achievement as by the time needed to reach a particular level of output. Clearly, this is no great problem for individuals who would otherwise be unoccupied and who might spend their years doing nothing productive. Such inactivity frequently leads to a host of emotional problems as the years go by.

Occupational Level and Mental Retardation. People earn their livelihood in many diverse ways. Few people realize that there are literally thousands of occupations. Some of these occupations have been traditional over many years. Yet, on the other hand, as society becomes more complex, new skills are needed as new positions appear.

A corollary to the observation that new jobs develop is the observation that jobs also disappear. The attrition rate is largely traceable to the impact of technology, and the jobs which disappear are largely manual or unskilled. This is not to say that all jobs created by technology are skilled and require high intelligence. Rather, the change in occupations over the years has been primarily a shift away from job situations involving solitary activity and the role of judgment. The worker today works with other people, and he is responsible not for his craftsmanship but for expensive machinery and its maintenance.

For example, earth-moving once consisted of using a shovel and, eventually, a horse and cart. The shift in the worker's responsibility has been from the care of his shovel, costing a few dollars, to the maintenance of a truck costing several thousand dollars. The motor skills required may not be greater, but the responsibility is far greater.

At present, jobs held by the mentally retarded are numerous and diverse. Saenger's report to the state of New York pointed out that the quite low-IQ subjects he studied had a "surprising" work history.

Twenty-seven per cent of his sample were working on a full- or part-time basis (47). Most of them did simple tasks for which they were paid. Jobs included such activities as sweeping, dusting, washing dishes, and carrying messages. Half of these people earned over twenty dollars each week. In a few cases the earnings went as high as sixty dollars a week. Some 90 per cent took pride in their work and enjoyed it.

A less comprehensive, earlier study by Delp and Lorenz followed the careers of a similar group of people (12). All had IQ's below 50. Ten of the individuals had been gainfully employed, and the majority of those living at home engaged in some activity. Interestingly, several were fairly steady readers, a provocative finding in view of the usual generalities about the lower limits of educability.

An interesting report to which we may turn is the work of Beckham in 1930 (3). He summarized a number of previous findings and systematically related intelligence to occupational activities beginning at MA 5. Table 11·1 shows some of the representative activities as grouped by Beckham.

A sardonic observation in this day of highly paid semi-skilled workers and lower-paid "white-collar" workers is that the retardate occasionally makes more money from an evening job than his teacher makes at his full-time job. An example of this is a teenager whose skilled services as a pastry cook were highly valued by a local bakery. The boy received an excellent income while still in school, having already surpassed his instructor, who had put in many years at his job.

Goldberg has surveyed the range of jobs held by the mentally retarded (21). In his analysis he canvassed a number of state institutions and received replies from sixty-five. It emerged that 125 different jobs were held by individuals who had received vocational rehabilitation services. Some of the positions held outside the institutions included that of farm helper, hotel worker, hospital aide, laundry worker, kitchen helper, gas-station attendant, and factory worker.

A 1960 study of women discharged from a mental-deficiency hospital in England has been reported by Brandon (6). Two hundred women were studied after an average of five years in the community. Of 108 who worked prior to admission to the hospital, 52 had been in domestic work. One hundred and sixty-seven were traced, of whom 114 were gainfully employed. Seventy-one were doing domestic work in hospitals; 42 were doing domestic work in private homes; and 46 were married, 31 having children. It was Brandon's conclusion that the women were not anti-social and were not a burden to the community they now resided in.

TABLE 11·1

OCCUPATIONAL SKILLS GROUPED BY MENTAL AGE
After Beckham, 1930 (3)

What Mental Ages of Five Can Do

Boys

1. Wash dishes
2. Sandpaper furniture
3. Scrub and polish floors
4. Feed and fold from mangle
5. Do simple domestic work
6. Be brush-makers' assistant
7. Handle cinders and garbage
8. Make nets
9. Cut rags in accurate strips

Girls

1. Follow a pattern in simple sewing
2. Pare vegetables
3. Cut rags in accurate strips
4. Wash dishes (by hand)
5. Sew rag carpet

What Mental Ages of Seven Can Do

Boys

1. Do rough painting
2. Do simple shoe repairing
3. Drive 2-horse team
4. Plow
5. Be blacksmith assistant
6. Cane chairs
7. Make brooms
8. Do simple carpentry
9. Do domestic work

Girls

1. Knit neckties and scarfs
2. Hemstitch (plain and Italian)
3. Cross stitch
4. Braid
5. Sew rags for rugs
6. Do simple domestic work
7. Iron (by hand)
8. Do simple packing of small articles (powder puffs, etc.)

What Mental Ages of Nine Can Do

Boys

1. Handle entire process of broom making
2. Operate foot-power printing press
3. Block paper into pads
4. Repair furniture
5. Paint toys
6. Handle higher processes of shoe repairing
7. Harvest vegetables and fruits
8. Make mattresses and pillows
9. Learn an alto horn and manipulate drums
10. Make fancy brushes

Girls

1. Knit stockings and mittens
2. Make fancy baskets
3. Make cloth toys
4. Make pottery
5. Operate automatic rug loom
6. Cut out and make dresses
7. Do plain cooking
8. Make pillow lace
9. Sew in lining (hat industry)
10. Sew mounts on cardboard
11. Sew buttons
12. Make novelties

What Mental Ages of Eleven and Twelve Can Do

Boys	Girls

Boys

1. Be competent janitors
2. Keep stock
3. Keep store (small)
4. Label and check
5. Be green house attendant
6. Care for lawns

Girls

1. Sew garters and powder puffs
2. Sew wire edges and facing in hats
3. Do simple library work
4. Do Italian cut work in embroidery
5. Handle power sealing in canning plant
6. Learn first violin, cello, flute, and clarinet

TRAINING

Too many school systems try to prepare the slower children for adult living merely by consigning them to trade schools. This particular practice is based on the fallacy that the absence of verbal skills is automatically compensated for. Because the child cannot handle the language arts, he is supposed to be a master of the manual arts. His education is geared to the proposition that he will be successful in nonverbal areas.

The inadequacies of this kind of thinking are fairly obvious. Children are not either good at "head" jobs or automatically good at "hand" jobs. Reflection on the nature of a machine or electrical shop suggests that it is not the best place for the slow learner. In fact, it is far less appropriate than the classroom, if only because the chance of injury is so great.

Clearly, some alternative school provisions for the habilitation of the slow learner are needed. McCartney has suggested that early experience can prepare a child for work later on (33). It is her suggestion that children with more than one handicap can begin to acquire rudimentary skills by playing with toys that require manipulation. Such toys as those which require hammering and assembling would be appropriate.

At a more advanced level, Westby-Gibson has offered an analysis of occupational factors to be considered in curriculum development (53). His conclusions were based on the judgments of a group of employers in San Mateo County, California. According to his report, the basic curriculum for the retarded should stress:

1. The development of personality skills.
2. The development of manual dexterity, coordination, and speed.

3. A degree of academic skill suitable for people who will be unskilled or semi-skilled workers.

4. Training in the use of basic tools.

5. Instruction in the handling of money and in following oral and written directions.

Attention to such considerations would ease the transition from school to work. This particular problem is acute, since many young people enter the labor force not because of a rational decision to seek work but because of dissatisfaction with school.

Occasionally the schools go beyond the suggestions offered by Westby-Gibson. Peace has reported a series of investigations in New York by people working with the would-be worker (39). He has analyzed the working situations which young special-class people are likely to encounter. The various job classifications in hospitals, restaurants, housing projects, and similar agencies employing people with minimal skills and abilities were investigated and summarized.

Work-study programs are the best hope for preparing young retarded persons to assume the major role of independent living—that is, obtaining and keeping a job. The programs are never easy to develop, because they fall between the several stools of state agencies for rehabilitation, schools, private health agencies, and parents' associations. In many cases their success or failure is due to ecological factors beyond the scope of program directors: local employment rates, the skilled or unskilled nature of local industries, the general level of acceptance for the handicapped shown by the community. In a 1965 publication, Miller and Danielson have discussed five particular problems of work-study programs (36). There are (a) administrative support, (b) community support, (c) agency support, (d) program development, and (e) curriculum development. Additional elements which Miller and Danielson presented in their study to which the reader might profitably turn are identification of pupils, additional costs, pupil promotion, and coordination of efforts.

Two relevant studies have been reported from Detroit by Bobroff (4, 5). He indicated that most of his cases were functioning well in the post-school years. Generally speaking, they exhibited satisfying and desirable social patterns. About one-half had been working for one employer for seven consecutive years or more. This is an encouraging finding in view of the comments made previously about job instability. An oversimplified standard of performance is the amount of money a worker earns. Bobroff reported that about one-half of the people he investigated were making around two dollars an hour.

Another study from Michigan, this one using subjects in Grand Rapids, was made by Rynbrandt (46). An interesting finding was the classification of post-school occupation among former special-class students according to their IQ's. The IQ 20-49 group were engaged in such occupations as house-cleaning and window-washing. The 50-69's worked as clerks, drill-press operators, truckdrivers, and farm workers. The 70-79's worked as bakers, bartenders, janitors, and messengers.

A smaller study, but one which offers opportunities for some comparisons which are important, is the work of Porter and Milazzo (43). It is one thing to demonstrate what happens to people who attend special classes; it is another to compare people of low ability who did attend special classes with those who did not. The subjects in this interesting study were all of the intelligence level which would indicate special-class enrollment. The failure to be enrolled in a special class was not a specific "treatment" in the experimental sense but reflected a lack of facilities for some of the children. Twelve subjects who had participated in a special-class program were matched with twelve subjects who had not. None of the special-class people had been arrested, while four of the others had been. The employment rate of the special-class people was four to five times better. At least partial self-support was earned by 91 per cent of the special-class, graduates, while only about one-third of the people who had not attended special classes were self-supporting to any extent. The smallness of the sample in this study was unavoidable. More comparisons of this sort are in order so that the effectiveness of special-class preparation for adulthood may be checked.

Vocational Training

The goals of training are as follows:

1. To prepare the retarded to work (1) in an industrial setting, (2) on a partially dependent basis in a non-competitive situation, or (3) in a protected milieu where they will not have to compete and will not have to meet industrial work standards.

2. To acquire those personal traits that make a person acceptable to others and which produce harmony in a group setting.

3. To develop those habits of persistence and industry that make a worker productive—habits such as being punctual, obeying orders, and following directions.

On the face of it there is nothing unique in this set of objectives. They are to a large extent the expectations that apply to normal people. Perhaps the biggest difference is that most people acquire these skills and learn to fulfill these role requirements *incidentally*. The absence of them is as detrimental to the normal individual as it is to the retarded individual. The point to this is that so much of what is adequacy in a work setting is a composite of intellectual skills; it is also a composite of social skills which may be present or absent in people of high, average, or low intelligence.

Generally speaking, school provisions for training the retarded towards good citizenship and effective work habits occur within a program of special class activities. Occasionally, preparation is offered as intensive, short-term, training, usually for people who are beyond school age. In such programs attention is paid to such issues as selection, prediction of vocational success, guidance, and placement. Often the agency responsible for training continues to support the individual when he is on the job, helping him to make adjustments and to perceive what is expected of him.

Selection of Students. Multiple criteria are used to select people for training. Obviously they cannot be profoundly retarded. They must be viewed as potential workers in a variety of settings. Not all are expected to train for competitive industry. Those who are expected to do so must be ambulatory, stable, capable of travelling alone, and fairly attractive.

The non-competitive worker may be less fortunate in terms of the criteria just considered. An intermediate category of worker has been suggested by Dubin; this is the person who occasionally works outside the sheltered situation (16).

Peck has reported the selection standards used at a training center near Austin (40). The trainees were between sixteen and twenty-five years of age. The intelligence quotients were in the range 50–80. There were no crippling handicaps, and there was no history of delinquency. The young men were expected to be free of significant emotional problems and to have good possibilities for placement. Compared to those of special classes, such standards are high, and the young men did not spend much more than one or two years at the institution. Clearly the program is not intended to serve a wide range of disabled people, and its standards of selection make its contribution quite specific.

The program served around twenty-six clients at a given time. This number is in marked contrast to most institution populations which are in the hundreds. It is unfortunate that optimal populations are usually defined on the basis of construction and maintenance costs rather than on the basis of service considerations. If populations were determined by service considerations, there would be many smaller programs able to make a qualitatively greater contribution.

Training. The young retarded worker is usually capable of mastering skills that have some industrial value. Simple assembling jobs will probably not be mechanized, and jobs such as preparing material for mailing are still largely manual tasks (the worker folds sheets of paper, stuffs envelopes, and puts stamps on them). Other skills, such as collecting pages and stapling, are necessary in most organizations, and the retarded may be trained to do such jobs even when quite handicapped.

A non-productive but equally vital part of training is the development of an appropriate worker-supervisor relationship. The industrial setting has standards of performance and conduct which the supervisor enforces. The retarded worker must learn to relate to his supervisors on their terms. The worker must also learn to respect the production quota established by his supervisors. The worker must learn to maintain his equipment in an acceptable way. Gunzberg has given an interesting account of a technique of evaluation which is recorded in a highly visual way allowing the trainee to see his progress. A value claimed for the system is that it provides a good basis for discussion of progress in training (*24*).

Prediction of Employability. One of the vital problems is the selection of trainees and the direction of their training towards sound occupational goals. According to Tizard and O'Connor, who have a good deal of experience in such matters, it is not wise to assume that intelligence alone will determine employability (*52*). They feel that psychometric measures are inadequate. This is entirely reasonable when one considers some of Goldberg's findings on the temperament of retarded individuals. He reported that the teachers of 256 young people, all moderately retarded, found them shy and fearful. Others were attention-seeking, aggressive, and stubborn. Clearly such traits are quite detrimental in a work situation (*21*).

On the other hand, Ferguson has reported evidence on the prediction of vocational potential which is fairly sanguine (*18*). He reports a correlation of .90 between Performance IQ on the *Wechsler Adult Intelligence Scale* and competitive employment status. A multiple correlation produced a coefficient of .955 when other scales were incorporated.

The approach used by Ferguson and others attempts to predict employment success in a fashion which Kolstoe has labelled *static,* and which he has applied to the skills, abilities and characteristics of people (*30*). Kolstoe has pointed out there are *dynamic* factors to be taken into account. These are the situational elements which elicit application of skills on the job. He feels that the way people use their skills, the personal traits which mediate their use, are not emphasized sufficiently. Essentially, he advocates people and their human complexity rather than linear equations as a context within which new hypotheses may be generated.

Guidance. The vital role of guidance is acknowledged in the amount of attention that is paid to interviews with trainees. DiMichael and Terwiliger reported data on 99 cases seen by rehabilitation counselors (14). They reported the mean number of interviews as 18.7, with the range extending from 2 to 50. A large number of follow-up interviews were conducted after the client had completed training and had been placed. The intent in these interviews was to help the worker understand his new job and the ground rules of his new milieu. Such objectives as understanding his fellow-employees and learning how to get along with them were considered. An additional and quite important problem that the rehabilitation counselor attended to was helping the retarded worker manage his earnings. Obviously, the hazards of new-found wealth are many, and the individual of limited intellect, much like his normal co-workers, needs to exercise caution.

Occupational Placement. When we consider the amount of energy and time consumed in the process of training, it is only reasonable to view eventual job selection as crucial. The adequacy of job placement and resultant adjustment are the test of all that has gone before (25).

The evidence indicates that adequate training is no guarantee that a given job situation will suit the worker completely or that he will fit into whatever organization he joins. This finding is reasonable when one considers that so few of the bright middle-class males judged "successful" are working in occupations easily and quickly related to their college preparation. A certain amount of changing seems to be normal and typical for all workers before they settle into a permanent niche.

Of 100 educable boys discharged from the Mont-St. Aubert institution in Canada, 79 per cent needed up to three placements (32). In the work at the McDonald Training Center in Florida, multiple job placements were necessary for 44 per cent of the trainees (18). Ferguson has also pointed out that better than one-half of the workers were still holding their first jobs. A similar observation has been made by Engel (17).

Failure in initial placement is undoubtedly due to many causes. A program may train a worker, but he is still responsible for his own performance on the job. Also, even if the worker is well motivated and the training has been adequate, there has to be a job available for him. Even if these requirements are met, the worker has to relate to other people in order to work well. Their acceptance and his perception of them, are intangibles that are quite important (29).

One approach to the complexities of placement is the "nesting" concept. It means that the job held by the worker is carefully developed by means of a search for accepting employers and agencies. Once a job has been lined up by using an approximation of job needs and worker skills, the position is incorporated into the training process as closely as circumstances permit. The position within industry is viewed as a protective setting into which a marginal worker can be placed. This is an approach which takes a guarded view of chances for survival in the economic market place under normal circumstances; it is also a highly individualized approach which presents its own unique problems of job identification. It is not an approach which stresses development of work personality, and it sets aside the value of allowing the potential worker to make a vocational choice. In those circumstances where job placement is not continuous with curricular precedents, and given little logistical support for worker evaluation and training, it has some merit. A curricular approach to training is preferable (31).

Another element that may be strategically raised at this point is the fact that placement hinges, in the last analysis, on acceptance by employers and supervisors. Employment of persons known to be retarded must surely be threatening to many workers who find their jobs downgraded by the tacit presumption that even intellectually limited persons can do them. Also, employers and supervisors must be willing to accept people who are different and who are known to have "something," often misunderstood, wrong with them. In effect, the criterion of success in placement may well be denied to persons whose training has carried them as far as its mission allows.

Despite the obstacles, and the very real fact that training programs are expensive, the results are encouraging. DiMichael has pointed out the return on the training of 592 persons in 1951 (13). Before rehabilitation they had earned a total of $35,900. In one year, after vocational rehabilitation, they earned $922,400. Projecting those earnings from 1951 to date indicates that occupational success is a realistic, attainable goal for many retarded persons. To this we may add two observations. The first is that the federal government has begun accepting retarded persons for selected occupation in agencies. This step is welcome because it adds a willingness to hire to a willingness to train workers for other people to hire. The second observation is that even highly developed industries, such as the toy industry, have found retarded workers able to compete. According to the *New York Times*, Remco Industries found that training thirty retarded persons provided them with good workers able to provide Remco with satisfactory work; absenteeism was 2 per cent, compared with 7 per cent, and they were able to maintain a higher rate for arriving at work on time (20).

The Multiple-Handicapped Worker. So far the discussion has considered the worker with one limitation. Quite frequently the handicapped have several disorders (50). For example, personality disorders and mental retardation may be found in individuals who are cerebral-palsied. There are many other disorders that may be found in such cases, since the term *multiple handicap* covers a symptom complex of considerable scope.

Salient limitations are usually mental retardation and physical incapacity to perform fine motor tasks. As Rosenberg and Moed have pointed out, poor work habits, social immaturity, and uncertainty also characterize cerebral-palsied individuals requiring vocational rehabilitation (44). The result is that training must be more closely tailored to abilities, which must be very carefully evaluated. Also, a great deal of care must be taken to increase the social effectiveness of the client.

A third point, an extension of the previous two, is probably most important. Far greater problems of occupational selection exist. In some cases there may be skills that are usable in industry (37). On the other hand, there may be minimal skills to be exercised only in a non-competitive, protected milieu.

Collins examined the qualities leading to success and failure in rehabilitating cerebral-palsied persons (9). Examining random samples within the categories of success and failure, he was able to reach some conclusions about relevant worker traits. He found Wechsler-Bellevue IQ's insignificantly different between groups when scores were analyzed as (1) full scale, (2) verbal, and (3) performance. Length of time and speech clarity were insignificant factors, but manual dexterity was significantly related to successful vocational rehabilitation.

The Sheltered Workshop. In the past, the approach to work possibilities has been grossly oversimplified. Either a worker could work in the industrial setting or he could not work at all. This meant that many people with some work potential, although handicapped (34), were non-productive.

Recent consideration of this problem has seen the emergence of work settings in which the handicapped can use their skills and can earn a little money. The money is not charity. It is a return for work which is economically meaningful, although not necessarily produced at the speed of the typical industrial setting. Much of the work is sub-contracted. Jacobs and Sherman have pointed out that such tasks as mailing, tag stringing, packaging, stapling, and simple assembly are within the capacities of quite seriously handicapped people (26).

An important problem is coordination of programs. The handicapped individual cannot be given a sense of dignity and a sound self-concept in a short period of time. Such perceptions are the culmination of many hours of dedication by rehabilitation workers and the integration of many efforts.

A good time perspective is needed. We need to see programming as an enterprise beginning with the earliest attempts to motivate when the individual is quite young. This would then be capitalized on in realistic school programs, such as that developed by Kolstoe and Frey (31), and then concluded by coordinated vocational training or by smooth entrance into a sheltered workshop. The end product would be the avoidance of rejection and maudlin sentimentality and the achievement of the highest social good—that is, respect for all people in their several unique modes of productivity and respect for their inherent dignity.

The Workshop Economy. In many communities workshops have been started with federal support; in such instances an assurance of financial aid is often provided to cover the first years of development and to stablize operations. The unspoken premise is that one can enter the current free market in which supply and demand maintain some sort of balance and establish a unit which will either be economically viable, or marginally so, with additional community finance, usually from the private sector. The expectation that this can be done with a work force not subject to the usual incentives is unsound. More particularly, the absence of an industrial climate and the ascendance of "educational" values all contribute to the precarious economics of workshop operations. The fact is that workshops are not usually viable economic units in a free market, and their fiscal plight is probably inevitable. Their salvation in an economy transported from the once-pivotal concept of personal skills to the impersonal ground of high-output automation lies in the inevitability of subsidy, and public subsidy in particular.

Viewed in this light the workshop stands, not as a marginal economic unit, but as a public utility to be invoked in the best interests of a minority of citizens. As we subsidize the high-school shop as a training device, so we should subsidize the community sheltered workshop as a place where training is possible for some and employment is possible for many. Specifically, those whose limitations are great—but not to the point of futility—can be employed productively. There is a degree of gain to be realized even from workers who cannot attain industrial norms of behaviors and productivity. The essential point of these comments lies in the necessity to change the economic premise on which federal funds are spent.

The institutional workshop is on safer ground; it can survive, but usually because it competes within the closed economic system of the state institution, serving other state agencies. Farms, for example, are probably not highly efficient in the sense of modern agricultural science, but the combination of underpaid or unpaid help and guaranteed markets for their canned goods, etc. allows them to play a marginal but safe role. Interestingly, economic processes within the closed economic systems of state institutions allow residents to develop the roles of open economic systems. Entrepreneurs emerge; bootleg car-washing and the exchange of services develop; and the roles persist, classically, although the institution's regulations may expressly curb economic initiative.

SUMMARY

This chapter has considered, first, some of the general goals of rehabilitation. These are the development of workers who can meet various standards of performance, the cultivation of those personality traits that lead to acceptance, and the encouragement of work traits of industry, application, and discipline. Second, a discussion of issues in the psychology of work was offered. Attention was called to problems of occupational stability and to the role that socio-economic level and non-intellectual factors play in vocational success. Third, the chapter has considered various rehabilitation issues, such as the selection of trainees, the courses of training, the evaluation of programs, and the role of guidance. The problems of the severely handicapped worker have been considered, with attention to the need to coordinate all programs in a time sequence from early childhood to adulthood.

BIBLIOGRAPHY

1. Baller, W., Charles, D. C., and Miller, E. L., "Antecedents of Change in Mentally Retarded Persons at Mid-Life: A Longitudinal Study," Vocational Rehabilitation Administration, U. S. Department of Health, Education, and Welfare, 1965.

2. Beard, R. J., "Industrial Therapy with Mental Defectives," *Am. J. Ment. Def.*, 1953, 57, 547-553.

3. Beckham, A. S., "Minimum Intelligence Levels for Several Occupations," *Personnel J.*, 1930, 9, 309-313.

4. Bobroff, A., "Economic Adjustment of 121 Adults, Formerly Students in Classes for Mental Retardates," *Am. J. Ment. Def.*, 1956, 60, 525-535.

5. ———, "A Survey of Social and Civic Participation of Adults Formerly in Classes for Mentally Retarded," *Am. J. Ment. Def.*, 1956, 61, 127-133.

6. Brandon, M. W. G., "A Survey of 200 Women Discharged from a Mental Deficiency Hospital," *J. Ment. Sci.*, 1960, *106*, 355-370.

7. Clarke, A. D. B., and Hermelin, B. F., "Adult Imbeciles, Their Abilities and Trainability," *Lancet*, 1955, *269*, 337-339.

8. Cohen, J. S., "An Analysis of Vocational Failures of Mental Retardates Placed in the Community after a Period of Institutionalization," *Amer. J. Ment. Defic.*, 1960, *65*, 371-375.

9. Collins; H. A., "Success and Failure in the Vocational Rehabilitation of the Cerebral Palsied," unpublished Ph.D. dissertation, St. Louis University, 1963.

10. Collman, R. D., and Newlyn, D., "Employment Success of Educationally Subnormal Ex-Pupils in England," *Am. J. Ment. Def.*, 1956, *60*, 733-743.

11. Collman, R. D., and Newlyn, D., "Employment Success of Mentally Dull and Intellectually Normal Ex-Pupils in England," *Amer. J. Ment. Def.*, 1957, *61*, 484-490.

12. Delp, H. A., and Lorenz, M., "Follow-Up of 84 Public School Special-Class Pupils with IQ's Below 50," *Am. J. Ment. Def.*, 1953, *58*, 175-182.

13. DiMichael, S., "Vocational Rehabilitation Works for the Mentally Retarded," *Personnel and Guid. J.*, 1953, *31*, 428-432.

14. _____, and Terwiliger, W. B., "Counselor's Activities in the Vocational Rehabilitation of the Mentally Retarded," *J. Clin. Psych.*, 1953, *9*, 99-106.

15. Dinger, J. C., "Post-School Adjustment of Former Educable Retarded Pupils," *Excep. Ch.*, 1961, *27*, 353-360.

16. Dubin, M. N., "The Sheltered Workshop—Some Important Considerations in Its Planning and Establishment," *Am. J. Ment. Def.*, 1956, *60*, 508-514.

17. Engel, A. M., "Employment of the Mentally Retarded," *Am. J. Ment. Def.*, 1952, *57*, 243-267.

18. Ferguson, R. G., *Habilitation of Mentally Retarded Youth*, Part II, "Evaluation of the Potential for Vocational Rehabilitation of Mentally Retarded Youths," Tampa, Fla., 1959.

19. Ferguson, T., and Kerr, A. W., "After-histories of Boys Educated in Special Schools for Mentally-handicapped Children," *Scot. Med. J.*, 1958, *3*, 31-38.

20. Freeman, W. M., "Retarded Found to Excel in Jobs," *New York Times*, Sunday, March 14, 1965.

21. Goldberg, I. I., "Coordination of Retardates' Experiences from School to Occupational Center," *Am. J. Ment. Def.*, 1958, *62*, 823-825.

22. _____, "A Survey of the Present Status of Vocational Rehabilitation of the Mentally Retarded Residents in State Supported Institutions," *Am. J. Ment. Def.*, 1957, *61*, 698-705.

23. Greene, C. L., "A Study of Personal Adjustment in Mentally Retarded Girls," *Amer. J. Ment. Def.*, 1945, *49*, 472-476.

24. Gunzberg, H., "Vocational and Social Rehabilitation of the Feeble-minded," in Clarke, A., and Clarke, A., *Mental Deficiency: The Changing Outlook*, London, Methuen, 1958.

25. Hitchcock, A. A., "Vocational Training and Job Adjustment of the Mentally Deficient," *Am. J. Ment. Def.*, 1954, 59, 100-106.

26. Jacobs, A., and Sherman, C., "Training Facilities for Severely Physically and Mentally Handicapped," *Am. J. Ment. Def.*, 1956, 60, 721-728.

27. Jordan, T. E., *et al.*, *Rehabilitation of the Adult with Cerebral Palsy*, Division of Vocational Rehabilitation, U. S. Department of Health, Education, and Welfare, 1961.

28. Kennedy, R. J. R., *A Connecticut Community Revisited: A Study of the Social Adjustment of a Group of Mentally Deficient Adults in 1948 and 1960*, U. S. Office of Vocational Rehabilitation, 1962.

29. Kolstoe, O. P., "An Examination of Some Characteristics Which Discriminate Between Employed and Not-Employed Mentally Retarded Males," *Amer. J. Ment. Def.*, 1961, *66*, 472-482.

30. _____, "State vs. Dynamic Factors in Predicting Employment Success of Mentally Retarded Young Adults," paper presented to the American Psychological Association, 1964.

31. _____ and Frey, R. M., *A High School Work-Study Program for Mentally Subnormal Students*, Southern Illinois University Press, 1965.

32. Lambert, J., and Racine, H., "Considerations Sur le Placement En Emploi Des Deficients Mentaux," *Canad. Psychiat. Ass. J.*, 1959, *4*, 107-119.

33. McCartney, L. D., "Providing Occupational Readiness for Young Mentally Deficient Children of the Non-Familial Type," *Am. J. Ment. Def.*, 1958, *62*, 625-633.

34. Machek, O., and Collins, H. A., "Preliminary Report of Evaluating and Classifying the Vocational Potential of the Cerebral Palsied," *Arch. Phys. Med.*, 1960, *41*, 434-437.

35. Michal-Smith, H., "A Study of the Personal Characteristics Desirable for the Vocational Success of the Mentally Deficient," *Am. J. Ment. Def.*, 1950, *55*, 139-143.

36. Miller, D. Y., and Danielson, R. H., *Work-Study for Slow Learners in Ohio*, Ohio State Department of Education, Columbus, 1965.

37. Neuschutz, L., *Vocational Rehabilitation for the Physically Handicapped*, Charles C. Thomas, 1959.

38. O'Connor, N., 'The Successful Employment of the Mentally Handicapped," in Hilliard, L., and Kirman, B., *Mental Deficiency*, Little, Brown, 1957.

39. Peace, W. F., "Workshop in Job Requirements in Occupational Areas of New York City," *Am. J. Ment. Def.*, 1949, *53*, 621-643.

40. Peck, J. R., "The Marbridge Plan: A Texas Experiment in Habilitation for Mentally Retarded Youth," *Excep. Ch.*, 1958, *24*, 346-350.

41. *Personnel and Industrial Relations:* Report of the President's Committee on Employment of the Physically Handicapped, U. S. Govt. Printing Office, 1958.

42. Peterson, L., and Smith, L. L., "A Comparison of the Post-School Adjustment of Educable Mentally Retarded Adults with that of Adults of Normal Intelligence," *Excep. Child*, 1960, *26*, 404-408.

43. Porter, R. B., and Milazzo, T. C., "A Comparison of Mentally Retarded Adults Who Attended a Special Class with Those Who Attended Regular School Classes," *Excep. Ch.*, 1958, *24*, 410-412.

44. Rosenberg, B., and Moed, M. G., "Messenger Service Training—An Aid to Habilitation," *J. Rehab.*, 1956, *22*, 12-13.

45. Roswell-Harris, D., "Industrial Training for the Mentally Subnormal in a Hospital Setting," *J. Ment. Def. Res.*, 1964, *9*, 76-80.

46. Rynbrandt, D. M., "A Study of the Socio-Economic Adjustment of People Who Have Attended the Auxiliary and Ungraded Classes of the Grand Rapids Public Schools," unpublished Ph.D. dissertation, Wayne State University, 1947.

47. Saenger, G., *The Adjustment of Severely Retarded Adults in the Community*, Report: New York State Interdepartmental Health Resources Board, Albany, 1957.

48. Shotwell, A., "Effectiveness of Institutional Training of High Grade Mentally Defective Girls," *Am. J. Ment. Def.*, 1949, *53*, 432-440.

49. Sloan, W., "Some Statistics on Institutional Provisions for the Mentally Handicapped," *Am. J. Ment. Def.*, 1955, *59*, 380-382.

50. Stein, Z., and Susser, M., "Estimating Hostel Needs for Backward Citizens," *Lancet*, 1960, 486-488.

51. Super, D. E., *The Psychology of Careers*, Harper & Row, Publishers, 1957.

52. Tizard, J., and O'Connor, N., "The Employability of High Grade Mental Defectives, II," *Am. J. Ment. Def.*, 1950, *55*, 144-157.

53. Westby-Gibson, H., "Certain Occupational Factors in Curriculum Development for Mentally Retarded Children," unpublished Ph.D. dissertation, University of California, 1957.

INDEX OF NAMES

Abernathy, E. A., 164, 178
Akesson, H., 25, 28, 31
Albert-Gasorek, K. J., 348, 355
Albini, J. L., & Dinitz, S., 339, 355
Allaway, N. C., 117, 141
Allen, F. J., & Diamond, L. V., 304, 306
Allen, F. J., & Gibson, R. M., 305, 306
Allen, R., & Collins, M. G., 216, 232
Alm, I., 242, 253, 267
Almack, C. J., 118, 137
Altman, C., 53, 73
Altus, W. D., 69, 73
Amatruda, C. S., 347, 357
Anastasi, A., 19, 21, 31, 203, 232
Anberg, A., 284, 311
Angelino, H., & Shedd, C., 127, 137
Apgar, V., 221, 237
Appleton, M. D., & Pritham, G. H., 291, 306
Aquinas, T., 279
Aronson, B. E., Aronson, S. M., & Volk, B., 303, 307
Arthur, G., 125, 137

Ascher, P., & Schonell, F. E., 298, 307
Aserlind, L., 56, 73
Atkins, L., O'Sullivan, M. A., & Pryles, C. V., 293, 307
Axline, V., 339, 355

Badt, M. I., 161, 175, 178
Baller, W., Charles, D. C., & Miller, E. L., 407-423
Bandera, E. A., & Churchill, J. A., 284, 307
Bangs, J. L., 159, 160, 178
Barclay, A., 233
Barlow, A., 285, 307
Barnett, C., 292, 311
Baroff, J. S., 206, 232
Barton, J., 257, 270
Batza, E. M., 159, 174, 175, 178
Bauer, A. M., 350, 358
Beard, R. J., 410, 423
Beck, C. S., McKhann, C., & Belnap, W., 342, 355
Beck, H. S., & Lam, R. L., 206, 232
Beck, S., 97
Becker, R. F., Flanagan, E., & King, J. E., 260, 268

Beckham, A. S., 409, 423
Beechley, R. M., 130, 138
Behrens, W. L., 348, 355
Beier, E. G., Gorlow, L., &
  Stacey, C. L., 209, 232
Bell, A., & Zubek, T. P., 116, 137
Bell, D. M., 175
Belnap, W., 342, 355
Benda, C. B., 278, 281, 291, 303,
  307
Benda, C., et al., 43, 74
Benda, C. E., & Melchior, J. C.,
  229, 232, 303, 307
Bender, L., 126, 137, 229, 232
Benirschke, K., 259, 269
Benoit, E. P., 4, 31, 111, 137, 216,
  234
Bensberg, G. T., 86, 103, 220, 232
Benton, A., 7, 31, 125, 138, 220
Bergsman, S., 291, 307
Berko, J., 173, 178
Berman, H. H., et al., 130, 138
Berman, H., Albert-Gasorek,
  K. J., & Reiss, M., 348, 355
Berman, P. W., 219, 220, 234
Bice, H. V., 296, 298, 302, 311
Bierman, J. L., 205, 252, 268
Bijou, S. W., & Werner, H., 161
  175, 178
Binet, A., 12, 19, 31, 89
Binet, A., & Simon, Th., 143, 178
Birch, C. B., 190, 235
Birch, J. W., 214, 232, 283, 315
Birch, J. W., & Mathews, J., 164,
  178
Black, D. A., 220, 238
Blackman, L. S., 133, 141, 391,
  403
Blanchard, I., 166, 168, 174, 178,
  330, 355

Blum, L., 300, 312
Bobroff, A., 415, 423
Boder, D. P., 147, 178
Boldt, W. H., 265, 268
Boll, S., 53, 74
Bond, G., & Fay, L. M., 124, 138,
  204, 232
Bonney, M. E., 118, 138
Book, J. A., 70, 74
Boshes, B., 284, 313
Bossard, H., & Boll, S., 53, 74
Bossio, V., 56, 77
Bothwell, D. R., 293, 307
Bowman, B. H., 305, 312
Boyd, D., 66, 74
Boyd, H., 216, 234
Brandon, M. W. G., 54-55, 412,
  424
Braunstein, P., 229, 234
Brill, K., & Joynson, M. G., 69, 74
Brodsky, M., 214, 233
Brown, F., 53, 74
Bruner, J., 23, 31, 126, 307
Buck, J., 212, 232
Bulin, E. V., 242, 270
Bumbalo, T. S., Morelewicz,
  H. V., & Behrens, W. L., 348.
  355
Burgmeister, B., & Blum, L., 300,
  312
Buros, O., 203, 232
Burt, C., 12, 13, 19, 31

Cain, F. L., & Levine, S., 85, 103
Caldwell, B., Manley, E. J., &
  Seelye, B. J., 38, 74
Campanelli, P. A., Pollock, F. J.,
  & Henner, R., 284, 306
Canter, A., 18, 215, 233
Capobianco, R. J., 134, 138

Carlson, H. B., & Henderson, W., 20, 31

Carlton, T., & Carlton, L. E., 175

Carroll, J. B., 150, 179

Carver, M. J., Wittse, H., & Wilson, C. L., 291, 308

Cassel, R. H., 7, 32, 229, 234

Cassidy, V., & Stanton, J. E., 391, 399

Centerwall, S. A., & Centerwall, W. R., 55, 74, 91, 103, 267, 269

Chambers, G. S., & Hamblin, R. C., 132, 138

Chapman, A. H., 227, 233

Chapman, L. J., & Pathman, J. H., 231, 233

Charles, D. C., 407-423

Chidester, L., 340, 356

Churchill, J. A., 284, 307

Churchill, L., 93, 103

Claireaux, A., 262, 268

Clarke, A. D. B., & Clarke, A. M., 126, 138, 281, 308, 326, 327, 356

Clarke, A. D. B., & Hermelin, B. F., 411, 424

Cleland, C. C., 86, 103

Clements, S., & Peters, J. E., 308

Clutterbuck, Dr., 344

Coffey, V. P., & Jessup, W. J. E., 241, 255, 257, 268

Cohen, J. S., 97, 103

Colbert, E. G., & Koegler, R. R., 229, 233

Coleman, J. C., 40, 74

Coleman, J. M., Iscoe, I., & Brodsky, M., 214, 233

Collings, J. L., 119, 141

Collins, H. A., 421, 424

Collins, M. G., 216, 232

Collman, R. D., & Newlyn, D., 408, 424

Collman, R. D., & Stoller, A., 308

Colton, K., 296, 298, 302, 311

Condell, J. F., & Town, M. H., 387, 399

Conquest, Dr., 344

Cooper, M., 26, 33

Corah, N., *et al.*, 283, 308

Corbett, G. R., 6, 34

Cotzin, M., 340, 356

Courville, C. B., 260, 269

Cowie, V. A., 348, 356

Crager, R. L., 214, 235

Crome, B., & Kirman, B., 260, 271

Cruickshank, W. M., & Raus, G., 298, 308

Culotta, C. S., 347, 357

Curtis, G. W., 259, 269

Cutler, R., 284, 286, 311

Cutts, R. A., 212, 233

Dagg, C. P., 281, 287, 314

Dancis, J., 305, 314

Daniel, P. M., & Stritch, S. J., 281, 308

Danielson, R. H., 415, 425

Dann, M., Levine, S. Z., & New, E., 285, 308

Daryn, E., 194, 233, 284, 308

Daum, M. P., 160, 174, 179

Davis, M. E., and Potter, E. L., 261, 270, 287, 308

Day R., and Haines, M. S., 342, 356

Day, R. W., & Wright, S. W., 250, 269

Dayan, M., 329, 354, 356

deCharms, R., 17, 33, 111, 135, 139, 175, 180, 208, 391, 401
della Porta, G. B., 293, 309
Delp, H. A., & Lorenz, M., 412, 424
Dennis, W., 241, 269
Dentler, R., & Mackler, B., 100, 103
de Prospo, C. J., 390, 400
Despert, J. L., & Pierce, H. D., 328, 356
Diamond, L. V., 304, 306
DiCarlo, L., 222, 233
DiMichael, S., 420, 424
DiMichael, S., & Terwiliger, W. B., 419
Dinger, J. C., 407, 424
Dingman, H., 101, 106, 292, 312
Dinitz, S., 339, 355
Doll, E. A., 64, 74, 322, 356
Donovan, H., 157, 179
Downey, K. J., 92, 103
Dredge, T. E., 349, 360
Drillien, C. M., 247, 269, 284, 285, 309
Drillien, C. M., & Wilkinson, E. M., 36, 74
Driscoll, S. G., Benirschke, K., & Curtis, G. W., 259, 269
Dubin, M. N., 417, 424
Dunn, L. M., 134, 138, 215, 233, 385, 399, 402
Dunsdon, M. I., 302, 309
Durling, D., & Benda, C. E., 130, 138
Dutton, G., 291, 309

Eames, J. H., 285, 308
Eccles, J. C., 18, 32, 279, 309

Edgerton, R. B., 100, 103, 122, 140
Edgerton, R., & Sabagh, G., 99, 100, 104
Edison, T., 13
Eichorn, D., 91, 106
Eidinova, M. B., & Pravdina-Vinarskaya, Ye., 346, 356
Ellis, N., 137, 138, 329, 356
Ellis, A., & Beechley, R. M., 130, 138
Ellson, D., Fuller, P. R., & Urmston, R., 353, 354, 357
Engel, A. M., 419, 424
Erhardt, L. L., 246, 270
Esen, F. M., & Durling, D., 350, 357
Essen-Möller, E., 29, 32, 115, 139, 242, 270

Farber, B., 44, 45, 47, 48, 50, 74-75, 121
Farber, B., Jenné, W., & Toigo, R., 93, 104
Fay, L. M., 124, 138, 204, 232
Feifel, H., 161, 179
Feigin, I., 305, 314
Fenichel, O., 61, 75
Ferguson, R. H., 418, 424
Ferguson, T., & Kerr, A. W., 406, 424
Finley, C. J., & Thompson, J. M., 205, 233
Fisch, M., 300, 301, 312
Fischer, A. E., & Moloshok, R. E., 252, 270
Fischer, A. E., Moloshok, R. E., & Rafton, E. H., 259, 270
Fischer, L., 285, 311
Flanagan, E., 260, 268

Folling, A., 304, 351

Font, M., 211, 234

Ford, D. D., Patterson, J. C., & Treuting, W. L., 240, 270

Forrer, G. R., 61, 75

Forssman, H., & Thyssell, T., 292, 310

Fouracre, M., & Thiel, E. A., 301, 310

Fowler, E., 168, 174, 180

Fox, W. W., and Parrotte, I., 389-400

Franceschetti, A., 241, 271

Francey, E., 382, 400

Francey, R. E., 325, 357

Fraser, J., & Mitchell, A., 293, 310

Freedman, A., 254, 275

Freedman, R. M., 284, 286, 311

French, J. L., 216, 233

French, L. A., & Suechting, R. L., 343, 357

Freud, S., 24, 61, 110, 282, 336

Frey, R. M., 390, 401, 422, 425

Friedman, E. C., & Barclay, A., 233

Frisina, R., 104, 179, 330, 359

Fuller, P. R., 353, 354, 357

Galambos, M., 350, 357

Galambos, R., 23, 32

Gallagher, J. J., 221, 233

Gallagher, J. E., Benoit, E. P., & Boyd, H., 216, 234

Galton, F., 112

Garrison, I. K., 384, 400

Genn, M. M., & Silverman, W. A., 285, 310

Gens, G. W., 156, 179

Gentry, J. T., Parkhurst, E., & Bulin, E. V., 242, 270

Gesell, A., Amatruda, C. S., & Culotta, C. S., 347, 357

Gibby, R., 111, 139

Gibson, D., & Pozsonyi, J., 130, 139

Gibson, R., 7, 32

Gibson, R. M., 305, 306

Ginglend, D. R., 384, 400

Girardeau, F., & Spradlin, J., 329, 357

Girvin, L., 382, 400

Gladwin, T., 14, 33

Glassman, L. A., 338, 357

Goda, S., 159, 174, 179

Goda, S., & Griffith, B., 175

Goffman, E., 98, 104

Goldberg, I. I., 412, 424

Goldfarb, W., Braunstein, P., & Scholl, H., 229, 234

Goldman, D., & Rosenberg, B., 194, 234

Goldman, W. J., 366, 400

Goldstein, H., 92, 104, 348, 357, 382, 400

Goldstein, H., Moss, J., & Jordan, L., 216, 234

Goldstein, K., 228, 234

Goldstein, M., 282

Goldstein, R., Landau, W. M., & Kleffner, F., 223, 234

Gorlow, L., 209, 232

Goshen, C. E., 57, 75

Gothberg, L., 132, 139

Gottsleben, R. H., 156, 166, 174, 179, 183

Graham, F. K., & Berman, P. W., 219, 220, 234

Graliker, B., 348, 359

Greenberg, M., Pelliteri, O., & Barton, J., 257, 270
Griffith, B., & Spitz, H., 175
Griffith, B. C., Spitz, H., & Lipman, R. E., 133, 139
Grigg, A. E., 127, 139
Grossman, C., 156, 184
Gruenberg, E., 292, 310
Gruenwald, P., 256, 270
Guiraud, P., & Roualt de la Vigne, A., 303, 310
Gunzberg, H., 418, 425
Gutman, A. B., 305, 310

Hafemeister, N. R., 383, 400
Haines, M. S., 342, 356
Haley, J., 59, 75
Hall, B., 291, 293, 310
Hall, J. G., Francey, E., & Girvin, L., 382, 400
Hallgren, B., & Sjogren, T., 71, 75
Halstead, W., 279
Hamblin, R. C., 132, 138
Hansen, E., 242, 270
Harkins, J. P., 59, 78, 153, 167, 173, 174, 183
Harlow, H. F., 305, 315
Harper, P., Fischer, L., & Rider, R. V., 285, 311
Hartogs, R., 124, 139
Haynes, J. R., & Sells, J. B., 219, 234
Hebb, D. O., 23, 32, 111, 282, 311
Heber, R., 122
Hedberg, E., 242, 270
Hedberg, E., et al., 258, 270
Hegge, T. F., 390, 400
Heilman, A., 300, 311
Heimer, C. B., Cutler, R., & Freedman, R. M., 284, 286, 311

Heiser, K., 340, 358
Helgason, T., 25, 32, 112, 117, 139
Henderson, R. A., 94, 104
Henderson, W., 20, 31
Henner, R., 284, 306
Hermelin, B. F., 411, 424
Herndon, C. N., 70, 75
Hersov, L. A., 195, 236
Hesseljo, R., & Anberg, A., 284, 311
Hicks, S. P., 240, 271
Higgins, J. V., 71, 75, 241, 271
Hill, A. S., 325, 358
Hilliard, L. T., & Kirman, B. H., 5, 32, 241, 271, 281, 311
Holt, K. S., 44, 47, 75
Hooft, C., et al., 305, 311
Hopkins, T., Bice, H. V., & Colton, K., 296, 298, 302, 311
Horner, F. A., et al., 352, 358
Hudson, M., 382, 400
Huizinga, J., 243, 274
Hungerford, R. H., deProspo, C. J., & Rosenzweig, L. E., 390, 400
Hurley, J. R., 53, 75
Hutchings, J. J., et al., 347, 358
Hutt, M., & Gibby, R., 111, 139
Hyland, H. H. 251, 271

Illingworth, R. S., & Birch, C. B., 190, 235
Inghe, C., 242, 271
Ingraham, F. D., & Matson, D. M., 344, 358
Ingram, V., 67, 77
Irwin, O. C., 174
Iscoe, I., 214, 233

Jackson, E., 53, 76
Jastak, J., 6, 33, 123, 126, 139, 206, 234
Jenné, W., 93, 104
Jervis, G., 260, 271, 342, 358
Jessup, W. J. E., 241, 255, 257, 268
John (case study), 17-18
John, S., 13
Johnson, A. P., 129, 142
Johnson, C. D., & Barnett, C., 292, 311
Johnson, G. O., 118, 139, 383, 401
Johnson, G. O., & Kirk, S. A., 118, 139
Johnston, A. W., & McKusick, V. A., 243, 271
Jolles, I., 210- 211, 235, 377, 401
Jolly, D., 37, 64, 75
Jordan, L., 216, 234
Jordan, P. H., 67, 77
Jordan, T. E., 33, 139, 180, 235, 271, 311, 358, 425
Jordan, T. E., & deCharms, R., 17, 33, 111, 135, 139, 175, 180, 208, 391, 401
Joyce, J., 146
Joynson, M. G., 69, 74

Kääriänen, R., & Dingman, H., 292, 312
Kallikak family, 72
Kanner, L., 3, 33, 62, 63, 125, 140, 227, 228, 238
Kanner, L., & Lesser, L., 229, 235
Kant, I., 287
Kantor, J. R., 58, 76
Kaplan, O., 117, 140
Karlin, I. W., & Strazzulla, M., 157, 180

Kastein, S., & Fowler, E., 168, 174, 180
Katzenstein, M., 263, 264, 272
Kelsey, F., 264
Kennedy, J. F., 81
Kennedy, L., 156, 174, 180
Kennedy, R. J. R., 406, 407, 425
Kenney, E. T., 56, 76
Kephart, N. C., 388, 401
Kerr, A. W., 406, 424
King, F. J., Bowman, B. H., & Moreland, H. J., 305, 312
King, J. E., 260, 268
Kirk, D. C., & Bauer, A. M., 350, 358
Kirk, S. A., 14, 33
Kirk, S. A., & McCarthy, J. J., 25, 33, 132, 217, 235, 334, 359
Kirman, B., 190, 235, 260, 271
Klatskin, H., Jackson, E., & Wilkins, L., 53, 76
Klebanoff, L. B., 53, 76
Klein, A., & Franceschetti, A., 241, 271
Kleffner, F., 223, 234
Kluge, W., 291, 312
Knobloch, H., 254, 271
Knobloch, H., & Pasamanick, B., 246, 256, 271, 283, 312
Koch, R., Sharp, I., & Graliker, B., 348, 359
Kodman, F., et al., 164, 180
Koegler, R. R., 229, 233
Koffman, O., & Hyland, H. H., 251, 271
Kogan, K. L., & Crager, R. L., 214, 235
Kolstoe, O. P., 170, 175, 180, 418, 419, 425
Kolstoe, O. P., & Frey, R. M., 390, 401, 422, 425

Kratter, F. E., 7, 33, 125, 129, 140, 248, 271, 305, 312

Kraus, J., 193, 237

Kraus, M. J., 205, 238

Kreindler, A., Unger, I., & Volanskii, D., 282, 312

Kronovet, E., 58, 77

Krout, M. H., 220, 235

Kugel, R. B., & Reque, D., 91, 104

Kugelmass, I. N., 278, 281, 312, 349, 350, 359

Lam, R. L., 206, 232

Lamm, S., & Fisch, M., 300, 301, 312

Landau, W. M., 223, 234

Larson, L. A., 359

Lassers, L., & Low, G., 171-172, 174, 181, 331, 359

LaValli, A., & Runge, L., 383, 401

Lawrence, P. J., 21, 33

Lazure, D., 226, 229, 235

Lee, E. S., 27, 33

Lehtinen, L., 388, 403

Lejeune, J., & Turpin, R., 250, 271

Leland, H., 122, 123, 140

Lemkau, P., Tietze, C., & Cooper, M., 26, 33

Lesser, L., 229, 235

Levin, J., 206, 237

Levine, S. Z., 285, 308

Levinson, A., 260, 272

Levy, S., & Perry, H. A., 258, 265, 272

Lewis, E., 352, 359

Liggins, J. C., & Phillips, L. I., 257, 272

Lillienfeld, A. M., & Pasamanick, B., 252, 272

Lipman, R. E., 133, 139

Little, W., 294, 312

Loomis, E. A., 340, 361

Lorenz, M., 412, 424

Loudon, J. B., 26, 34

Louttit, R., 354, 359

Lovell, C., 389, 402

Low, G., 171-172, 174, 181, 331, 359

Lubman, C., 157, 181

Lucey, J. F., 262, 272

Lunzer, E., 135, 141, 391, 403

Luria, V., 7

Lyle, J. G., 174, 175, 267, 272, 328, 359

Lyons, W. F., 157, 183

McCarthy, D., 150, 151, 153, 181

McCarthy, J. J., 25, 33, 132, 217, 235, 334, 359, 380

McCartney, L. D., 414, 425

McCaw, W. R., 383, 402

McClelland, D., 111, 235

McDonald, A. D., 285, 313

McDowell, F. B., 87, 105

McKeown, J., 242, 272

McKhann, C., 342, 355

McKusick, V. A., 243, 271

McLaurin, R. L., & Matson, D. D., 133, 140, 343, 360

McMurray, J. G., 221, 236

McNeill, W. D. D., 131, 140

McPherson, J. R., 164, 181

MacAndrew, C., & Edgerton, R., 122, 140

MacDonald, F. J., 395, 402

MacGillivray, R., 292, 312

MacMahon, B., & McKeown, J., 242, 272

MacNab, G., 345, 359
Machover, K., 212
Mackie, R. P., Williams, H., & Dunn, L. M., 402
Mackler, B., 100, 103
Magaret, A., 204, 206, 238
Magoun, W., 23, 33
Makita, K., 230, 236
Malamud, N., 280, 287, 313
Malzberg, B., 115, 140, 260, 272
Manley, E. J., 38, 74
Mary, K., 110
Mary (case study), 55
Masket, L. J., 160, 174, 181
Masland, R. L., Sarason, S. B., & Gladwin, T., 14, 33
Matheny, W. D., 299, 314
Mathews, J., 157, 164, 178, 181
Matson, D. D., 133, 140, 343, 344, 358, 360
Mautner, H., 291, 313
Maxwell, J., 19, 33
May, A. M., 241, 273
Mead, G. H., 10, 33
Meader, M. H., 174
Mecham, M., 174, 181, 207, 332, 360
Mein, R., 153, 157, 163, 175, 184
Mein, R., & O'Connor, N., 162, 175, 182
Meindl, J. M., 344, 360
Melchior, J. C., 229, 232, 303, 307
Mellin, G. H., & Katzenstein, M., 263, 264, 272
Mellman, W. J., 174
Menkes, J. H., 305, 313
Menninger, K., 195, 236
Metraux, R., 149, 151, 182
Meyer, H., 64, 76
Meyers, C. E., 386, 402

Michael-Smith, H., 340, 360, 410, 425
Michel, J., & Carney, R., 174
Milazzo, T., 416, 426
Millen, D., & Danielson, R. H., 415, 425
Millen, J. E., & Woollam, D. H. M., 240, 272
Miller, E. A., & Rosenfeld, G., 300, 313
Miller, E. L., 407-423
Minear, W. L., 296, 298, 313
Mitchell, A., 293, 310
Moloshok, R. E., 252, 259, 270
Moore, B. C., McGee, E. S., & Sindzinski, R. M., 304, 313
Moore, O. K., 380
Moorhead, P. S., Mellman, W. J., & Wenar, C., 174
Moreland, H. J., 305, 312
Morelewicz, H. V., 348, 355
Morello, A., et al., 345, 360
Morris, E. F., 65, 76
Moss, J., 216, 234
Mowrer, O. H., 152, 182
Munson, S. E., & May, A. M., 241, 273
Murray, H., 110, 209, 236
Myklebust, H., 152, 182
Myklebust, H. R., & Boshes, B., 284, 313

Narabayashi, H., et al., 346, 360
Neel, J. V., 242, 273
Nelson, M. M., 245, 273
Neuhaus, E. C., 384, 402
New, E., 285, 308
Newland, T. E., 216, 236
Newlyn, D., 408, 424
Nice, M. M., 150, 182

Noce, R. H., Williams, D. B., & Rapaport, W., 350, 360
O'Connor, N., 162, 175, 182, 408, 418, 426
O'Connor & Hermelin, 174
Ohlsen, R. H., 161, 175, 182
Ohlsen, R. L., 391, 402
Oliver, J. N., 327, 328, 360
Orme, J. E., 214, 236
Orr, K., 206, 236
Orzack, L. H., 89, 105
Osgood, C. E., 10, 132, 170
Osgood, C. E., Suci, G. J., & Tannenbaum, P. H., 148, 182
O'Sullivan, M. A., 293, 307

Page, J. D., 325, 360
Paine, R. S., 305, 313
Palm, J., 77, 112, 241, 273
Papania, N. A., 161, 175, 182
Parkhurst, E., 242, 270
Parnicky, J., & Zigler, E., 88, 105
Parrotte, I., 389-400
Partington, M. W., 305, 314
Pasamanick, B., 33, 126, 140, 242, 246, 256, 271, 273, 283, 312
Pasamanick, B., & Lillienfeld, A. M., 257, 273, 261
Pathman, J. H., 231, 233
Patterson, J. C., 240, 270
Patterson, L. L., 65, 77
Patton, R. E., & Weinstein, A. S., 92, 105
Paulet, W., 5-6
Pavlov, I., 7
Peace, W. F., 415, 426
Peck, J. R., 417, 426
Pelliteri, O., 257, 270
Peltin, S., 177, 141

Penman, A. S., & Dredge, T. E., 349, 360
Penrose, L. S., 28, 30, 34, 250, 273, 291, 314
Perlstein, M., 294
Perry, H. A., 258, 265, 272
Peters, J. E., 308
Peterson, L., & Smith, L. L., 406, 426
Pettigrew, T., 204, 236
Pevzner, M. S., 7, 34
Phelps, W. M., 299-300, 314
Phillips, L. I., 257, 272
Phillips, V. P., 71, 77
Piaget, J., 111, 141, 146, 182
Pierce, H. D., 328, 356
Plutchik, R., & Kronovet, E., 58, 77
Pollock, F. J., 284, 306
Poole, J., 149, 182
Popp, C. E., Ingram, V., & Jordan, P. H., 67, 77
Porter, R. B., & Milazzo, T., 416, 426
Porter, R. B., Collings, J. L., & McIver, M. R., 119, 141
Porteus, S. D., & Corbett, G. R., 6, 34
Portnoy, B., & Stacey, C. L., 127, 141
Potter, E. L., 261, 270, 287, 308
Pozsonyi, J., 130, 139
Pravdina-Vinarskaya, Ye., 346, 356
President's Commission on Mental Retardation, 6
Pribram, K., 282, 314
Pringle, M. L., & Bossio, V., 56, 77
Pritham, G. H., 291, 306
Pryles, C. V., 293, 307

Quinn, K. U., & Durling, D., 353, 361

Rapaport, D., 146, 182
Rapaport, W., 350, 360
Raus, G., 298, 308
Ravenette, A. T., & Hersov, L. A., 195, 236
Rawnsley, K., & London, J. B., 26, 34
Ray, C. G., *et al.*, 348, 361
Reece, R. E., 156, 184
Reed, E. W., & Phillips, V. P., 71, 77
Reed, S. C., Reed, E., & Palm, J., 77, 112, 241, 273
Reiss, M., 348, 355
Reitan, R., 279, 314
Répond, A., 48-49, 77
Reque, D., 91, 104
Rettig, J., 350, 361
Richards, B. W., & Rundle, A. T., 241, 277
Richards, T. W., & Sands, R., 56, 77, 91, 106
Rider, R. V., 285, 311
Ridler, M. A. C., & Shapiro, A., 291, 314
Riello, A., 159, 183
Riese, H., 382, 402
Rigrodsky, S., 160, 183, 331, 361
Rimland, B., 230, 236, 282
Robb, H. P., 350, 361
Robinson, N. M., & Robinson, H. B., 285, 286, 314
Roger (case study), 16
Rogers, C., 60, 77
Rogers, M. E., Lillienfeld, A. M., & Pasamanick, B., 192, 237

Rosenberg, B., & Moed, M. G., 421, 426
Rosenfeld, G., 300, 313
Rosenthal, F., 173, 183
Rosenzweig, L. E., 390, 400
Rosenzweig, S., 127
Rouault de la Vigne, A., 303, 310
Rouse, S. T., 379, 380, 403
Roy, V. I., 237
Ruby, D. O., & Matheny, W. D., 299, 314
Rundle, A. T., 241, 277
Runge, L., 383, 401
Runner, M. N., 241, 243, 245, 274
Runner, M. N., & Dagg, C. P., 281, 287, 314
Rychlak, J. F., & Wade, I., 372, 403
Rynbrandt, D. M., 416, 426

Sabagh, G., *et al.*, 93, 94, 106
Sabagh, G., & Edgerton, R. B., 99, 100, 104, 346, 361
Sabagh, G., & Windle, C., 92, 106
Saenger, G., 45, 51, 93, 94, 106, 119, 120, 127, 136, 141, 411
Safford, H. W., 265, 274
Saltzman, S., 204, 237
Samuels, I., 23, 34
Sands, R., 56, 77, 91, 106
Sarason, S., 14, 33, 136, 141, 209, 237, 339, 361
Saucier, J. F., 45, 77
Sawyer, G. M., 292, 314
Scally, B., & McKay, D., 29
Schacter, F. F., & Apgar, V., 221, 237
Schacter, F. F., Meyer, L. R., & Loomis, E. A., 340, 361
Scheerenberger, R., 82, 106

Schipper, M. I., 52, 77
Schonell, F. E., 298, 300, 302, 307, 314
Schonell, F., & Watts, B., 46, 78
Schlanger, B., 86, 91, 106, 158, 162, 174, 175, 183, 332, 361
Schlanger, B. B., & Gottsleben, R. H., 156, 166, 183
Schlesinger, E., 246, 274
Schlesinger, E. R., Allaway, N. C., & Peltin, S., 117, 141
Schmid, W., Lee, C. H., & Smith, P. M., 293, 314
Schneck, L., 303, 314
Scholl, H., 229, 234
Schuell, H., 226, 237
Seelye, B. J., 38, 74
Sells, J. B., 219, 234
Shafter, A. J., 96, 106
Shapiro, A., 291, 314
Shapiro, M. I., 193, 237
Shedd, C., 127, 137
Sherrington, C. S., 279, 314
Shotwell, A., 409, 426
Siegel, G., 59, 78, 153, 173, 175, 183
Siegel, G., & Harkins, J. P., 59, 78, 153, 167, 173, 174, 183
Siertsma, B., 152, 183
Sievers, D. J., 174, 217, 237
Silberman, J., Dancis, J., & Feigin, I., 305, 314
Silverman, W. A., 285, 310
Silverstein, A. B., 130, 141, 205, 237
Simon, Th., 143, 178
Sindzinski, R. M., 304, 313
Sirkin, J., & Lyons, W. F., 157, 183
Sjogren, T., 71, 75
Skeels, H., 69, 78

Skodak, M., & Skeels, H., 69, 78
Skinner, B. F., 152, 154, 183
Sloan, W., 97, 106, 211
Sloan, W., & Cutts, N., 204, 237
Smith, J. O., 175
Smith, L. L., 406, 426
Smith, P. M., 293, 314
Sparks, H. C., & Blackman, L. S., 391, 403
Spencer, E. F., 387, 403
Spencer, H., 290
Spitz, E. B., 344, 362
Spitz, H., & Blackman, L. S., 133, 141
Spradlin, J., 24, 329, 357
Stacey, C. L., & Levin, J., 206, 209, 232, 237
Stanton, J. E., 391, 399
Stedman, D., & Eichorn, D., 91, 106
Stein, Z., & Susser, M., 4, 34, 43, 44, 54, 78
Stein, Z., Susser, M., & Lunzer, E., 135, 141, 391, 403
Steinman, J., Grossman, C., & Reece, R. E., 156, 184
Sterling, H. M., 299, 315
Sternlicht, M., 205, 238
Sternlicht, M., & Wanderer, Z., 130, 141
Stevens, G. D., 283, 315, 370, 403
Stevens, G. D., & Birch, J. W., 283, 315
Stoddard, H. M., 328, 362
Stoller, A., & Collman, R. D., 247, 258, 274, 308
Stowe, M. M., 66, 78
Strauss, A. A., 128, 141, 219, 238, 282, 315, 388, 403
Strauss, A. A., & Kephart, N. C., 388, 401

Strauss, A. A., & Lehtinen, L., 388, 403

Strazzulla, M., 157, 167, 174, 180, 184, 337, 362

Strickland, R. G., 172, 184

Stritch, S. J., 281, 308

Suci, G. J., 148, 182

Suechting, R. L., 343, 357

Super, D., 408, 426

Susser, M., 4, 34, 43, 44, 54, 78, 135, 141, 391, 403

Tanino, Y., 348, 362

Tannenbaum, P. H., 148, 182

Tapia, F., 305, 315

Tarjan, G., 267, 274

Tarjan, G., et al., 93, 94, 106

Tarjan, G., & Dingman, H., 101, 106

Tarjan, G., et al., 156, 184

Taussig, H., 264, 274

Templin, M., 149, 151, 184

Terwiliger, W. B., 419

Thiel, E. A., 301, 310

Thompson, C. W., 116, 142

Thompson, C. W., & Magaret, A., 204, 206, 238

Thompson, J. M., 205, 233

Thorne, F. C., 339, 362

Thyssell, T., 292, 310

Tietze, C., 26, 33

Tisdall, W., 175, 379, 391, 404

Tizard, J., & Loos, F. M., 131, 142

Tizard, J., & O'Connor, N., 410, 418, 426

Toigo, R., 93, 104

Tolman, N. G., & Johnson, A. P., 129, 142

Tong, J. B., & McKay, G. W., 94, 106

Town, M. H., 387, 399

Trippe, M., 114, 142

Treuting, W. L., 240, 270

Tucker, B. E., 260, 275

Turkel, H., 348, 362

Turpin, R., 250, 271

Unger, I., 282, 312

Urmston, R., 353, 354, 357

Vaughn, A. O., 174

Van Pelt, J. F., & Huizinga, J., 243, 274

Vera Cruz, P. G., 343, 362

Volanskii, D., 282, 312

Volk, B., 303, 307

Wade, I., 372, 403

Waisman, H. A., 263, 274

Waisman, H. A., & Harlow, H. F., 305, 315

Wakefield, R. A., 43, 78

Walker, G. H., 37, 78

Wallace, H. N., 305, 316, 352, 363

Walters, R. H., 204, 238

Walton, D., & Black, D. A., 220, 238

Wanderer, Z., 130, 141

Warkany, J., 245, 262, 274, 290, 316

Warren, S. A., 392, 404

Warren, S. A., & Kraus, M. J., 205, 238

Watts, A. F., 150, 184

Webster, D., 287

Weiner, B. B., 384, 404
Weinstein, A. S., 92, 105
Wenar, C., 174
Wendlund, L. V., Urmer, A. H.,
  & Safford, H. W., 265, 274
Wepman, J., 132, 148, 171, 180,
  217, 231, 235
Werdegar, K., 6, 34
Werner, H., 161, 175, 178, 211,
  220, 238
Westby-Gibson, H., 414, 426
Wheeler, L. R., 19, 34
Whitney, E. A., 136, 142
Wiener, G., et al., 285, 286, 316
Wigger, O. L., 392, 404
Wilkins, J. L., 332, 363
Wilkinson, E. M., 36, 74
Williams, H., 402
Wilson, C. L., 291, 308
Wilson, J. G., 245, 275
Wilson, L., 157, 164, 184
Wilson, M. G., et al., 258, 275
Windle, C., 92, 106
Winitz, H., 110, 184
Winterbottom, 53, 79
Winthrop, H., 132, 142
Wirtz, M., 383, 404
Witschi, E., 245, 275
Wittse, H., 291, 308

Wolfensberger, W., Mein, R., &
  O'Connor, N., 153, 157, 163,
  175, 184
Woodward, M., 85, 142
Woollam, D. H. M., 240, 272
Worchel, T. L., & Worhel, P., 52,
  79
Worhel, P., 52, 79
Wortis, H., & Freedman, A., 254,
  275
Wortis, J., 389, 404
Wright, S. W., 250, 269
Wunsch, W. L., 130, 142

Yacorzynski, G. K., & Tucker,
  B. E., 260, 275
Yakovlev, P. I., 5, 34

Zellweger, H., 241, 275
Ziegler, E., & Williams, J., 91,
  107
Zigler, E., 88, 105
Zimmerman, G. T., & Burg-
  meister, B. B., 349, 350, 353,
  363
Zubek, T. P., 116, 137
Zuk, G., 24, 34, 48, 66, 79, 231,
  238

INDEX OF SUBJECTS

Ability, 371
Abortion, 257
Absenteeism, 470
Accidents, 410
Achievement, functional, 134
Achievement motive, 409
Adaptive behavior, 7, 8, 89, 122-123
Adolescence, 132, 157, 373, 389-391, 406
Adoption, 191
Adrenalin, 291
Age, 115-117, 332
Aggrandizement, 99
Amelioration, 321
American Association on Mental Deficiency, 372
Amino-acids, 306
Analysis levels, 188-189
Anecdote, 188, 199
Anemia, 200
Animals, 245
Anoxia, 265, 283
Aphasia, 42, 194, 217, 222-226
Articulation, 330-331
Ashkenazi, 303
Athetosis, 275
Audiometry, 164-165, 196, 224

Autism, 226-230
Autistic theory, 331

Bakery, 412
Baltic Sea, 303
Basque, 149
Billy, 199-201
Blood disorders, 261
Bone age, 348
Boys, 242
Brachycephaly, 287
Brain, 282
  cerebellum, 295
  cerebrum, 279
  cortex, 222, 282, 283
  fontanelle, 291, 343
  frontal lobes, 282
  reticular formation, 282
  tissue, 282
  ventricle, 289
Brain injury, 128, 141, 161, 194, 218-221, 226, 281-282
Brain-storming, 379

Carotid artery, 342
Case-study, 187, 195-201

441

Cataract, 257
Catholic, 199
Cerebral palsy, 155, 246, 294-302, 318, 330
Chemotherapy, 318
Children, 412
Cholera, 246
Chromosomes, 249-251
Chromosomal error, 130
Classroom activity, 377-385
Cleft palate, 155, 241
Clinician, 192
Community, 406
Compensation, 414
Concept attainment, 133
Counseling
    awareness, 62-63
    eclectic, 61
    goals, 337-339
    group, 67, 337, 340
    indicants, 338
    issues, 62
    learning, 338
    non-directive, 60
    play, 340
    problems, 63
    psychoanalysis, 60
    steps, 66
    transfer, 338
Craniostenosis, 287
Cretinism, 302-303, 343, 347
Curability, 320
Cure, 319
Curricula, 368
Cyanosis, 262

Data language, 163, 166
Deaf retarded, 330
Deanol, 12, 354
Death, 44

Defamilization, 90
Deletion, 250
Delinquency, 127
Demography, 242
Denver system, 249
Development, 277-316
Developmental quotient, 242
Diabetes, 252, 259, 318
Diagnosis, 42-43, 231
Divergent thinking, 379-380
DNA, 249
Down's Disease (see Syndromes)
Dyad, 173
Dye, 245

Ecology, 415
Economic adjustment, 407
Educable, 372
Education, 365-404
    achievement, 391-392
    brain-injury, 388-389
    clinical, 370, 386
    curriculum, 374, 378
    diagnosis, 381
    enrollments, 366
    evaluation, 391-392
    goals, 370-371
    Herbartian, 385
    hometraining, 397
    instruction, 373, 385-386
    language, 379-380
    model, 393
    practice, 366
    preschool, 14, 379-381
    placement, 374-375, 377
    problems, 368, 388-389
    reading, 383
    teachers, 366, 378, 386-388, 396
Electroencephalography, 7, 23
Electro-shock, 350

Emotional disturbance, 226-230
Encephalitis, 265
Epidemiology, 246, 258
Epilepsy, 95, 345
Epistemology, 11, 279
Erythroblastosis, 304, 341
Evaluation
    prediction, 190
    purposes, 189-191
Excellence, 409
Exogenous-endogenous, 128

Factor analysis, 279, 292
Family, 35-79
    adjustment, 40-43
    disorganization, 94
    integration, 48
    reactions, 46-49
    retarded, 68-72
    size, 40
    strategies, 45-46, 49-51
    triad, 59
    types, 43-46
Feral children, 325
Fertility, 71
Fetal life, 284
    wastage, 284
Fetal loss, 251-255
Fetus, 245
Fluoridation, 29
Folling's disease (see
    Syndromes)
Forme fruste, 251
Foster home, 84, 96
Frustration, 65
Funeral, 200-201

Galactocemia, 251
Galanthamine, 346

"Garden-variety defective," 136
Genes, 249
Genetics, 2, 241
Geriatrics, 95
Girls, 408
Glutamic acid, 41, 352-354
Gonadal immaturity, 130
Government, 420
Growth, 191
Guidance, 410

Handicapped worker, 421
Haploid, 250
Hare lip, 261
Hawthorne effect, 328
Health, 374
Hearing loss, 163-165
Hematology, 291
Hematoma, 344
Hemoglobin, 256
Hepatitis, 247, 258
Heredity, 248
Hexagon, 227
Higher nervous activity, 265
Homelife, 15
Homes, 335
Hormones, 245
Hospitalization, 201
Housing projects, 415
Human movement, 132
Human nature, 1
Hyaline membrane, 259
Hydrocephalus, 93, 281, 345, 349

Idiot, 143
Illinois State Department of
    Mental Hygiene, 93
Illusions, 133
Imbecile, 143

Inbreeding, 241
Income tax, 83
Incurability, 34
Independence training, 53
Independent living, 405-426
Intelligence, 408
Intersex, 250
Interview, 194
Iowa studies, 326
IQ, 19, 55, 326, *passim*

Jaundice, 262, 304
Jobs, 406

Kauai pregnancy study, 252
Kernicterus, 201, 304
Kindergarten, 325
Kennedy-Johnson
    administrations, 18

Laborers, 408
Language, 143-185
    acquisition, 148
    articulation, 159-160
    categories, 144-148
    corpus, 231
    deaf, 163-164
    incidence, 156
    Lapp, 149
    lexicon, 162
    listening, 144
    mazes, 173
    morphology, 147, 173
    mutism, 155, 158
    oral, 174
    philology, 148
    phonemes, 159, 160
    pitch, 167

Language—*Cont.*
    reading, 145
    research, 164-175
    semantic differential, 148
    sentence length, 150
    speaking, 144
    structure, 175
    stuttering, 166
    syndromes, 163-168
    syntax, 147, 156, 231
    therapy, 168-169, 329-334
    thinking, 145
    training, 329
    type-token, 147, 169
    vocabulary, 149, 150, 160-163,
        175
    writing, 145
Larynx, 148
Laundry, 329, 409
Lead, 266
Longitudinal study, 247
Lissajou figures, 221
Literature, 2
Little's disease (*see* Syndromes)

Magic Bullet, 322
Malformations, 287
Malnutrition, 201
Maple Syrup disease, 305, 352
Maternal age, 242, 261
Maternal values, 328
Maturity, 12
Measured intelligence, 8
Mechanisms, 280
Medical summary, 278
Meningitis, 266
Meningocele, 281
Mental Age, 203, 375, 413
Mental hospital
    administrator, 87

Mental Hospital—*Cont.*
  attendants, 86
  bureaucracy, 89
  child care, 101
  populations, 82, 88, 91
  resident, 81-107
  services, 84-89
  social system, 97
  total institution, 99
  training, 87, 88, 89, 102
  types, 83-84
Mental illness, 2, 95, 96
Mental retardation, *passim*
  codification, 6, 9-10
  definitions, 3-11
    codified, 9-10
    discriminative, 3
    factorial, 11-12
    functional, 7
    neural, 7
    nuclear, 10
    ontological, 4-5
    phenomenal, 8
    phylogenetic, 6
    residual, 3
    social, 7
    synoptic, 3
    tautological, 4
  discovery, 36-40
  epidemiology, 25-30
  inductive approach, 11-29
Metabolism, 349
Metasystem, 240
Microcephaly, 93
Migration, 27-28
Mind, 278-279
  dualism, 278
  monism, 279
Mongolism, (*see* Syndromes)
Monkeys, 282
Morphogenesis, 281

Mortality, 291, 407
Mortification, 99
Mother, 51
  health, 256-259
  high risk, 56
  interaction, 58
  Negro, 254
Motivation, 129
Mueller-Lyer illusion, 133

Naevoid amentia, 288
National Association for
    Retarded Children, 367
Neural satiation, 134
Neuroses, 2, 210
New York Times, 420
Number, 374
Nutrition, 255-256
Nurture, 87

Oasthouse disease, 305, 315
Objectives, behavioral, 331
Obstetric problems, 259-261
  anesthesia, 260
  anoxia, 260
  diabetes, 260
  placenta, 260
  trauma, 259, 260, 265
Occupations, 407, 412, 416
  level, 411
  selection, 417
Occupational therapy, 398
Oligophrenia, 7
Operant conditioning, 89
Operation Headstart, 216
Opisthotonos, 305
Oxycephaly, 287
Oxygen, 285

Paraplegia, 243
Parents, 38-39, 152
  perceptual distortions, 67
  retarded, 69
Pedagogy, 385
Penetrance, 248
Perseverating, 409
Personality tests, 207-213
Pertussis, 265
Pesticides, 266
Phenylaniline, 352
Phenylpyruvic amentia (see
  Syndromes)
Phocomelia, 264
Phoneme, 147, 331
Physical conditioning, 327
Pitch, 330
PKU (see Syndromes)
Place names
  Cities
    Austin, Texas, 417
    Baltimore, Maryland, 26,
      160, 392
    Chicago, Illinois, 44, 50
    Des Moines, Iowa, 159, 184
    Detroit, Michigan, 415
    Elmtown, 97
    Glasgow, Scotland, 406
    Grand Rapids, Michigan,
      416
    Kauai, Hawaii, 113, 137,
      247, 252
    Leningrad, USSR, 255
    Lincoln, Illinois, 131
    Los Angeles, California, 20,
      43, 68
    Milwaukee, Wisconsin, 5, 6
    Middletown, 97
    Mont-St. Aubert, Quebec,
      419
    Nancy, France, 347

Place names—Cont.
  Cities—Cont.
    New York, New York, 45,
      51, 98, 252, 257, 415
    Philadelphia, Pennsylvania,
      27, 328
    Prague, Czechoslovakia, 245
    St. Louis, Missouri, 392
    San Mateo, California, 414
    Toronto, Ontario, 325
    Singapore, Malaya, 287
    Stockholm, Sweden, 242,
      254
    Watertown, South Dakota,
      247
  Counties
    Cook County, 93
    Lancashire, England, 391
    Malmohus, Sweden, 391
    Onondaga County, New
      York, 28, 29, 113, 114
  States
    Florida, 332
    Illinois, 83, 87, 92, 94, 264,
      387
    Minnesota, 69, 71
    New Jersey, 296, 298, 302
    New York, 92, 242
    North Carolina, 70
    Rhode Island, 26
    Tennessee, 19
    Wisconsin, 89
  Countries
    Africa, 242
    Australia, 46, 193, 290
    Belgium, 352
    Canada, 45, 346
    Denmark, 242, 290, 293
    Finland, 252
    France, 26

Place names—*Cont.*
  Countries—*Cont.*
    Great Britain, 13, 47, 54, 94,
      95, 131, 410
      England, 28, 29, 326, 412
      Northern Ireland, 29, 117
      Scotland, 36, 72
    Holland, 243
    Iceland, 25
    Iran, 246
    Ireland, 352
    Israel, 194
    Japan, 346, 348
    Lebanon, 243
    New Zealand, 21, 257, 332
    Soviet Union, 346
    Sweden, 29, 70, 71, 115, 245,
      284, 292, 352
    Switzerland, 352
    Tristan da Cunha, 26
    United States, 242, 254, 352,
      367
Placebo, 322, 354
Placement
  failure, 419
Placenta, 252, 256
Police record, 406
Poliomyelitis, 239, 265
Poverty, 286
Pregnancy, 47, 52, 243, 284
Prematurity, 168, 252-255, 284-
  286
  achievement, 285
  adolescence, 286
  development, 285-286
  hearing, 284, 285
  social class, 286
  survivors, 284
  vision, 285
Preschool, 327
Primary process, 146

Programmed learning, 385
Project Headstart, 286
Projective techniques, 208-213
Protein, 256
Pseudofeeblemindedness, 125
Psychoanalysis, 60, 146
Psychodiagnostics, 187-237
Psycholinguistics, 385
Psychotherapy, 349

Radiation, 242
Readers, 412
Readiness, 214, 216-217
Reading, 165, 190, 377
Recreation, 398
Reinforcement, 152, 328
Reliability, 202
Religion, 48, 49, 355, 368
  Catholic, 48, 49, 93
  Jewish, 48, 93
  Protestant, 49, 93
Reproductive casualty, 252
Research, 243-247
  disciplines, 243
  group, 244
  integration, 244
  tools, 244-247
Reserpine, 349
Residential agencies, 405, 417
  Abilene State School (Texas),
    67
  Arizona State School, 304
  Children's Hospital
    (Philadelphia), 345
  Columbus State School
    (Ohio), 256
  Dixon State School (Illinois),
    93, 131
  Fort Wayne State School
    (Indiana), 160

Residential agencies—*Cont.*
Fountain Hospital (London), 328
Laurel District Training School (Maryland), 95
Pacific State Hospital (California), 93, 100, 101, 166, 346
Parsons State Hospital and Training School (Kansas), 122, 329
Rosewood State School (Maryland), 160
Southbury Training School (Connecticut), 340
Vineland Training School (New Jersey), 168, 223, 340, 380
Wisconsin Central Colony, 89, 380
Residential living, 81-107
abandonment, 96
absenteeism, 96
child care, 101
cottage life, 89, 100
day-room, 87
discharge, 84, 96
elite, 100
enrollment, 82, 92
entrepreneur, 101
entry, 90, 93, 94
family contact, 92
half-way house, 96
home placement, 90-92, 96
overcrowding, 82
recommitment, 94
waiting list, 93
Reticular formation, 230
Retrolental fibroplasia, 285
Rh-factor, 341-342

Rubella, 224, 256-257
Runaways, 163

Scaphocephaly, 287
Schemata, 280-281
Schizophrenia, 146, 229
School, 365
Scientific management, 143
Segregation, 368
Selective mating, 29
Self-care, 410
Sensory development, 154
Sheltered workshop, 421-423
Sicca-cell, 348
Signs, 374
Skeletal age, 242
Social age, 207
Social competence, 117-122
Social policy
efficiency, 82
institutions, 82
sterilization, 345-346
Social-vocational efficiency, 15-17
Socialization, 328
Special class, 407, 416
Special Education, 85, 325-327
Speech therapy, 329-333
Sphincter, 227, 229
Spiral after-effect, 221
Sterilization, 99, 345-346
Steroids, 348
Stigmata, 130
Subjectivity, 188
Supervision, 410
Suture, 343
Syndromes
Arnold-Chiari, 281
Cerebral palsy (*see* Little's disease)
Cretinism, 266

Syndromes—*Cont.*
Down's Disease, (Mongolism)
10, 37, 93, 128, 130-131,
165-166, 242, 261, 290-
293, 330, 348
cytology, 293
mortality, 291, 292
reproduction, 292
stigmata, 291, 292
Folling's disease
(Phenylpyruvic amentia,
Phenylketonuria, PKU)
42, 129, 168, 251, 262, 304-
305, 351, 352
detection, 305
incidence, 304
mechanisms, 305
signs, 305
Gargoylism (*see* Hurler's
disease)
Hartnup disease, 305, 311
Heller's disease, 229
Hurler's disease (Gargoylism),
243, 251, 275, 289
Hydrocephalus, 289-290
Little's disease, 49, 294-302
definition, 294
growth, 298-299
illness, 299
intelligence, 299-302
topology, 297-298
types, 294-296
Mongolism (*see* Down's
disease)
Kanner's disease, 229
Minimal brain injury, 129, 140,
155
Morquio's disease, 288
Niemann-Pick disease, 304
PKU (*see* Folling's disease)

Syndromes—*Cont.*
Rud's syndrome, 293-294
Strauss syndrome, 283
Sturge-Weber syndrome, 288
Tay-Sachs disease, 303, 309,
313, 318
Von Recklinghausen's
Disease, 195, 251, 288
Syntax, 330

Tacts, 160
Tails, 72
Taxes, 368
Taxonomy, 283
Teaching, 190
Teratogenic agents, 262, 263
Tests, 202-218
Ad Hoc Scale of Verbal
Ability, 170, 175
Advanced Performance Scale,
215
Ammons Full Range Picture
Vocabulary Test, 161
Bernreuter scale, 208
Blacky Pictures, 212
Bryngelson and Glaspey Test
Cards, 159
California Test of Mental
Maturity, 203
California Test of Personality,
208
Cattell Infant Intelligence
Scale, 300
Children's Picture Information
Test, 214
Coloured Progressive Matrices
(1947), 196, 197
Columbia Mental Maturity
Scale, 206, 214, 215
Davis-Eells Games, 203

Tests—*Cont.*
Draw-a-Man Test, 214, 232
Durrell Analysis of Reading Difficulty, 217
EEG, 201, 223, 224
Family Problems Test, 56
Full Range Picture Vocabulary Test, 215, 233
Gesell Development Scale, 254
Goldstein-Scheerer Scale, 220
Graham-Kendall Test, 220
Harrison-Stroud Reading Readiness Profiles, 217
House-Tree-Person Test, 211-212
Human Figure Drawing Test, 212
Illinois Test of Psycholinguistic Ability (ITPA), 25, 170, 175, 180, 217, 333, 334
Leiter International Scale, 206
Make a Picture-Story Test, 212
Michigan Picture Test, 196, 197
Minnesota-Multiphasic Personality Inventory, 208, 349
Minnesota Teacher Attitude Inventory, 387
Nebraska Test of Learning Aptitude, 206-207, 215
Observational Scale for Language Ability, 170
Parent Attitude Research Instrument, 328
Parsons Language Sample, 24, 172
Peabody Picture Vocabulary Scale, 215-216
Primary Mental Abilities Test, 203

Tests—*Cont.*
Progressive Matrices Test, 213-214
San Francisco Inventory of Communicative Effectiveness, 172, 174, 180
Stanford Binet Scale, 203-204, 211, 321
Szondi Test, 212
Thematic Apperception Test, 132, 209
Verbal Language Development Scale, 207
Vineland Social Maturity Scale, 207, 213, 325, 376
Wechsler Adult Intelligence Scale, 265, 418
Wechsler Intelligence Scale for Children, 29, 196, 205-206
X-ray, 223, 224, 245
Tetralogy of Fallot, 291
Thalidomide, 263-264
Therapy, 317-363
chemotherapy, 323, 347-354
functional, 323, 324-335
psychotherapy, 323, 335-341
surgery, 323, 341-346
Thyroid, 348
Time, 132
Toe-walking, 229
Token systems, 329
Toys, 414
Toxemia, 257
Trainable, 369, 372
Training, 414-418
Transfer, 410
Translocation, 250
Tranquilizers, 347, 349-351
Treatment, 319

Trimester, 257
Trisomy, 250
Tuberous sclerosis, 251, 288
Twinning, 245
Tyrosine, 305

U-medication, 348
Urban Living, 406

Validity, 202
Vitamins, 322
Vocational adjustment, 97

failure, 97
Voting, 407
Ward, 345
War on Poverty, 18
Washington University, 283
Watson-Crick model, 249
Wetzel grid, 299
WICHE, 386
Women, 412
Work, 408-409
    failure, 407, 408
    history, 407
    productivity, 409, 411
    stability, 415